C0-AXB-418

Circuits and Machines in ELECTRICAL ENGINEERING

Volume II. MACHINES

BY JOHN O. KRAEHENBUEHL
AND MAX A. FAUCETT

CIRCUITS AND MACHINES IN ELECTRICAL ENGINEERING. *Second Edition*
Volume I. Circuits
Volume II. Machines

BY JOHN O. KRAEHENBUEHL

ELECTRICAL ILLUMINATION

Circuits and Machines in ELECTRICAL ENGINEERING

Volume II. MACHINES

JOHN O. KRAEHENBUEHL, M.S., E.E.
Professor of Electrical Engineering, University of Illinois

MAX A. FAUCETT, M.S., E.E.
Professor of Electrical Engineering, University of Illinois

Second Edition
1947

New York · JOHN WILEY & SONS, Inc.
London · CHAPMAN & HALL, Limited

SECOND EDITION
Third Printing, December, 1949

PRINTED IN THE UNITED STATES OF AMERICA

PREFACE TO SECOND EDITION

The philosophy of the second edition of the text is the same as that of the first edition. The arrangement of the text has been changed at the suggestion of a number of users of the first edition. Since the text has been used for electrical engineering students as well as for other engineering students, the material has been changed to meet both needs. The request for the additional material influenced the decision to divide the text into two volumes, one on circuits and one on machines.

The second volume is confined to electrical machinery and has been arranged with the machines separated into two groups, direct-current and alternating-current, rather than into generators and motors as in the first edition. The material in the original converter and rectifier chapter has been divided into two parts, electronic devices and machines. Electronic devices are discussed in Volume I, and the machine portion is included with direct-current generators in this volume.

The transformer chapter has been expanded to include a discussion of harmonics. Harmonic problems are being brought to the attention of individuals in the operating divisions of utilities. These problems are not confined to the electrical engineer only; those whose interests are in electronic controls as well as power generation also find that they must consider harmonic problems.

New problems have been added throughout the text and, as in the first edition, the attempt has been made to give problems which lead to analysis rather than to substitution into expressions which appear in the developments.

The authors are indebted to those who have contributed ideas and suggestions for making the revisions in this new edition.

J. O. K.
M. A. F.

University of Illinois
Urbana, Illinois
May, 1947

PREFACE TO FIRST EDITION

This book, which is written for those who wish a knowledge of the fundamentals in electrical engineering, may be used as a first course for electrical engineering students, but it is written primarily for non-electrical engineering students who take electrical engineering as a secondary subject. For a period of twelve years the authors have used this method of presenting electricity as a general subject, dealing with the general system and developing the specific system as a special case. By combining the concepts of alternating current and direct current, it is possible to develop the subject with less repetition. The student, moreover, is not handicapped by having first to study principles of direct current and later to modify his point of view to develop the work in the more general field of alternating-current electricity. The rapid expansion of the subject has made it necessary either to neglect that which is new or to eliminate much that is basically necessary. By using the new method of approach, the authors find that the student is less confused and, duplication having been eliminated, there is time for material on new developments.

This book is the revision of a preliminary work which has passed through two editions and three years of classroom use, embodying ideas of four instructors and comments from many interested students. The electrical circuit is developed with the view of using circuit fundamentals in the analysis of machines. In developing the subject, stress is placed on physical analysis rather than upon mathematical derivations. If a mathematical development seems advisable, however, it is included but in such a way as not to encourage memorizing. The material does not develop either new or radically different interpretations but approaches the material from a new method of analysis. Demonstration problems and figures are kept simple, thereby eliminating much descriptive material in the text proper. The subject is treated qualitatively rather than in a quantitative or design manner. Those things that make only one or two per cent difference in the result are neglected or merely mentioned and not elaborated. Basic ideas are frequently repeated and reference is made to fundamental material in previous chapters, not by paragraphs but as to chapter content, so that the student will be encouraged to consider the whole instead of only a part of the correlating material. By means of this repetition, the connecting link between electric and magnetic circuits and their relationships to the machines is fused.

The problems have been chosen for the purpose of developing analysis, not for substituting numerical data into derivations developed in the book. The working of the problems should enable the student to recognize and use the fundamental principles that underlie the functioning of electrical circuits and the operation of machines. Electronics, which occupies approximately five per cent of the text, has not been included for its novelty, consideration being given only to fundamentals and equipment found in use at present. The specialist will find that his field has been neglected, for it is not the intent of the book to be encyclopedic in nature. These special subjects will be mentioned for the student who is interested in doing additional outside work, but they are not handled in detail. The chapters which explain applications are necessarily merely an outline of the possible treatment of this division.

Acknowledgment is made at the point of insertion for the material which has been furnished by manufacturers and commercial organizations. The authors recognize, in special appreciation, the assistance given by Mr. H. N. Hayward and Mr. L. L. Smith, members of the electrical engineering staff at the University of Illinois, who have taught classes in which the preliminary editions have been used. Their criticisms and suggestions have aided the authors to develop approaches and clarify vague statements. Mr. Hayward has contributed one-third of the problems in the book. Professor C. A. Keener read and criticized the preliminary material on machines. Mr. E. F. Heater of the Engineering Experiment Station aided in the checking and arrangement of the drawings.

J. O. K.
M. A. F.

University of Illinois
Urbana, Illinois
November, 1938

CONTENTS

CHAPTER 1

MACHINE CONSTRUCTION AND WINDINGS

1. Introduction. The growth of the electrical industry, the ever-decreasing cost of generation and distribution, and the increased uses of electrical equipment have been due largely to the rapid developments in rotating machines. During the last decade, the developments in petroleum refineries, electrolytic refineries, pulp and paper mills, the rubber industry, cement mills, lumber mills, and steel mills have been aided materially by motors and generators designed for operation under the special requirements of each of these industries.

The general name dynamo is used to classify all these rotating electrical machines. When mechanical power is converted to electrical power, the dynamo is a generator and, when converting electrical power to mechanical power, the dynamo is a motor. Thus, the fundamental difference between a motor and generator is not in the construction of the machine, but in the way the machine is used. All machines have two electrical circuits, namely, an armature circuit and a field circuit, and the different methods of construction and operation determine the particular kind or type under which a machine may be classified. In every machine the operation depends upon relative motion between the magnetic field and the armature conductors carrying current. For this reason the magnetic field may be stationary while the armature rotates, or the armature may be stationary while the magnetic field rotates. In special cases, both may be rotated.

2. Classification of Machines. The two main classes of dynamo machines are the a-c machines and the d-c machines. Omitting the acyclic machine, there is, however, very little difference in the two types. Any d-c machine, with the previous exception, has an a-c voltage generated in its armature and, by the use of a device called the commutator, rectification is obtained and the machine may be used on d-c systems. Any d-c machine may be used as an a-c machine if slip rings are connected symmetrically to the armature windings.

Because it is necessary to rectify the induced voltage in d-c machines, the armature is always rotated and the commutator, which is integrally connected to the armature winding, rotates at the same speed. The external connections to the armature circuit are made through the carbon brushes, which complete the circuit with the commutator. This requirement in construction obviously limits the electrical and mechanical capacities of the d-c machines. Considerable attention is required to keep the brush contacts clean, to keep the brush pressure sufficient to give good contact and, in addition, to prevent excessive wear of the copper commutator bars. Although large currents can be carried through the brush contacts, capacities seldom exceed 5000 kilowatts for a generator and 7500 horsepower for a motor. The maximum permissible voltage at the present time is about 1500 volts per commutator and this limits the capacity of d-c machines.

The difficulty of insulating between commutator bars (to prevent flashovers between brush holders) limits the voltage which can be used. High voltage d-c machines have a relatively small current rating because of the difficulty in insulating the armature conductors. The added insulation also reduces the size of conductor which can be used for a given armature slot.

A-c machines do not require a commutator connected to the armature and, for this reason, the windings may be stationary and the magnetic field rotated. This type of construction has both mechanical and electrical advantages since it is easier to make electrical connections to the armature winding when it is stationary, and since better protection can be provided for the armature leads which carry current at relatively high potentials. The only moving contacts required, therefore, for most a-c machines are those for the field circuit which require direct current at a low potential.

The capacities of a-c machines are not limited as are those of d-c machines. Alternators having capacities up to 165,000 kilovolt-amperes and generated voltages of 24,000 volts, and motors of 7500 horsepower are in use at the present time. This, no doubt, has been one of the important factors in the more rapid growth of a-c systems than of d-c systems.

3. D-C Machine Construction. During the last decade, the construction of electrical machines has been changed because of the introduction of large presses and electric welding. Originally, most parts of the machines were made of cast iron and, because of its low permeability, the machines were larger in dimensions than are the modern ones. On the other hand, almost all machines, today, are made, wherever possible, of rolled steel slabs welded together and, because of its high permeability, the size of the machine magnetic circuit and its entire dimensions are decreased.

The important parts of a d-c machine are magnetic frame (or yoke), field poles, armature, brushes and brush rigging, bearings, and base or bed plate.

The magnetic frame (or yoke) consists of high grade steel rolled into shape and fastened to the bed plate by means of supporting feet, which are electrically welded to the yoke. In the larger machines, the frame is split horizontally to aid in the assembly of the machine parts, and the two sections are bolted together.

The field poles and interpoles consist of sheet steel laminations riveted together. The use of laminated poles reduces the iron losses, which are produced by eddy currents in the pole face. The shape of the pole face depends upon the performance characteristics desired, and careful consideration is usually given to this particular feature, especially if the machine is to have large load fluctuations. The shunt field coils consist of a large number of turns and are wound of insulated (usually cotton-covered) wire and shaped on insulated forms. The series and interpole windings consist of a few turns of strip copper. The series field winding is placed on the main field poles over the shunt field winding, where it is securely held in position, and the interpole winding is placed on a small narrow-faced pole between the main field poles.

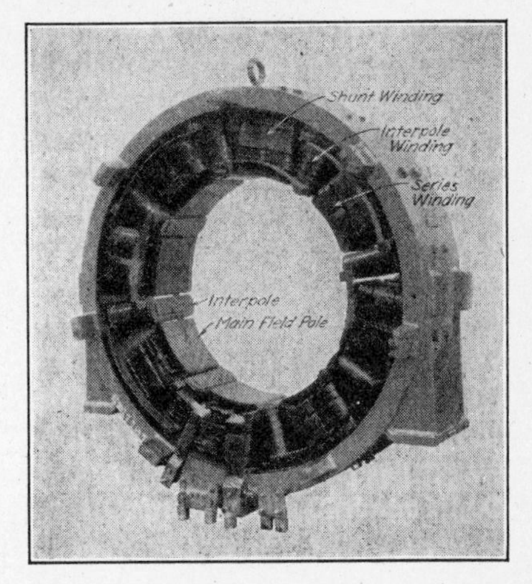

Fig. 1–1. Field structure of a d-c machine showing the main field poles and the interpoles. (Courtesy of Allis-Chalmers Mfg. Co.)

The larger generators are usually supplied with a compensating winding to compensate for the main field flux distortion which is caused by sudden changes in load. These windings are similar to those of the armature, except that the windings are placed in slots cut in the main pole face. These windings are fully insulated and are connected in series with the series field and armature windings. Figure 1–1 shows the field structure of a compound generator. The frame is of rolled steel and is split to aid in assembling the armature in the machine. The interpole winding and series field winding are usually connected in series. Figure 2–1a shows the same type of machine with the addition of the compensating winding placed in each main pole face. The addition of this compensating winding obviously increases the cost of the machine and, therefore, would be placed only on machines subjected to abnormal load

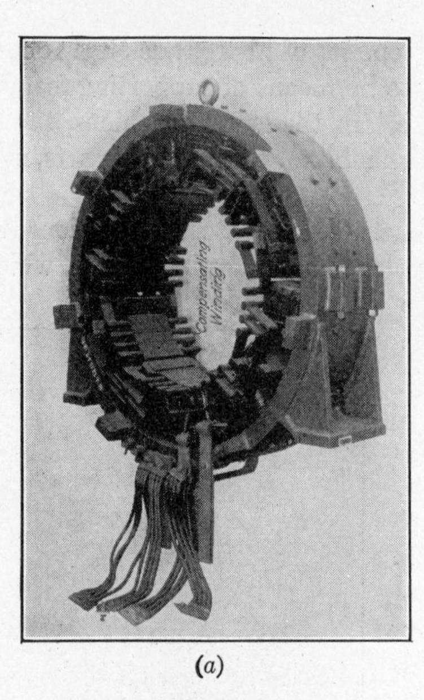

(a)

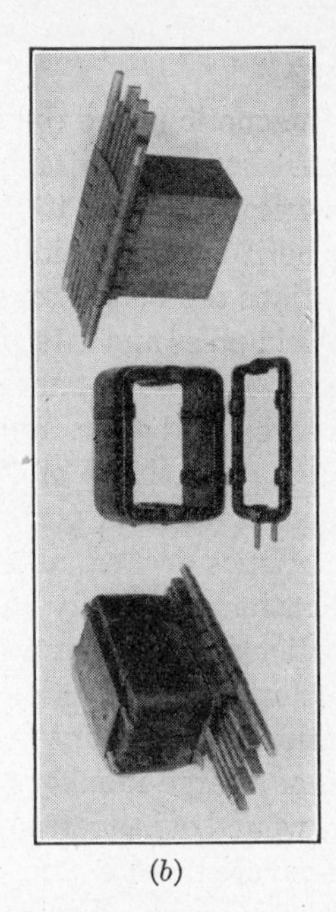

(b)

Fig. 2–1. (a) The position of the compensating windings with respect to the main field poles and the interpoles. (b) Construction of the field pole showing the shunt, series, and compensating windings. (Courtesy of Allis-Chalmers Mfg. Co.)

Fig. 3–1. Field structure and brush rigging for a 1000-hp, 300–600-rpm motor (Courtesy of Allis-Chalmers Mfg. Co.)

conditions. The field poles are each bolted to the outside frame. Figure 2–1b shows the laminated field pole and coils for a machine of this type. The compensating bars are fastened in the pole face and con-

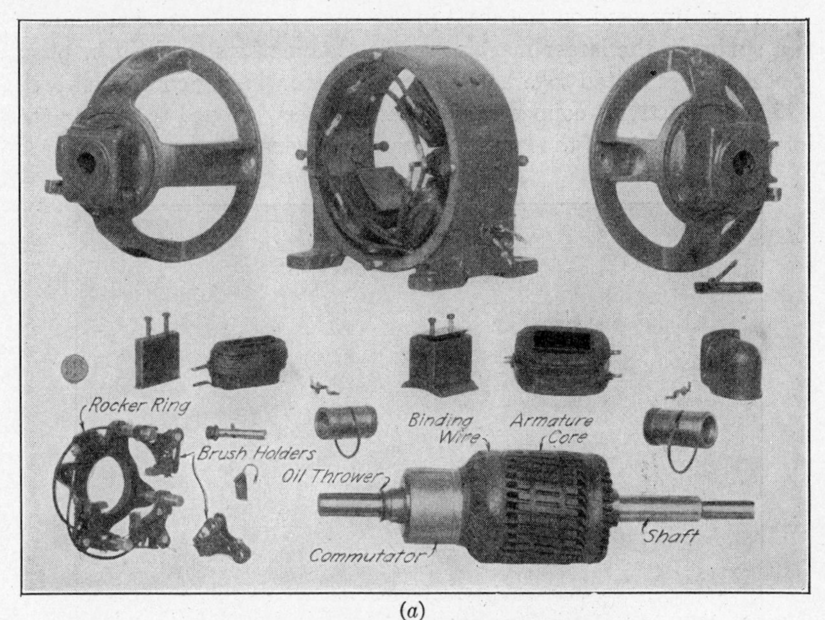

(a)

(b)

FIG. 4–1. (a) Parts of interpole shunt-wound machine. (b) The assembled machine. (Courtesy of General Electric Co.)

nected together with heavy bars. The shunt field coil and series field coil are wound separately and are thoroughly insulated.

Figure 3–1 shows the field structure and brush rigging for a heavy-duty machine. The electrical connection to the brushes is made through the two insulated bars on the two sides of the support for the brushes. Alternate sets of brushes are connected to the same bar.

The armature core consists of laminated steel punchings (usually silicon steel) pressed on the shaft in the smaller machines or assembled on a spider in the larger machines. The laminations are held in place by cast flanges bolted together. The armature winding consists of coils of high conductivity copper wire or bars properly shaped to fit into the slots on the surface of the laminated core. The insulated coils are placed

Fig. 5–1. A 7000-hp, 50–120-rpm, twin-unit motor. (Courtesy of Allis-Chalmers Mfg. Co.)

in the slots and held in position by insulated wedges. The windings are also held together by the use of steel binding bands placed around the windings.

The commutator consists of a large number of high grade copper bars, accurately wedge shaped, the outer surfaces of which form a true cylindrical surface. The bars are insulated from each other by mica and are held in place by mica-insulated end rings. Slots are cut in each bar for soldering the ends of the coil windings to the individual bars.

The carbon brushes have the proper hardness to prevent excessive wear on the commutator and the proper contact area to carry the armature current without excessive heating. The brush yoke and brush rigging may be fastened to the machine frame or, in the large machines, may be assembled and fastened to the base, independent of the machine yoke. The brush holders are insulated from their support as the brushes make contact to the commutator and have a voltage between them equal to the system voltage.

Figure 4–1*a* shows the various parts of a shunt-wound dynamo. It will be noted that the armature winding consists of formed coils each carefully shaped to fit in the armature slots. Binding wire has been wound around the armature winding near the two ends and center to hold the windings in position. Figure 4–1*b* shows the assembled machine. The brushes may be shifted on the commutator in order to obtain good commutation, as the load changes but, if the machine has interpoles, the brushes need not be shifted after once having been properly set. The brush pressure on the commutator is adjusted by individual springs on each brush.

Figure 5–1 shows a heavy-duty, slow speed, twin-unit motor. Because of the heavy current flow, the brush holders are heavily constructed and the brush contact on the commutator is large. This type of motor is used in steel-mill service. The bearings for this unit are very heavy so that they can withstand the stresses which occur during the operation of the mill. The heavy compensating windings can be seen on the left-hand unit of the motor.

Figure 6–1*a* shows a single-unit heavy-duty motor. In addition to the series field winding and interpoles, this motor has a compensating winding. The current capacity is more than the capacity of either of the units shown in Fig. 5–1. This is shown by the increase in size of the commutator and brush rigging. The machine is mounted on a fabricated steel base. The field coils are shown in Fig. 6–1*b*, and the field windings are placed around an insulated form of the same size as the field pole.

4. A-C Machine Construction. Fundamentally, the a-c machines and d-c machines are alike. The real difference between the two classes is the necessity of having a commutator on the d-c machine. The stationary part of the a-c machine is called the stator and the revolving member the rotor.

The stator frames are designed to withstand all mechanical stresses and, as in the d-c machines, this frame may be cast iron or fabricated steel, depending upon the machine capacity and magnetic density in the iron. The laminated armature punchings are of high grade steel and are built up with lap joints in the yoke (or frame) to reduce the magnetic circuit reluctance. These laminations are held from slipping, by either keys or projecting lugs, which can be securely fastened to the frame. In the larger machines, the armature core may consist of several sections, with each section built of laminated iron punchings. These sections are carefully assembled into a completed iron structure which appears as one perfect punching.

The speed at which the machine is operated controls the shape and size of the armature as well as the rotating field. The high speed (turbine drive) machines have few poles and the armature windings are connected for a small number of poles. On the other hand, there is a larger number of poles in the slow speed (engine or water wheel drive)

(a)

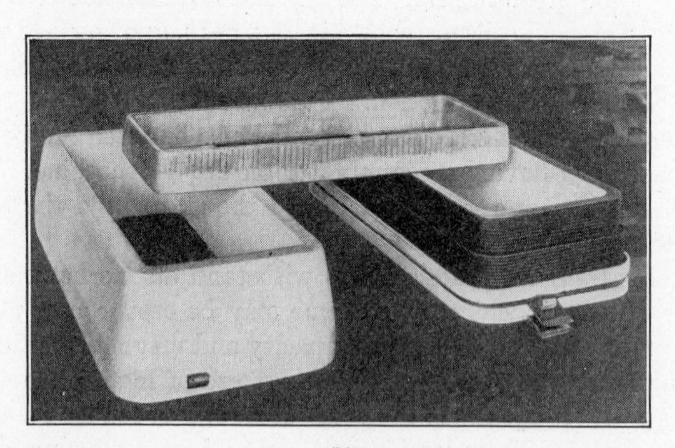

(b)

FIG. 6-1. A 4500-hp, 600-volt, 125–282-rpm, d-c motor. (Courtesy of Allis-Chalmers Mfg. Co.)

machines, and the windings are connected for a larger number of poles. The high speed rotors have non-salient poles; the slow speed rotors have salient poles. The armature coils for both types of machines are form-wound coils and, if one fails, it can be removed and a new one installed with a minimum amount of labor. The ventilation is very important, and considerable work is required by the designer to insure proper cooling. Ventilation may be accomplished by fans on the rotor or by air forced from some auxiliary source. In the latter case, the machine is totally enclosed.

The rotor core for slow speed units is often made of cast iron and, in large units, the spider is machined and slotted to hold the individual poles of the machine. The windings for these poles are similar to those for

(a)

(b)

FIG. 7-1. (a) Engine-type alternator without rotor bearings. (b) Rotor of engine-type alternator showing field coils and amortisseur windings. (Courtesy of Allis-Chalmers Mfg. Co.)

the d-c machines, and the connection of the ends to the d-c source of excitation is accomplished through two slip rings.

The rotor for the high speed machines is usually a solid steel forging and is slotted for the individual coil windings. This type of rotor has non-salient poles, and the finished rotor is smooth on the surface in order to reduce the air friction loss.

The class of alternating machines just discussed required some auxiliary means of d-c excitation for the field of the machine. In single machine installations, this may be furnished by a small d-c generator direct-connected to the rotor shaft but, if several a-c machines are placed in the same plant, a large separately driven d-c generator may be used to supply the excitation for the several machines.

Figure 7-1*a* shows a view of an engine-driven alternator of the slow speed type. The frame is cast in two sections with provisions for mounting on a separate base or on the engine base. The rotor is shown without bearings for mounting on an engine shaft. The rotor for this type of alternator (Fig. 7–1*b*) is a welded plate spider with the individual field coils mounted on the rim. The d-c supply to the revolving field is connected through the insulated slip rings fastened to the rotor. It

(*a*)

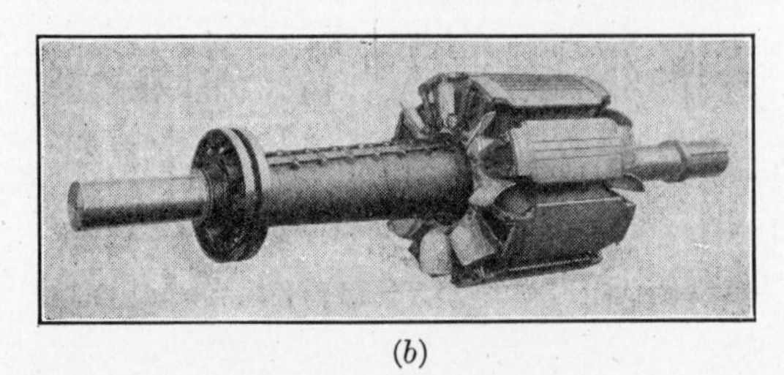

(*b*)

FIG. 8–1. (*a*) Detail view of rotor showing field poles, field coils, and amortisseur winding. (*b*) Rotor of a high speed engine-type alternator with a solid spider. (Courtesy of Allis-Chalmers Mfg. Co.)

is possible to increase the rotor weight for flywheel effect and, in this manner, eliminate the necessity of a separate flywheel. An amortisseur winding is shown on the rotor. This winding consists of bars embedded in the pole faces and connected to common bands on the two sides of the poles. Although it is quite similar in construction to the compensating winding of the d-c machines, its purpose is to prevent hunting, which is sudden variations in the speed of the rotor.

The detailed view of Fig. 8–1*a* shows the field pole windings and amortisseur winding of a rotor of the slow speed engine type. The speed of a rotor of this type is approximately 100 to 200 revolutions per minute. In Fig. 8–1*b* is shown the rotor of a high speed synchronous motor. Fundamentally, the design of the rotor is the same as in the slow speed machine but, because of the increased peripheral velocity

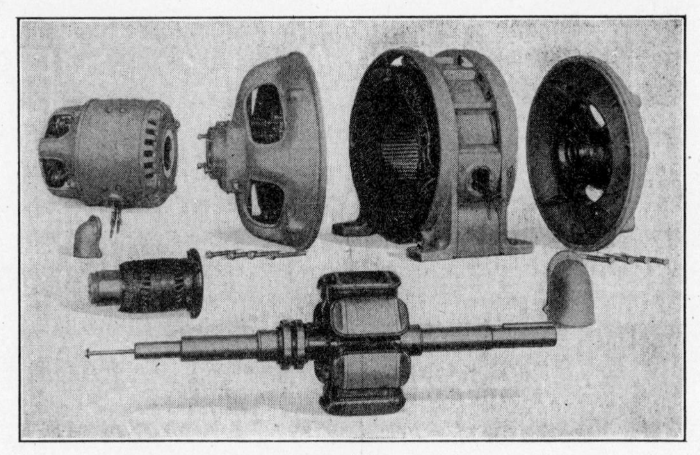

(*a*)

(*b*)

FIG. 9–1. (*a*) Dismantled view of a typical small alternator with a direct-connected exciter. (*b*) Assembled machine and exciter. (Courtesy of Allis-Chalmers Mfg. Co.)

of the rotor, the field poles are dovetailed into the solid iron spider and the field coils are held in place by heavy wedges. In nearly every case, the field poles are built of laminated steel punchings.

Figure 9–1 shows a dismantled view and an assembled view of a typical small a-c generator with a direct-connected exciter. The generator armature winding is on a laminated core held together by two cast end frames, and the bearing housings, which are machined castings, are fastened to these end frames. The rotor has a solid spider of the type shown in Fig. 8–1*b*. The small d-c exciter for the field winding fastens on the end of one bearing housing with its armature directly connected to the field winding of the a-c generator.

The six views of Fig. 10–1 show the sequence in assembling the stator and rotor of a turbo-alternator. The stator yoke consists of a fabri-

Fig. 10–1.

cated steel structure which has been machined to hold the armature laminations. These laminations are stacked in the yoke and held in place by end clamps. The formed armature coils are placed in the slots and the ends of the coils are fastened together to give a three-phase source of voltage. The large openings in the yoke are the ventilating ducts for the armature. The views of the rotor show the assembled field windings and the ventilated coil retaining rings. The coils are embedded in the iron to reduce the windage loss in the rotor. Rotors for large machines sometimes weigh several tons.

Figure 11–1 shows the stator and rotor of an 8850-horsepower, 360-revolution per minute synchronous motor used to drive a motor-generator set for steel mill service. The rotor of the machine has an amortisseur winding which is bolted to the spider and each field pole is

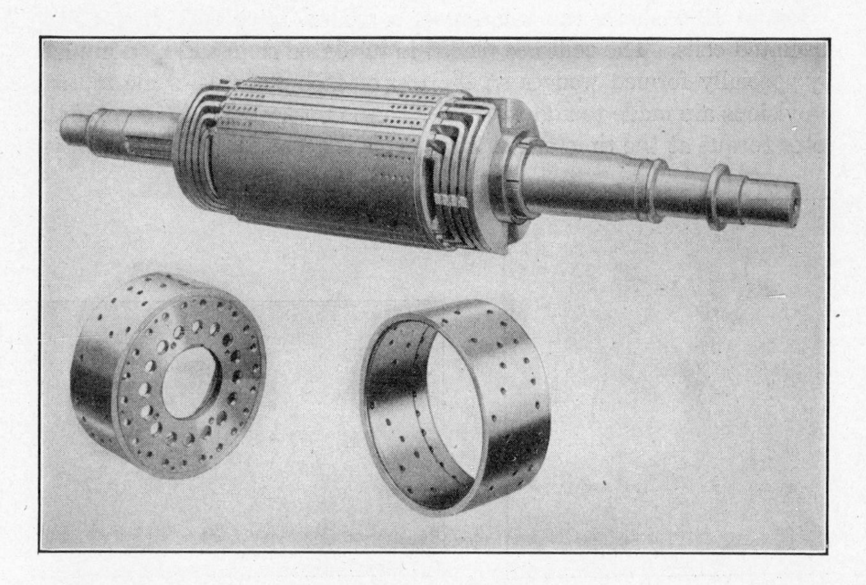

FIG. 10–1. Stator and rotor construction of a modern turbo-alternator. The machine rating is 9375 kva, 80% power factor, 11,500 volts, 3-phase, 60 cycles, 3600 rpm. (Courtesy of Allis-Chalmers Mfg. Co.)

dovetailed into this spider. The construction of the stator is similar to that of the alternator in Fig. 10–1.

The induction motor is the most widely used a-c motor. The stator (armature) of the induction motor is similar in construction to the synchronous motor stator. The rotor, however, obtains its excitation from the stator winding by induction, as suggested by the name of the motor.

The rotor is a closed circuit winding, and the induced rotor voltage supplies the necessary rotor current. The rotor winding may consist of insulated conductors connected together; or of bare copper bars. Both types of windings are embedded in slots on a laminated steel core.

Figure 12–1 shows the winding of a wound rotor with formed and insulated coils. The coils are placed in insulated slots and held in place by specially formed wedges at the top of each slot. In some motors, provisions are made to add resistance to the rotor circuit to increase the rotor torque at the time of starting. This is accomplished in two ways:

(a)

(b)

FIG. 11–1. Stator and rotor of an 8850-hp, 360 rpm synchronous motor used in the steel mill industry for driving motor-generator sets. (Courtesy of Allis-Chalmers Mfg. Co.)

(1) by bringing the ends of the rotor windings to the slip rings and connecting resistance between the slip rings, (2) by incorporating the resistance into the rotor structure and having it short-circuited after starting by means of centrifugal devices or by means of a rod external to the rotor.

Figure 13–1 shows typical rotor laminations for the various types of induction motors. The torque developed by the rotor is influenced by the depth and shape of the winding slots. The motor performance is controlled by the kind of rotor used.

Figure 14–1 shows the construction of a squirrel cage rotor for an induction motor. Although the construction of the rotor differs for different manufacturers, the rotor consists essentially of a one-piece cast grill, copper bars, and a laminated iron core. This particular rotor winding consists of two closed electrical circuits. The small bars form a winding having a high resistance and a low reactance because of the small cross section of the bar and the high reluctance of the magnetic circuit. The large bars form a winding having a low resistance and a high reactance at starting, because the cross section is large and the magnetic circuit reluctance is low. In this type of construction, the laminations

(*a*) (*b*)

(*c*)

FIG. 12–1. (*a*) The slotted rotor without windings. (*b*) Partially wound rotor. (*c*) Wound rotor showing slip rings. (Courtesy of General Electric Co.)

shown in Fig. 13–1*c* are used. Figure 15–1 shows the complete rotor assembled on the shaft.

WINDINGS

The armature windings of electrical machines may be divided into two classes: open circuit and closed circuit. As suggested by the name, an open circuit winding does not close on itself but forms a continuous path of many conductors in series, terminating at the two ends of the winding. In polyphase machines, there are more than one of these windings, identical in construction but displaced from each other electrically by the required angle of displacement, which depends upon the number of phases. The closed circuit winding has a complete electrical circuit closed upon itself. Thus, each closed circuit winding in a two-pole machine has two parallel paths. It is possible to think of a closed

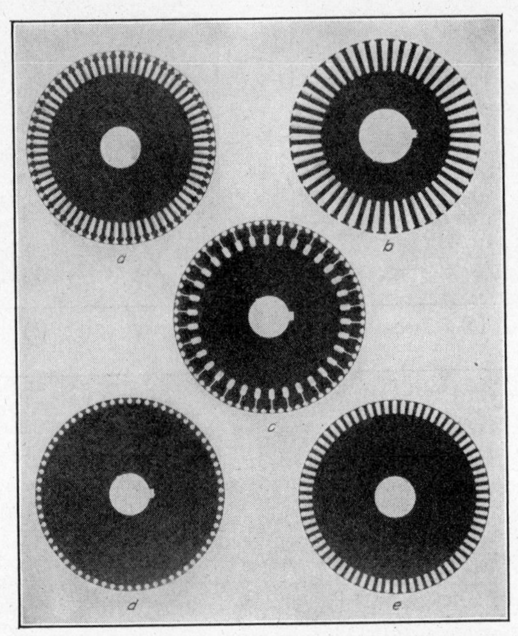

FIG. 13–1. Typical rotor laminations for induction motors: (*a*) normal torque, low starting current; (*b*) wound rotor; (*c*) high torque, low starting current; (*d*) high torque, high slip; (*e*) normal torque, normal starting current. (Courtesy of General Electric Co.)

circuit winding as two open circuit windings connected in parallel between the terminal connections. Figure 16–1 shows the principle of the open circuit and closed circuit windings. The power ratings of the two machines as indicated in (*a*) and (*b*) would be identical. The voltage of (*b*) would be one-half that of (*a*) because only $N/2$ turns are available between terminals, but the current capacity of (*b*) would be two times that of (*a*). This makes the power rating of the two types of windings the same. The coils for both types of windings are formed separately and insulated and then placed in the insulated slots. The end connections of the coils are fastened together and the ends, themselves, are thoroughly insulated from each other.

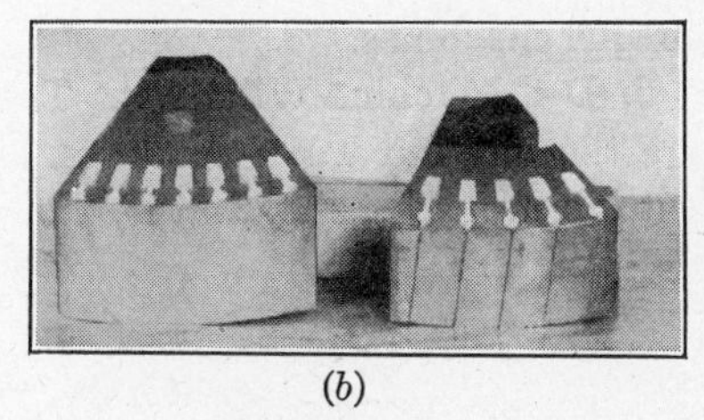

(a) (b)

Fig. 14–1. (a) Sectional view of a cast winding for a squirrel cage rotor. The iron laminations were removed with acid. (b) Two sections of a cast aluminum squirrel cage rotor showing the closed slot and partially open slot design. (Courtesy of General Electric Co.)

Fig. 15–1. Complete cast aluminum squirrel cage rotor. (Courtesy of General Electric Co.)

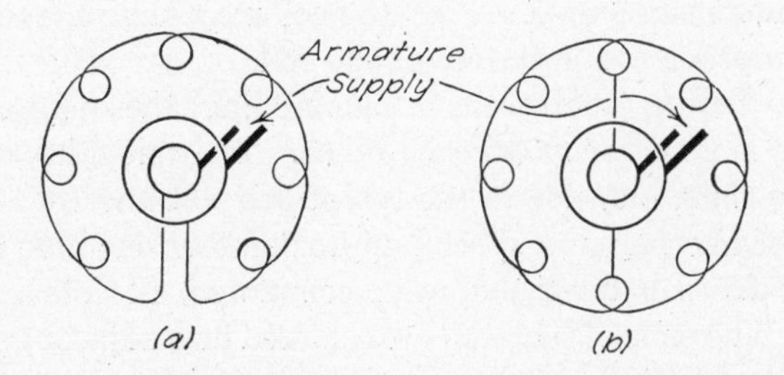

Fig. 16–1. (a) Open circuit winding. (b) Closed circuit winding.

One type of winding is made of insulated copper bars shaped to fit in the slots, with the end connections of the windings brazed, welded, or bolted together. Another type of winding is composed of many turns of insulated wire which has been formed and shaped into a coil to fit the armature slots. The connections of the windings are brazed together. The formed coil of several turns of wire is widely used in the smaller machines.

5. D-C Machine Windings. The windings used for most d-c machines are the lap and wave windings. Nearly all d-c armatures are wound with form-made coils; that is, the coils are wound, insulated, and shaped

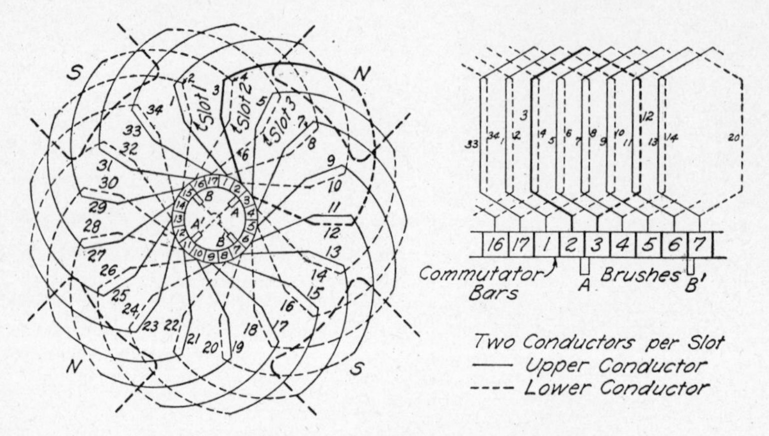

FIG. 17–1. Simplex lap winding for d-c machines.

ready for the armature slots by a special machine. The sides of the coil should be spaced so that, when one coil side is under a north pole, the other coil side is approximately under a south pole. This spacing is called the coil pitch and should be approximately equal to the pole pitch. In some instances, however, the coil may have a fractional pitch in order to improve commutation of the coil.

In the lap winding (adjacent coils overlapping) the successive coils are placed in the slots adjacent to each other. The coil sides are placed in the armature slots, one side in the top of one slot and the other side in the bottom of another slot, spaced approximately one pole pitch apart. The winding closes on itself and, when completed, all slots are filled with conductors. The ends of each coil are soldered into adjacent commutator bars. The brushes are placed in such a way with respect to the poles that the difference in potential between brushes is the maximum voltage generated in the band of conductors between them.

As the winding closes on itself, a simplex * lap winding has as many parallel paths for current through the armature as there are poles and as many brushes are required as there are poles. In a four-pole machine with a simplex lap winding, four brushes are necessary and there are four parallel paths through the armature winding. Figure 17–1 shows the developed winding of a four-pole machine which has a simplex lap winding. The position of the four brushes is shown and it will be noted that the brushes short-circuit the coils, which do not have a voltage generated in them at the instant the direction of the current flow is reversed.

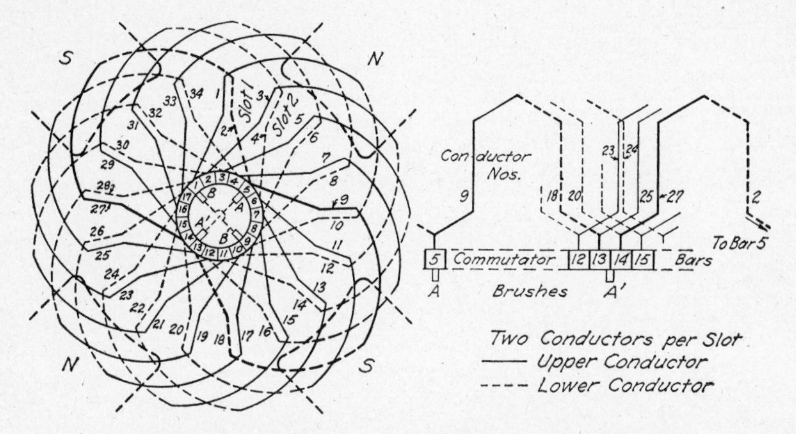

Fig. 18–1. Simplex wave winding for d-c machines.

In machines of large capacity, the windings may be more complicated than the one just indicated. The coils may be of such a number and pitch that several of the simplex windings may be placed in parallel on the same armature. In this event, the winding is called a multiplex lap winding and the number of parallel paths for the current is equal to the number of poles multiplied by the degree of multiplicity.

The wave winding differs from the lap winding in the shape of the coil and the number of paths through the armature. The wave winding, instead of having coils placed adjacent to each other, advances around the armature many times before the slots are filled and the winding closes on itself. This type of winding usually has more conductors in series between brushes and, consequently, can be made to produce a higher voltage. To balance this advantage, there are only two parallel paths

* A simplex winding is a single-coil winding. When there are two or more simplex windings in parallel the winding is a multiplex one.

through the armature winding, regardless of the number of poles and, for this reason, the current capacity of the machine is less than it would be if a lap winding were used.

Figure 18–1 shows the development of a simplex wave winding for a four-pole machine. It will be noted that, although the machine has four poles, there are only two paths for the current through the winding.

The two types of windings have advantages and disadvantages, and the type of the winding used depends upon the kind of machine in which it is to be used. The wave winding, for example, has the advantage that it supplies a higher potential for the same number of poles and conductors than a lap winding. It has another advantage in that the voltage generated is supplied by the series conductors under all the poles of the machine, and any variation in field strength of the poles or of the air gap do not produce unequal currents in the windings. It is often necessary in the lap-wound machines to use equalizers between corresponding points in the various paths to balance the currents in the armature windings.

It is possible to use only two sets of brushes for the wave winding, regardless of the number of poles. This is an advantage, especially for motors which are not readily accessible. Two examples of motors which are practically inaccessible are the railway and crane motors, and if wave windings are used on these motors the servicing of the brushes is made easier.

When large currents are necessary, the lap winding is more satisfactory because of the increased number of armature paths. The maximum current per path, which is limited by the size of the conductor, is approximately 250 amperes and, for this reason, heavy current machines require many parallel paths which can be obtained only by lap windings.

The comparison of the simplex lap and wave windings can be summarized as (1) the lap winding has as many paths for the current as the machine has main poles; (2) the wave winding has only two paths for the current, regardless of the number of poles.

6. A-C Machine Windings. The d-c machines use closed circuit windings and the minimum number of parallel paths between terminals (brushes) is two. For a-c machines, either the open circuit or the closed circuit winding may be used, but the former is more common. Thus, the d-c machine winding may be employed as an a-c winding, but the reverse is not generally true unless the latter is reentrant or closes on itself. The rotary converter which ties together both a-c and d-c systems uses a closed winding. This machine has a revolving armature.

In the a-c winding, the conductors of a particular phase may be placed in one slot under a pole or they may be distributed among several slots under a pole. The first method is called the concentrated winding and the second, the distributed winding. The distributed winding is used if possible since a distribution of the windings around the armature will

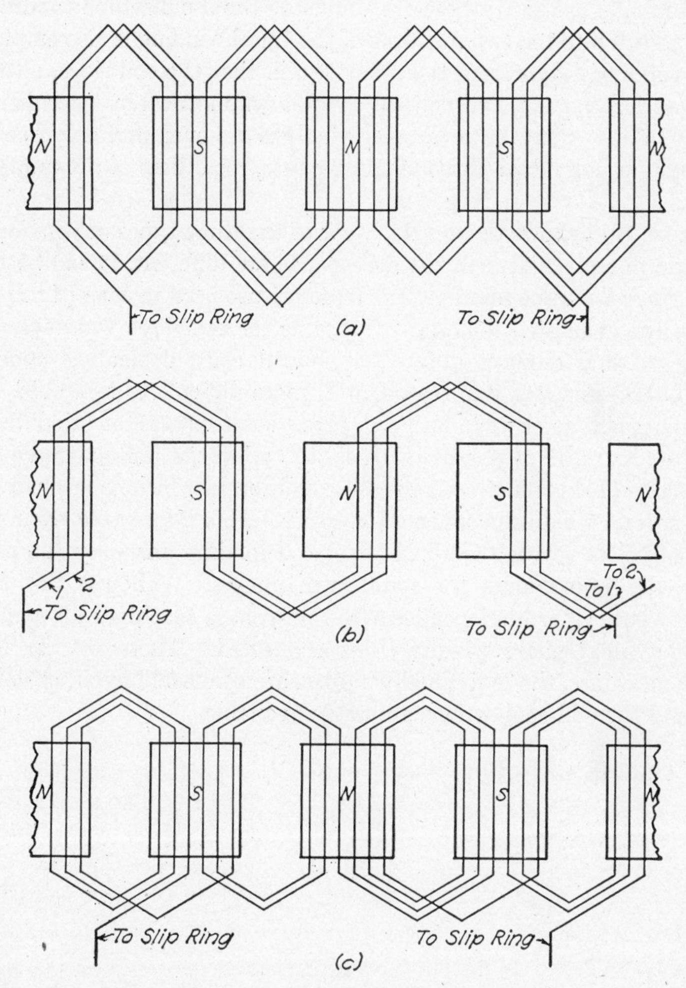

FIG. 19–1. Distributed winding for a-c machines: (*a*) lap winding; (*b*) wave winding; (*c*) spiral winding.

help to distribute the losses uniformly and, as a result, aid in dissipating the heat generated. Also the distribution in several slots reduces the reactance of the armature winding. Two conflicting conditions affect the armature reactance; that is, as the pitch factor is increased the total flux cut is increased, and at the same time the winding reactance is increased. The result is a compromise regarding the armature voltage per coil and reactance per coil required to give satisfactory machine performance. For a-c machines, both the lap and wave windings (barrel windings) are used; these are similar to the d-c machine windings.

In addition to the two mentioned, the spiral winding is also employed. This winding differs from the other two in that the coil sides, although symmetrical in generated voltage, are not symmetrical in space distribution. In any event, however, the windings are open and only one path through an individual phase winding exists, regardless of the number of poles.

Figure 19–1 shows the development of the three types of windings for a single phase. Although the coil shapes are different, it will be noted that, since the same number of conductors are used in each of the three types, the generated voltage is the same for the three windings. The spiral winding requires differently shaped coils, depending upon the distribution and, for this reason, it is more difficult to assemble. The added advantage of wave form, however, compensates for the difficulty.

As the number of phases increase, the windings become more complicated. This is illustrated by the condition in which each phase may have several windings connected in series. This means that each phase can consist of several windings displaced in time phase by the proper angle, depending upon the number of phases. Although the single-phase windings are independent, the polyphase machines always have the individual phase windings interconnected. Therefore, for three-phase machines, the individual windings are connected in either delta or star and the end connections are made available.

CHAPTER 2

THE MAGNETIC CIRCUIT

The circuit chapters have dealt with the electrical circuit in a manner which presupposes that the voltages on (or in) the system are definitely established and that conditions are not transient but steady state. When a machine is operating, it fulfills the requirements of an electrical circuit, but it depends for its operating performance not only upon its electrical characteristics (governed by the impedance of the windings) but also upon the properties of the magnetic circuit.

Whereas the electrical system is subjected to rather accurate and rigorous treatment, the magnetic system is not easily confined and, therefore, the results cannot be predicted so accurately as can those for the electrical system. Many of the magnetic designs depend more upon judgment and experience than upon theoretical treatment. Even the previous history of the material may influence the result and it is possible to have different magnetic conditions for the same excitation.

Many of the magnetic circuit problems depend on "cut and try" or "trial and error" methods for their solution. In the magnetic circuits,

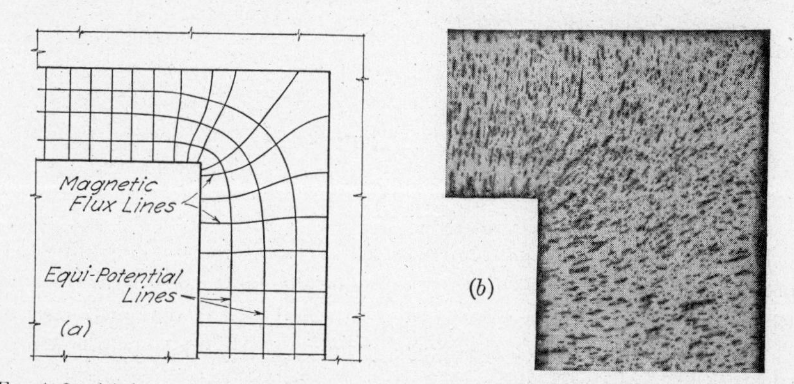

FIG. 1–2. (*a*) A magnetic field for an inside and outside corner. (*b*) Iron filing pattern of the same magnetic field.

the mathematical expressions contain both $\mathcal{B}$ and μ which are dependent upon each other. Under these conditions, it is necessary to assume a value for one of these unknowns and solve for the other. This method must be continued until the two values check for the material considered.

Sometimes several trials are necessary before the proper relationships are established. Often the amount of "fringing" (leakage of flux) is dependent upon knowledge of the configuration of the magnetic path and, since this is not reducible to mathematical treatment alone, it is necessary to confirm the results by either past experience or further investigations. It is possible, by means of templates, to determine the nature of the flux distribution in air gaps; this can be supplemented by actual flux plotting for the determination of the reluctance. Figure 1–2 shows a simple arrangement, using templates, for determining the flux distribution in an air gap, and also the corresponding flux plot for the arrangement.

1. Magnetic Units. The history of the attempt to establish units for the calculation of magnetic circuits has been one of considerable argument and, even at the present time, there is no definite international nomenclature or system, except for a few isolated units, by which to measure or express important magnetic relationships. Table I–2 gives the name, symbol, and unit of the magnetic units adopted by the International Electrotechnical Commission in 1930.

TABLE I–2

CGS MAGNETIC UNITS AND THEIR NAMES

Name	Symbol	Unit
1. Magnetomotive force	$\mathcal{F}$	Gilbert [1]
2. Magnetizing force	$\mathcal{H}$	Oersted [1]
3. Magnetic flux	ϕ	Maxwell [1]
4. Magnetic flux density	$\mathcal{B}$	Gauss [1]
5. Magnetic permeance	$\mathcal{P}$	
6. Permeability (absolute)	μ	
7. Magnetic reluctance	$\mathcal{R}$	

[1] International Electrotechnical Commission, 1930.

The magnetic field and reluctance have been treated in Chapter 4 of Volume I under the analysis of the inductance in the electrical system; therefore, the treatment here will be confined to the magnetic circuit alone. Table II–2 gives a summary of the magnetic relationships which are of interest to the engineer.

2. Magnetic Materials. The usual classification of materials is *magnetic*, where the permeability is greater than one; *non-magnetic*, where the permeability is unity; or *diamagnetic* (of little interest to the engineer), where the permeability is less than one. Though machines are constructed with magnetic materials, non-magnetic materials are frequently encountered and must be considered in engineering design, in connection with both the high reluctance and benefits derived from their use in controlling the reluctance of the magnetic circuit. By proper selection of the magnetic materials, the designer concentrates the flux, reduces the reluctance, and minimizes the losses. Iron, in its many forms and combinations, is the most common magnetic material used in the construction of electrical machinery.

TABLE II–2

IMPORTANT MAGNETIC RELATIONSHIPS

Name	Relationship	
1. Magnetomotive force	$\mathcal{F} = \phi\mathcal{R}$	$\mathcal{F} = 0.4\pi NI$
2. Magnetizing force	$\mathcal{H} = f/m$	
3. Magnetic flux	$\phi = \mathcal{B}A$	
4. Magnetic flux density	$\mathcal{B} = \phi/A$	
5. Magnetic permeance	$\mathcal{P} = 1/\mathcal{R}$	
6. Permeability	$\mu = \mathcal{B}/\mathcal{H}$	
7. Magnetic reluctance	$\mathcal{R} = l/\mu A$	
8. Series reluctance	$\mathcal{R} = \mathcal{R}_1 + \mathcal{R}_2 + \mathcal{R}_3 \cdots$, etc.	
9. Parallel reluctance	$\frac{1}{\mathcal{R}} = \mathcal{P} = \frac{1}{\mathcal{R}_1} + \frac{1}{\mathcal{R}_2} + \frac{1}{\mathcal{R}_3} \cdots$, etc.	

f is the force in dynes, m is the pole strength, A is the area, l is the length (in cgs units). Other symbols are given in Table I–2.

Cast iron is used in the frames and housings of the machines and acts as a poor auxiliary path for the flux. Contrasted to this are the steels, which are alloyed to produce magnetic materials of very low loss and high permeability and are used in the laminated structures of machines, making excellent paths for the flux. Some of the irons have the ability to retain much of the magnetism even after the exciting force is removed. The permanent magnets in the meters are of carbon and alloyed steels and are capable of retaining their magnetism indefinitely, whereas magnetic cores of induction coils and electromagnets are frequently composed of a large number of fine wires and have practically no residual magnetism. In some of the cores, the material is even more finely subdivided by grinding the magnetic material into a fine powder and forming the core by high pressure.

Besides alloying and composition, previous history is another factor which enters into the characteristics of a magnetic material. The point at which the magnetizing cycle stopped when last used and the previous maximum value of flux density are of importance. The composition of the material is very important, for it determines the ability of the material to handle flux; the crystalline structure and even the temperature, if carried high enough, will affect the magnetic properties. Finally, magnetic properties of the materials are influenced by the maximum flux passed through the material and the number of recurrences of the flux cycles. These conditions are so complicated that only by repeated experimentation upon specific material is it possible to have a reliable record of the magnetization characteristic of any material, and two pieces of the same run of material may not be the same. The composite curve used in design applies only in a general way to a specific material. In a production process, it is not unusual to obtain a machine definitely inferior or superior to the average. If this particular machine is dismantled and assembled again with its parts distributed and incorporated into several other machines of the same type, no difference in characteristics will be noticed in the reassembled machines.

3. Magnetization Curves. Inspection of Table II–2 shows that the magnetic circuit has the following relationships:

$$\mathcal{B} = \frac{\phi}{A} \qquad (a\text{–}2)$$

$$\phi = \frac{\mathfrak{F}}{\mathcal{R}} \qquad (b\text{–}2)$$

$$\mathfrak{F} = 0.4\pi NI \qquad (c\text{–}2)$$

$$\mathcal{R} = \frac{l}{\mu A} \qquad (d\text{–}2)$$

If the equations (b–2), (c–2), and (d–2) are substituted in (a–2), the expression for $\mathcal{B}$ becomes

$$\mathcal{B} = \frac{0.4\pi NI\mu}{l} = 1.257\,\frac{NI\mu}{l} \qquad (e\text{–}2)$$

Reference to Fig. 6–2 shows that there is a definite relationship between $\mathcal{B}$ and μ and, therefore, it is necessary to have curves showing the relationship between permeability and flux density. The work may be simplified if the permeability and the ampere-turns are combined so that the magnetomotive force per unit length of path is given. These curves, when taken for a given magnetic material, are known as the magnetization curve for the specific material. Curves given in Fig. 2–2 show the magnetization curves for the usual class of materials used in magnetic circuit design for machines. These curves are typical of the material in general and are not absolute curves for any actual material being used in design.

The curves in Fig. 2–2 are drawn with flux density per square inch and ampere-turns per inch of length (the English system of units). Since

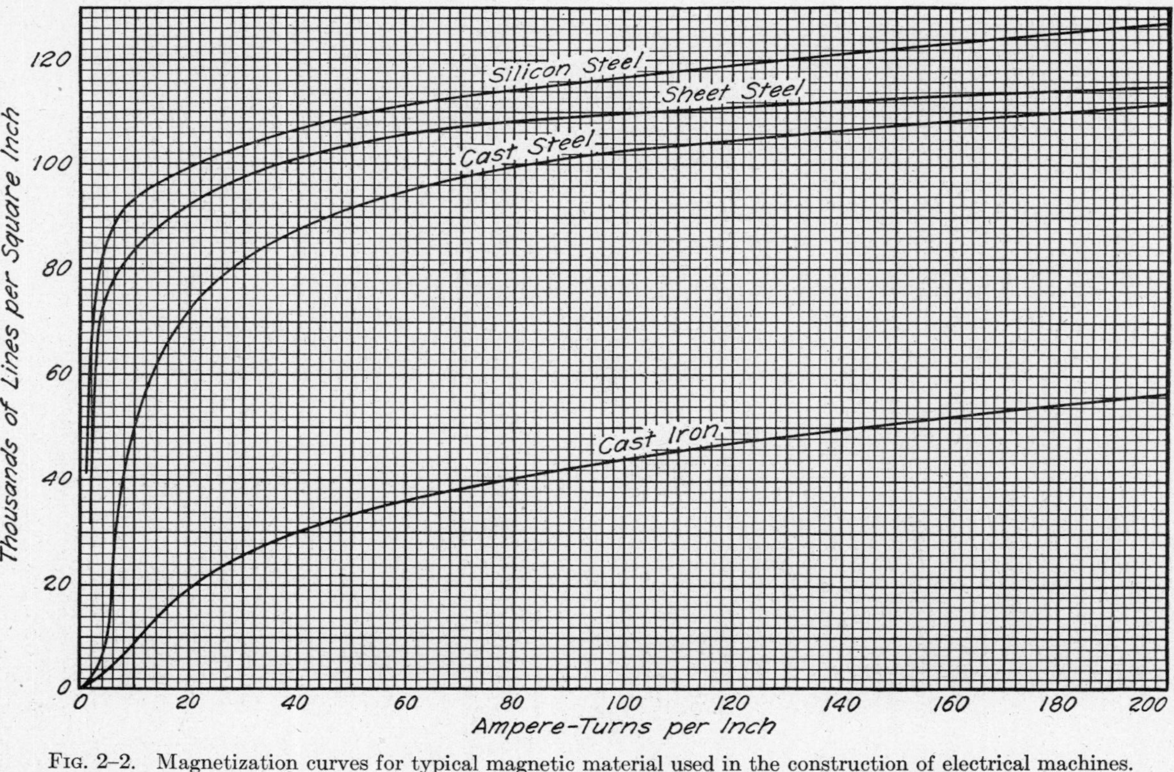

FIG. 2–2. Magnetization curves for typical magnetic material used in the construction of electrical machines.

most of the design in the United States is developed with the English unit, it is better to express the curves in these units rather than in the international units.

From the curves in Fig. 2–2 it will be noted that the flux increases proportionally with the ampere-turns through a limited range of excitation, but beyond that range additional ampere-turns do not produce proportional additional flux. The bend in the curve is called the "knee" of the curve and, beyond this point, the magnetic material approaches "saturation." For economy, magnetic circuits are so designed that they approach the knee of the curve but do not enter into the region of saturation. There is no definite point on the magnetization curve at which saturation begins.

4. Calculation of Ampere-Turns. In the calculation for ampere-turns, the amount of magnetomotive force necessary to produce the flux in a definite path is determined by the length of the path, the flux density, and the class of material. Assuming that it is necessary to determine the magnetomotive force to produce a flux density $\mathcal{B}$, from equation (e–2), the ampere turns will be

$$NI = 0.796 \frac{\mathcal{B}l}{\mu}$$

where the length is in centimeters and the flux density in gausses. When the medium is air, the permeability μ is unity. If, however, the determinations are to be made in English units, the conversion changes the expression to

$$NI = 0.796 \frac{\mathcal{B}}{(2.54)^2} \times \frac{2.54l}{\mu}$$

$$NI = 0.313 \frac{\mathcal{B}l}{\mu}$$

where the flux density $\mathcal{B}$ is in lines per square inch and the length l is in inches, with the total exciting force in ampere-turns.

By using the curves in Fig. 2–2, the factor 0.4π and the permeability are avoided. If the cross section of the path and the total flux are known, the number of ampere-turns per inch may be read from the curve after the lines per square inch have been determined.

5. Magnetic Circuit Calculations. Magnetic circuit calculations are best illustrated by means of problems using the magnetization curves.

Example a. Determine the ampere-turns necessary to produce 18×10^4 lines of flux in the air gap of the magnetic circuit shown in Fig. 3–2 (the core of silicon steel). To take care of the fringing in this small gap, the effective area is obtained by adding the length of the gap to the dimensions of the section of the steel path.

$$\mathcal{B}_{AB} = \mathcal{B}_{CD} = \frac{18 \times 10^4}{2 \times 1.5} = 60{,}000 \text{ lines per square inch}$$

$$l_{AB} + l_{CD} = 8 + 7.8 = 15.8 \text{ in.}$$

From the curve Fig. 2–2, 1.5 ampere-turns per inch are required and

$$NI = 1.5 \times 15.8 = 23.7 \text{ ampere-turns}$$

$$\mathcal{B}_{BC} = \mathcal{B}_{AD} = \frac{18 \times 10^4}{1.5 \times 1.5} = 80{,}000 \text{ lines per square inch}$$

$$l_{BC} + l_{AD} = 6 \text{ in.} + 6 \text{ in.} = 12 \text{ in.}$$

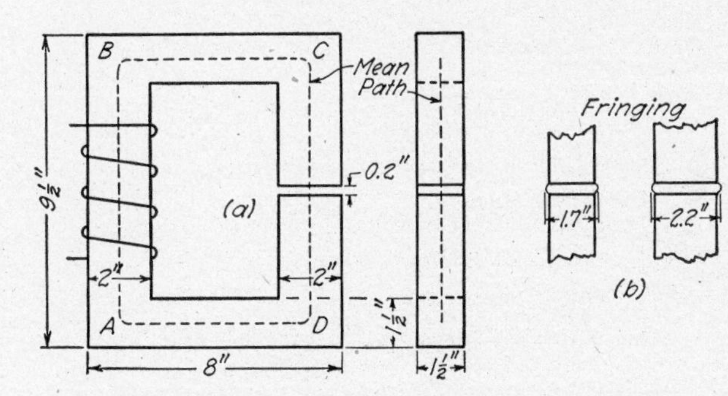

FIG. 3–2. Magnetic circuit calculated in Example *a*.

From the curve Fig. 2–2, 3.5 ampere-turns per inch are required and

$$NI = 3.5 \times 12 = 42 \text{ ampere-turns}$$

$$\text{Air-gap } NI = 0.313\mathcal{B}l = 0.313 \times \frac{18 \times 10^4}{1.7 \times 2.2} \times 0.2$$

$$= 3013 \text{ ampere-turns}$$

$$\text{Total } NI = 24 + 42 + 3013 = 3079 \text{ ampere-turns}$$

Note that 98 per cent of the total ampere-turns are needed for the air gap alone.

Example b. Determine the number of ampere-turns necessary to produce 27×10^4 lines of flux in the middle core of the magnetic structure shown in Fig. 4–2.

$$\mathcal{B}_{AB} = \mathcal{B}_{DE} = \frac{13.5 \times 10^4}{1.5 \times 1.5} = 60{,}000 \text{ lines per square inch}$$

Since this is a parallel magnetic circuit, only one of the parallel paths is considered. The mean length of the path will be

$$l_{AB} + l_{BC} + l_{CF} + l_{FA} = 8 \text{ in.} + 6.75 \text{ in.} + 8 \text{ in.} + 6.75 \text{ in.} = 29.5 \text{ in.}$$

$$29.5 \times 13 = 383.5 \text{ ampere-turns}$$

The value 13 is determined from the curves in Fig. 2–2.

The foregoing are simple magnetic circuits that may be used in electrical equipment. Figure 5–2 shows the magnetic circuit for a d-c machine. Though each field coil produces ampere-turns exciting two paths, as in Example *b*, the problem is much more complicated than in

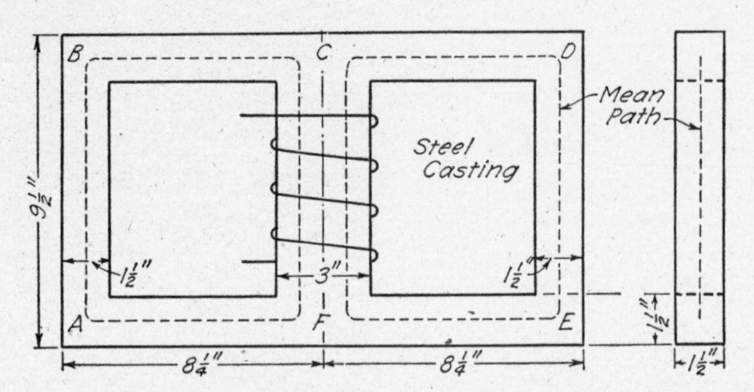

FIG. 4–2. Magnetic circuit calculated in Example *b*.

Example *b*; the solution of this type of problem should be studied under machine design. Empirical coefficients are used in this type of solution.

The foregoing examples have been solved by using curves for the specific material, so stated that the value 0.4π and the permeability need not be considered independently. If the circuit shown in Fig. 3–2

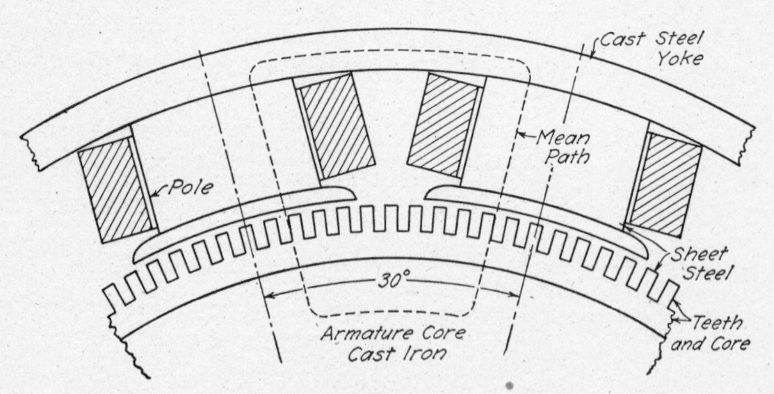

FIG. 5–2. Magnetic circuit of a generator.

is considered with the permeability curve (Fig. 6–2), the problem becomes one of "cut and try" or "trial and error." This type of problem is not unusual in the engineering field. The most satisfactory method of obtaining a solution is to assume a value in excess of the true value and one less than the true value; then, if a straight line relationship between the two points is assumed, the third solution will be accurate enough for most engineering determinations. The closer the two assumptions are to the true value, the more accurate will be the result, since the quantities do not usually vary linearly with respect to each other.

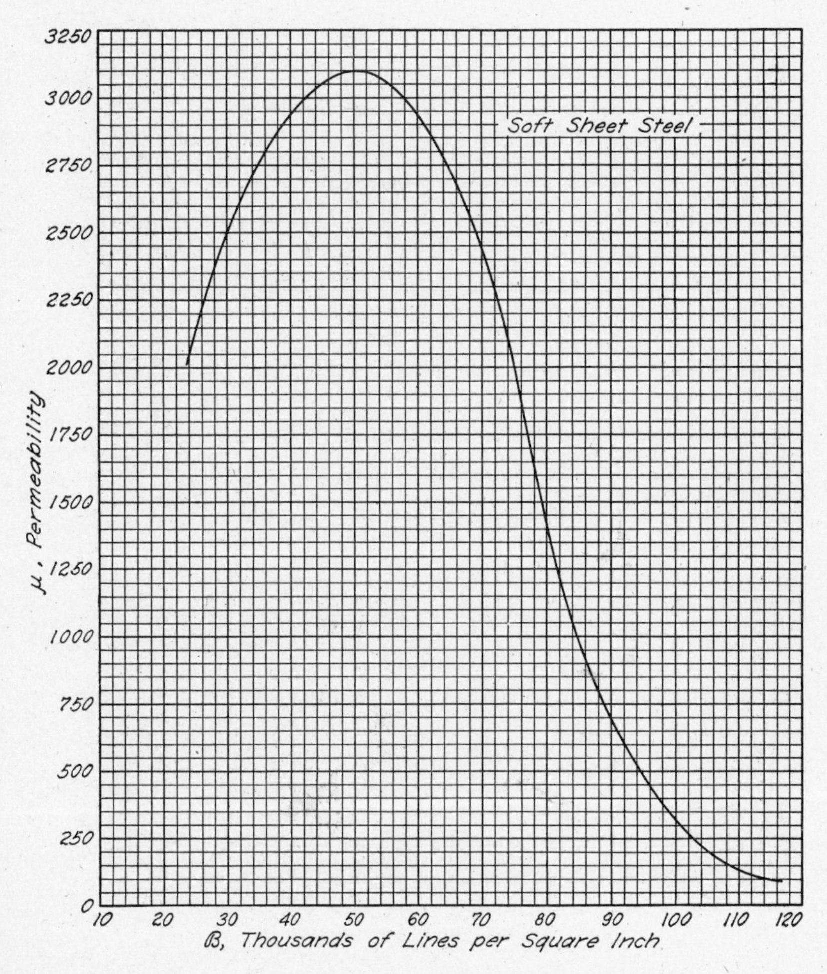

FIG. 6–2. Permeability flux density curve for sheet metal.

Example c. What would be the flux density and the total flux for the magnetic circuit shown in Fig. 3–2 if the coil carries 3.08 amp and has 1000 turns, and if the core is built of sheet steel?

To solve this problem, it is necessary to assume some flux density, and the density in the two different sections of the core will be inversely proportional to cross-sectional area, 3:2.25. Therefore, the reluctance of the air gap, uprights, and cross pieces will be different, the air-gap reluctance remaining constant regardless of the flux density.

General:

Reluctance of the air path

$$\mathcal{R}_A = \frac{0.2 \times 2.54}{(2.2 \times 1.7)(2.54)^2 \times 1}$$

$$= 0.0210$$

Reluctance of the uprights

$$\mathcal{R}_u = \frac{(8 + 7.8) \times 2.54}{(2 \times 1.5)(2.54)^2 \times \mu_u}$$

$$= \frac{2.074}{\mu_u}$$

Reluctance of the cross pieces

$$\mathcal{R}_c = \frac{(6 + 6) \times 2.54}{(1.5 \times 1.5)(2.54)^2 \times \mu_c} = \frac{2.100}{\mu_c}$$

Flux caused by m.m.f.

$$\phi_t = \frac{3.08 \times 1000 \times 0.4\pi}{\mathcal{R}_t} = \frac{3870}{\mathcal{R}_t}$$

First assumption:

$$\mathcal{B}_u = 70{,}000 \text{ lines per square inch}$$

$$\mu_u = 2450 \text{ (Fig. 6–2)}$$

$$\mathcal{B}_c = 93{,}400 \text{ lines per square inch}$$

$$\mu_c = 540 \text{ (Fig. 6–2)}$$

$$\mathcal{R}_A = 0.0210 \qquad \mathcal{R}_u = 0.00085 \qquad \mathcal{R}_c = 0.00389 \qquad \mathcal{R}_t = 0.02574$$

$$\phi = \frac{3870}{0.02574} = 150{,}100 \qquad \text{Calculated} \begin{cases} \mathcal{B}_u = 50{,}030 \\ \mathcal{B}_c = 66{,}800 \end{cases}$$

Second assumption:

$$\mathcal{B}_u = 50{,}000 \text{ lines per square inch}$$

$$\mu_u = 3100 \text{ (Fig. 6–2)}$$

$$\mathcal{B}_c = 66{,}700 \text{ lines per square inch}$$

$$\mu_c = 2650 \text{ (Fig. 6–2)}$$

$$\mathcal{R}_A = 0.0210 \qquad \mathcal{R}_u = 0.00067 \qquad \mathcal{R}_c = 0.00079 \qquad \mathcal{R}_t = 0.02246$$

$$\phi = \frac{3870}{0.02246} = 172{,}000 \qquad \text{Calculated} \begin{cases} \mathcal{B}_u = 57{,}330 \\ \mathcal{B}_c = 76{,}400 \end{cases}$$

By the first assumption, the calculated value is low; by the second assumption, the calculated value is high. The true value must lie between the two assumed values (consider a linear relationship).

Third assumption:

$$\mathcal{B}_u = 56{,}700 \text{ lines per square inch}$$

$$\mu_u = 3030 \text{ (Fig. 6–17)}$$

$$\mathcal{B}_c = 75{,}500 \text{ lines per square inch}$$

$$\mu_c = 1970$$

$$\mathcal{R}_A = 0.0210 \qquad \mathcal{R}_u = 0.000685 \qquad \mathcal{R}_c = 0.001065 \qquad \mathcal{R}_t = 0.02275$$

$$\phi = \frac{3870}{0.02275} = 170{,}000 \qquad \text{Calculated} \begin{cases} \mathcal{B}_u = 56{,}700 \\ \mathcal{B}_c = 75{,}500 \end{cases}$$

By the assumption of a straight line relationship (linear relationship) between the assumed and the calculated values, the third assumption gives a total flux of 170,000 lines per square inch. This degree of accuracy is better than could usually be expected in the actual performance of the finished magnetic circuit.

Total flux, approximately 170,000 lines.
Upright sections, approximately 57,000 lines per square inch.
Cross sections, approximately 76,000 lines per square inch.

Though this example by trial and error shows an interesting approach to an engineering problem, it would be better in this type of problem to change Fig. 6–2 to a curve similar to the one given for sheet steel in Fig. 2–2, where the flux density would be plotted against ampere-turns per inch. The expression for making the conversion would be

$$NI_{\text{per inch}} = 0.313 \frac{\mathcal{B}}{\mu}$$

where $\mathcal{B}$ would be the flux density in lines per square inch and μ would be the permeability (both are read from the curve in Fig. 6–2).

6. Losses in the Magnetic Circuit. It has already been pointed out that there is no loss of energy in maintaining a magnetic flux. If the flux is established in an air-core coil, the only loss comes from the I^2R losses of the copper on either a-c or d-c, this loss being radiated as heat. If, however, a magnetic material is introduced into the magnetic field of the coil, a wattmeter will indicate additional loss when the coil is attached to an a-c system. There will be additional loss in the d-c system, but it is relatively small because it occurs only when the system is opened or closed. Since this reversal of current occurs continuously in an a-c system, the loss is appreciable.

These losses, caused by the presence of magnetic material in the magnetic circuit, are a combination of both eddy current and hysteresis losses.

7. Hysteresis. A magnetic circuit containing magnetic materials has the ability to produce two or more different and independent values of flux density with the same field intensity. Both in testing and in operating electrical equipment, hysteresis affects the characteristics of the machine under consideration. It is desirable to be acquainted with this fact so that the peculiar phenomenon (which must be accepted) may also be recognized.

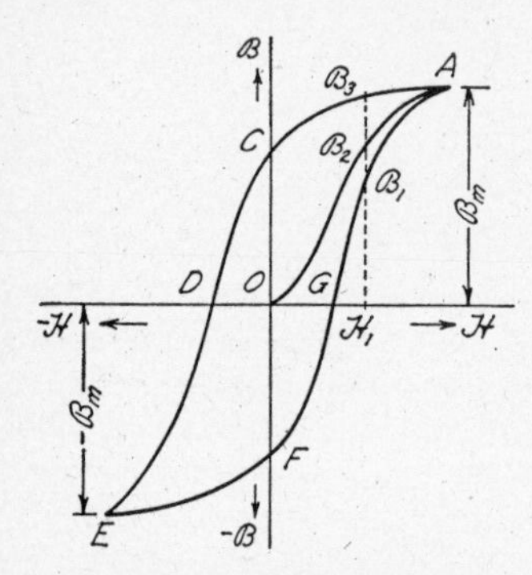

FIG. 7–2. Hysteresis loop showing three values of magnetic induction at one value of magnetic intensity.

In Fig. 7–2, the excitation of a magnetic circuit, which has previously been reduced to zero residual flux density, is traced. Starting at the point O, with zero excitation (magnetic intensity) and zero induction (flux density), the magnetic intensity is increased until point A is reached. The resultant curve is the normal magnetization curve for the material under consideration. This curve is similar to the curves given in Fig. 2–2. Its maximum excitation gives the maximum flux density $\mathcal{B}_m$, important in the magnetic cycle, because both the hysteresis loss and the eddy current loss are dependent on its value.

If the exciting force is decreased, the curve does not return along the same path but follows the path A to C and, after the exciting force is removed, there remains a magnetic induction equivalent to OC called the *remanence* or, more commonly by the engineer, *residual magnetism*. In order to bring the material to the point of zero magnetic induction, it is necessary to reverse the excitation, equal to OD (*coercive force*), reducing the flux density to the point D. If the reversed excitation is continued in order to obtain a negative maximum flux density $(-\mathcal{B}_m)$ equivalent to the positive maximum flux density, the curve reaches point E. By reducing the excitation to zero, the curve reaches the value F, leaving OF as a remanence. Again the reversal of the excitation will cause the curve to follow the FGA to point A. This completes the excitation versus magnetic induction cycle, and these curves form the hysteresis loop.

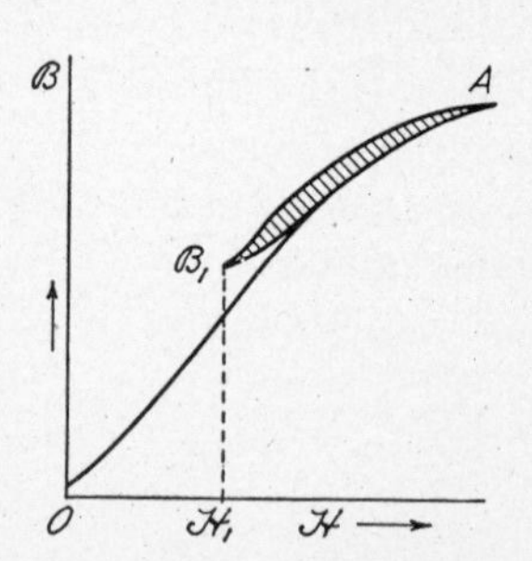

FIG. 8–2. Showing a small hysteresis loop on the magnetization curve caused by a reversal cycle.

In Fig. 7–2, at the excitation $\mathcal{H}_1$, three separate and distinct flux densities, $\mathcal{B}_1$, $\mathcal{B}_2$, and $\mathcal{B}_3$ (one for each portion in the history of the magnetic cycle), may be obtained. It is not necessary to follow the complete cycle as shown to obtain the hysteresis loop. If the excitation is continued to the maximum value shown in Fig. 7–2, then reduced as shown in Fig. 8–2, to a value $\mathcal{H}_1$, and increased again, there will be formed a small hysteresis loop which closes on the original normal magnetization curve. The smaller one is as truly a hysteresis loop as if the cycle had been carried through a reversal of equal flux density.

The hysteresis loop varies with the class of material. Figure 9–2 shows hysteresis loops for two different classes of magnetic material. One with low permeability, cast iron, gives the broad and large area loop; one with high permeability, Permalloy, gives the small area loop. These two represent extremes of the range of magnetic materials.

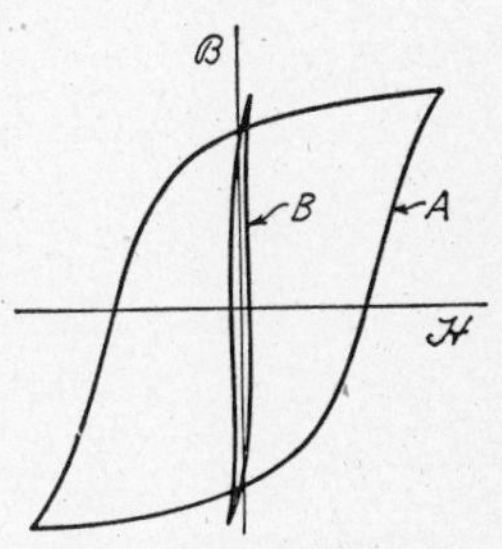

FIG. 9–2. Hysteresis loops for two different classes of magnetic material: (A) material of low permeability; (B) material of high permeability.

8. Hysteresis Losses. In addition to being of magnetic importance, hysteresis represents a definite loss to the electrical system. The heat produced in an iron core placed in a magnetic circuit gives evidence that there is a loss. If the circuit has a commercial frequency (25 to 60 cycles per second) impressed upon it, the heat represents the energy loss that must be supplied by the generator or power source.

A study of a magnetic circuit which is assumed to be free from resistance—the pure inductive system—will show the amount of energy lost in the hysteresis cycle. Assume such a system with length l, area A, and with N number of turns. The induced electromotive force in this system will be

$$e = -N\frac{d\phi}{dt}\times 10^{-8}$$

$$\phi = A\mathcal{B}$$

Therefore,

$$e \doteq -NA\frac{d\mathcal{B}}{dt}\times 10^{-8} \qquad (f\text{–}2)$$

From e–2,

$$\mathcal{B} = \frac{0.4\pi NI\mu}{l}$$

but

$$\frac{\mathcal{B}}{\mathcal{H}} = \mu$$

Therefore,

$$\mathcal{H} = \frac{0.4\pi NI}{l}$$

and

$$I = \frac{\mathcal{H}l}{0.4\pi N} \text{ amperes}$$

The impressed electromotive force is equal and opposite to the induced electromotive force, and the work is equal to VIt.

$$dw = (-vi\,dt) = AN\frac{d\mathcal{B}}{dt} \times \frac{\mathcal{H}l}{0.4\pi N}\,dt = \frac{Al}{0.4\pi}\,\mathcal{H}\,d\mathcal{B}$$

It should be noted that the energy is independent of time and depends only upon the fact that a cycle must be completed to close the energy loop.

$$\text{Volume} = Al$$

$$\frac{1}{0.4\pi} = \text{constant} = K_h$$

Therefore,

$$dw = K_h V \mathcal{H}\,d\mathcal{B}$$

$$W = K_h V \int_0^{1 \text{ cycle}} \mathcal{H}\,d\mathcal{B} \text{ ergs per cycle}$$

and, if the volume is reduced to 1 cubic centimeter, the expression becomes one of loss per cubic centimeter per cycle.

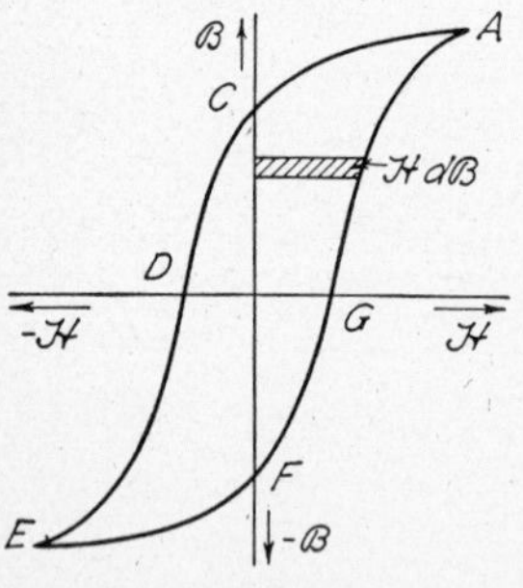

Fig. 10–2. The area of the hysteresis loop is proportional to the energy dissipated during a cycle.

Referring to Fig. 10–2, the energy loss per cycle per cubic centimeter is given by $1/0.4\pi$ (area of the loop in proper units). This requires that the specific loop be determined for the material under consideration and that the area be taken to determine the loss per cubic centimeter per cycle. There is no functional relationship between $\mathcal{B}$ and $\mathcal{H}$ which enables the integral expression to give a general solution.

A study of the loop will show that the area would increase rapidly as the maximum density is increased; this is true if any surface is compared with one of its linear dimensions. In order to avoid the necessity of measuring the area of the hysteresis loops for specific materials, Steinmetz determined the general law regarding the increase of areas of loops as a function of the maximum flux densities and found it to be according to the exponent 1.6, though with some of the high permeability materials it is more nearly 1.7. After making an elaborate study of magnetic materials, Steinmetz formulated the following expression:

$$W_h = n\mathcal{B}_m^{1.6}V \text{ ergs per cycle} \quad \text{or} \quad n\mathcal{B}_m^{1.6}V10^{-7} \text{ joules per cycle}$$

where n is a coefficient depending on the kind of material. These coefficients for the common magnetic materials are given in Table III–2. $\mathcal{B}_m$ is the maximum flux density expressed in gausses and V is the volume of the magnetic material in cubic centimeters. If expressed on the base of one cycle per second, the value becomes watts per cycle.

TABLE III–2

VALUE OF COEFFICIENT TO BE USED IN THE STEINMETZ EXPRESSION FOR HYSTERESIS LOSS

Material	Coefficient
1. Cast iron	0.014
2. Cast steel	0.008
3. Forged steel	0.007
4. Average sheet steel	0.003
5. Good sheet steel	0.002
6. Silicon sheet steel	0.001

Example d. A sheet steel core made from good sheet steel measures 3 in. by 3 in. and is 14 in. long. What will be the hysteresis loss per cycle in watts if the maximum flux density is 95×10^3 lines per square inch?

$$W = 0.002 \times \left[\frac{95 \times 10^3}{(2.54)^2}\right]^{1.6} \times (3 \times 3 \times 14)(2.54)^3 \times 10^{-7}$$

$$\begin{aligned}
&\log 2 \times 10^{-3} = 7.30103 - 10 &&= 7.30103\text{–}10\\
&\log[9.5 \times 10^4]^{1.6} = 4.97772 \times 1.6 &&= 7.96435\\
&\log[1/(2.54)^2]^{1.6} = -0.40483 \times 3.2 &&= -1.29546\\
&\log 1.26 \times 10^2 = 2.10037 &&= 2.10037\\
&\log (2.54)^3 = 0.40483 \times 3 &&= 1.21449\\
&\log 10^{-7} = 3.0000 - 10 &&= 3.00000\text{–}10\\
&\log W_h &&= 20.28478\text{–}20
\end{aligned}$$

$$W_h = 1.93 \text{ joules per cycle}$$

These losses are produced in the magnetic circuit when the flux changes, and the total loss is measured on the completion of a cycle regardless of the time involved. In the a-c system, this takes place every cycle but, in the d-c system, it takes place only in a switching cycle or at the change of load (that is, whenever there is a closing, opening, or changing in the system). In the d-c machine, the hysteresis and eddy current losses take place in the pole faces and the armature core but, in the a-c machine, every part of the magnetic circuit produces these losses.

In designing electrical equipment, it is impossible to eliminate the effect of hysteresis, but this may be reduced by choosing materials, in the magnetic group, of high permeability and correspondingly low hysteresis loss.

9. Eddy Current Loss. All the heat produced in the magnetic material present in a changing magnetic field is not caused by hysteresis alone, for it is possible to place non-magnetic material in a magnetic field and obtain a resultant heating which cannot be accounted for by hysteresis loss. It can be shown that there are concealed currents circulating in the material because an induced electromotive force is generated when a conductor is located in a varying magnetic field.

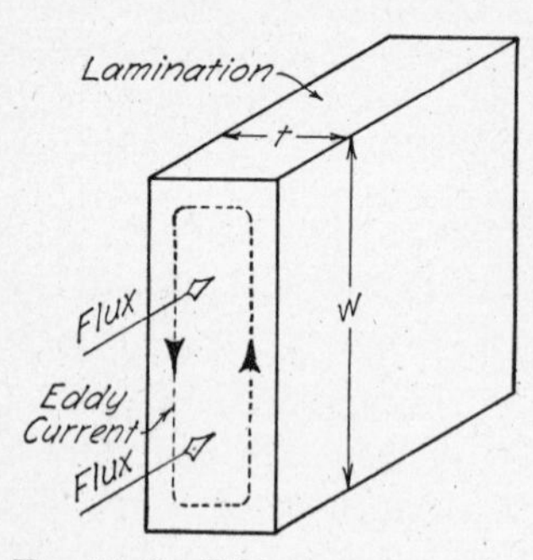

FIG. 11–2. Eddy current path in a lamination of sheet metal.

Shown in Fig. 11–2 is a section of a lamination of sheet magnetic material in which the thickness t is relatively small with respect to the width w. The flux is entering the edge of the lamination as it would in normal machine design. This flux creates, in the direction shown, a circulating current in the lamination caused by the change of flux. The induced electromotive force will be

$$e = -\frac{d\phi}{dt} \times 10^{-8}$$

$$e = -A\frac{d\mathcal{B}}{dt} \times 10^{-8}$$

If the flux is caused by a sinusoidal condition, the equation for the instantaneous flux is

$$\mathcal{B}_i = \mathcal{B}_m \sin \omega t$$

If this is substituted in the equation for the induced electromotive force, the effective voltage will be

$$E = \frac{2\pi A}{\sqrt{2}} f\mathcal{B}_m \times 10^{-8}$$

$$E = kf\mathcal{B}_m$$

The iron path is practically a pure resistance: therefore, the current and voltage are in phase and the power consumed in the path will be

$$W_e = \frac{E^2}{R}$$

$$W_e = K_e f^2 \mathcal{B}_m{}^2$$

The power consumed from the generating system is directly proportional to the square of the frequency and the square of the maximum flux density. The frequency in a rotating machine can be converted to terms of machine speed whenever desired.

Example e. What will be the effect on the eddy current losses in a transformer (*a*) if the frequency is doubled, (*b*) if the flux density is doubled, (*c*) if both the frequency and the flux density are doubled at the same time?

(*a*) $$W_e = K_e(2f)^2\mathcal{B}_m{}^2 = 4K_e f^2\mathcal{B}_m{}^2$$

(*b*) $$W_e = K_e f^2(2\mathcal{B}_m)^2 = 4K_e f^2\mathcal{B}_m{}^2$$

(*c*) $$W_e = K_e(2f)^2(2\mathcal{B}_m)^2 = 16K_e f^2\mathcal{B}_m{}^2$$

in terms of the original frequency and flux density.

The eddy current loss depends upon the factors mentioned above and a coefficient which includes the area of the path. The frequency and the flux density are a part of the necessary factors in the functioning of the machine and are not easily controlled, but the manipulation of the cross section of the path gives the designer a control over the loss. To reduce the eddy current loss to a minimum, the path may be reduced in area by laminating the magnetic circuit. This is accomplished by building the magnetic structure of thin sheets so placed that the total flux enters them at their edge, causing the circulating current to flow perpendicularly to the sheet where the greater resistance is encountered and, at the same time, the total flux is not hindered. To limit the eddy current to an individual sheet, these sheets are often oxidized or japanned on one side, introducing insulating material in the possible electrical circuit.

10. Separation of Hysteresis and Eddy Current Losses. If the value of the iron losses (core losses) is determined at two frequencies it is possible to separate the eddy current loss from the hysteresis loss. During the tests the flux density must be kept constant. The total iron loss may be expressed by

$$W_{e+h} = K_e f^2 \beta_m{}^2 + K_h f \beta_m{}^{1.6}$$

where β_m is a constant.

$$W_{e+h} = K_e' f^2 + K_h' f$$

$$\frac{W_{e+h}}{f} = K_e' f + K_h'$$

The final equation gives a linear relationship between the ratio of iron losses to frequency and the frequency. If the intercept of this line is multiplied by frequency the hysteresis losses at that frequency are obtained and if the variable portion is multiplied by the frequency the eddy current loss is obtained.

11. Electromagnets. The pull of an electromagnet is usually based on Maxwell's Law which states that

$$\text{Pull in dynes} = \frac{\mathcal{B}^2 A}{8\pi}$$

where $\mathcal{B}$ is the lines per square centimeter and A is the area in square centimeters. This statement assumes no air gap and no leakage flux; therefore, it is merely an approximation. Expressing the pull in pounds and the other factors in units of the English system, the coefficient becomes

$$F = \frac{\mathcal{B}^2 A}{72{,}130{,}000}$$

where $\mathcal{B}$ equals the lines of flux per square inch and A is the area in square inches.

Example f. A horseshoe lifting magnet has an area of 20 sq in. on each of its poles and a flux density of 70×10^3 lines per square inch. What will be the lifting force of the magnet in pounds?

$$F = \frac{(70 \times 10^3)^2 \times (2 \times 20)}{72{,}130{,}000}$$

$$= 2717 \text{ lb}$$

Magnets are used in control equipment and for various signal and communication circuits. In large sizes they are used for lifting scrap iron and in handling magnetic materials. For lifting they may be of two types as shown in Fig. 12–2. The first is the horseshoe type and the second, an annular type.

Some of the factors entering into the operation of a magnet are the inductance, the shortening of the air gap (with the accompanying increase of flux and reluctance change), and the arrangement of the magnetic structure.

A-c magnets are calculated by the above expression when the effective ampere-turns are used, and they differ from the d-c magnet in core loss hysteresis and eddy current losses. In a single-phase magnet, the flux passes through a zero point and it will hum excessively. This hum may be removed by the use of a shading coil, consisting of a closed copper ring placed in the pole piece so that the flux will pass through it.

The general expressions given for magnetic pull cannot be relied upon to give accurate results. For accurate determination of the pull of magnets and proper design for specific application, reference should be made to works explaining the empirical conditions that must be considered. The following references will be found helpful.

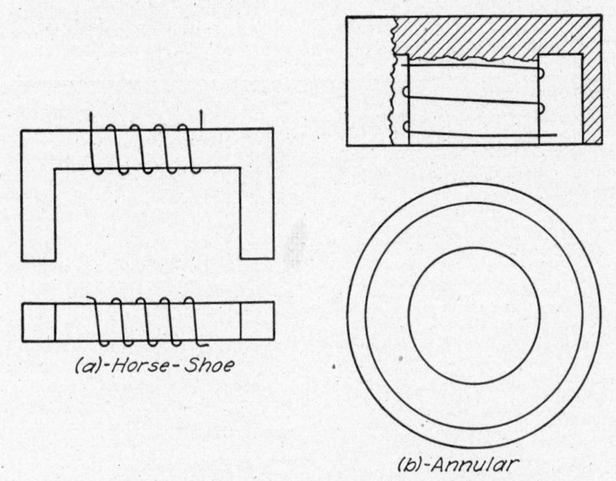

FIG. 12–2. Types of electromagnet armature structures.

REFERENCES

CARICHOFF, E. R. "On the Design of Electromagnets for Specific Duty," *Electrical World*, 1894, Vol. 23, pp. 113–212.

LINQUIST, D. L. "Alternating-Current Magnets," *Electrical World*, 1906, Vol. 47, p. 1295.

UNDERHILL, C. R. "Operation of Plunger Electromagnets," *Electrical World*, 1912, Vol. 59, p. 1388.

UNDERHILL, C. R. "Alternating-Current Electromagnets," *Electrical World*, 1914, Vol. 63, p. 260.

UNDERHILL, C. R. "Solenoids, Electromagnets and Electromagnetic Windings," *Proc. A.I.E.E.*, April, 1914.

WIKANDER, R. "Economical Design of Direct Current Magnets," *Trans. A.I.E.E.*, Vol. 30, p. 2019.

THOMALEN. "The Stroke of Alternating Current, Electromagnets," *Electrician* (London), 1918, p. 257.

PROBLEMS

1–2. A rectangular bar 8 cm long, has a pole strength of 900 emu concentrated at the poles. Assume the magnet located in free space and determine (*a*) the magnetic intensity at a point in line with the plane of the face of the north pole located at (0, 0) and 6 cm (0, 6) from the bar center line, and (*b*) the direction of the resultant force with respect to the magnet axis (X, X').

2–2. Determine the length of a magnetic circuit which has a total flux of 3×10^5 maxwells produced by 400 ampere-turns. The area of the magnetic circuit is 5 sq in. and the permeability of the material is 1.5×10^3.

3–2. A magnetic circuit 50 cm in length has an area of 10 sq in. and the material has a permeability of 750. (*a*) What magnetomotive force will give a flux of 6×10^4 maxwells? (*b*) What current is required if there are 200 turns on the exciting coil?

4–2. Two rings, the section of each being 2 in. by 2 in., are placed side by side. One ring is of cast steel and the other of silicon steel, and the mean length is 30 in. What will be the total flux if the exciting coil has 2100 ampere-turns?

5–2. Using the magnetic curves (Fig. 2–2) determine the permeability for cast iron and cast steel when the ampere-turns are 20, 40, 60, 80 per inch respectively.

6–2. Determine the number of ampere-turns necessary to establish a flux of 3.75×10^5 maxwells in a cast-steel ring which has a mean length of 21.67 ft and an area of 5 sq in. An air gap in the path is 0.5 in. long and has an average section of 10 sq in. including the fringing.

For Probs. 7 through 10, use the following magnetization curve data:

NI/in.	10	20	30	40	50	60	80	100	140
Kilomaxwells/sq in. (cast steel)	33	62	75	81	86	90	95	98	103
Kilomaxwells/sq in. (cast iron)	8	20	28	33	37	40	43	48	53

Best results will be obtained if these curves are drawn on an 8½ in. by 11 in. cross-section sheet.

7–2. A cast steel core of rectangular form has an outside dimension of 14 in. by 8 in. with an opening of 11 in. by 4 in. The core is 1½ in. thick. The long sides have a section of 2 in. by 1½ in. and the short sides a section of 1½ in. by 1½ in. There is a 0.2-in. air-gap in one of the 14-in. sides where the fringing causes a 30 per cent increase in the air-gap area. If the air-gap flux is to be 21×10^4 maxwells determine the ampere-turns necessary.

8–2. Using the same core form and cross sections as in Prob. 7 with the outside dimensions 9½ in. by 8 in. and no fringing at the air gap, determine the number of turns on the coil if 10 amp produce 18×10^4 maxwells in the air gap.

9–2. A magnetic circuit 4 in. thick (overall dimensions 20 in. by 14 in.), has two upright cores 8 in. long and 4 in. by 4 in. in section. The top and bottom yokes are 20 in. long and 3 in. by 4 in. in section. If the cores are of cast iron and the yokes of cast steel determine the flux density of the cores when the magnetic circuit has 2078 ampere-turns.

10–2. The same magnetic circuit as described in Prob. 9. The top yoke has a ¼ in. air gap inserted forming two pole pieces each 9⅞ in. long. Determine the flux in the air gap when the magnetic circuit is magnetized with 7160 ampere-turns and air-gap fringing is neglected.

11–2. What is the pull in pounds for an electromagnet 10 cm long with a section 2 cm by 2 cm for a magnetizing force of 30 ampere-turns, if the core material has a permeability of 5000 units?

12–2. The core loss in a machine is 800 watts at 60 cycles with 40 per cent hysteresis loss and 60 per cent eddy current loss. What will be the magnitude of each loss at 25 cycles if the flux density remains constant?

13–2. If the core loss at 60 cycles is 40 watts, 80 per cent hysteresis and 20 per cent eddy current, at what frequency will the total losses double if the flux density remains constant?

14–2. With the flux density remaining constant the core losses at 60 cycles and 30 cycles respectively are 2200 watts and 800 watts. Determine the hysteresis and eddy current loss at 60 cycles.

15–2. Use a different method for solving Prob. 14 than was previously used.

CHAPTER 3

MAGNETOMOTIVE FORCE, LEAKAGE REACTANCE, ARMATURE REACTION

All electrical machinery depends upon electrical and magnetic characteristics for operation. The electrical circuit is relatively simple and capable of accurate solution, whereas with the magnetic system the problem is much more difficult. If the conditions caused by the magnetomotive force which influence the final characteristic have been established, the machine may be represented by an equivalent electrical circuit. This permits a comparatively simple solution by circuit theory. If the induced voltage cannot be established, the problem becomes complex.

The resultant magnetomotive force is controlled by two separate types of influence: first, that portion created by the main field to establish a magnetomotive force for specific purposes; and, second, a magnetomotive force caused by the current passing through the machine windings to satisfy the demands of the load. Since it is physically impossible to establish independent magnetic fields in a common magnetic circuit, the result is a composite field, this field being the controlling factor in the generation of electromotive force.

Detailed study of the influence of magnetomotive forces which are secondary to the established magnetomotive force in the machine is essential to the fundamental study of machine performance and characteristics. These secondary magnetomotive forces are known as leakage reactance and armature reaction magnetomotive forces. The leakage reactance and the armature reaction magnetomotive forces set up by the load affect the resultant field and change the result derived from the established main-field magnetomotive force. Leakage reactance and armature reaction are controlled by the load and by the load alone. The phenomenon of armature reaction is not important in a machine unless the machine is loaded. There may be a slight phenomenon of armature reaction in a d-c generator caused by the internal use of current for excitation at no load, or by the no-load currents in motors..

1. Time and Space Relationships. In the study of the magnetic field and electrical characteristics in machine operation, it is necessary to consider both the time and space relationships of the various quantities involved. In the study of electrical circuits, the time relationship is used extensively, presupposing sinusoidal waves.

Figure 1–3 shows a plot of the time relationship between the current and the voltage in a system containing resistance and inductance where

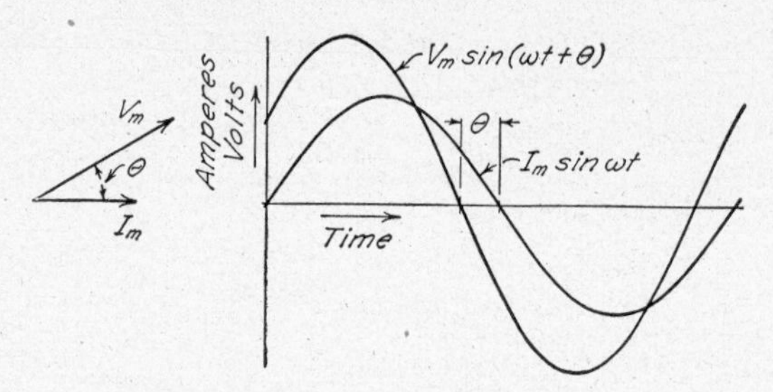

FIG. 1–3. Time relationship between current and voltage in a system containing resistance and inductance.

the current lags, in time relationship, behind the voltage that produces it. This presupposes uniform angular velocity and same frequency for the revolving vectors which represent the sine waves of voltage and current. The term "time relationship" is frequently expressed as "time phase," meaning that the angular relationship between e and i with respect to a reference is expressed as the number of electrical degrees displacement between e or i and the reference.

2. Space Relationships. In electrical engineering, when dealing with magnetic fields, it is frequently necessary to express the space relationship between two magnetic fields as an angular displacement which is fixed in space. Figure 2–3 shows two solenoids spaced at 90° to each other, forming fields that will have magnetomotive forces at 90 space degrees. This space relationship is called "space phase" displacement of the magnetomotive forces, and is a fixed position which these magnetomotive forces have in relation to any chosen reference. Frequently, a magnetomotive force may be of rotating type but, if such a force rotates at the same speed as the armature with which it is associated, it is sometimes convenient to speak of the space relationship of this magnetic field with respect to the armature. Therefore, it is possible for a magnetomotive force to be in

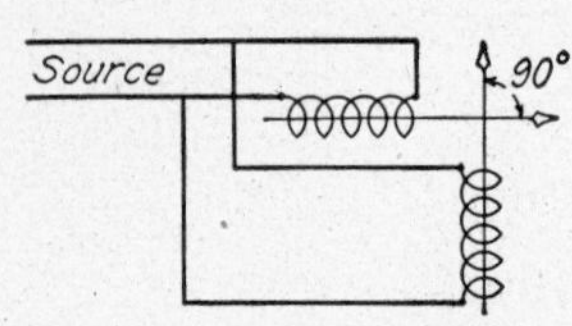

FIG. 2–3. The magnetomotive forces of two coils at 90° in space relationship.

space relationship with a rotating armature and in time relationship with a current that produces it.

3. Combination Time and Space Relationship. Figure 3–3 shows two coils having equal magnetomotive forces spaced at 90° to each other, one having high resistance and the other having high inductance in series with the windings. In space relationship, these magnetic fields are at 90° to each other; in time relationship, the current in the resistance coil will be approximately in phase with the applied voltage, whereas the current in the inductance coil will be approximately 90° behind the applied voltage.

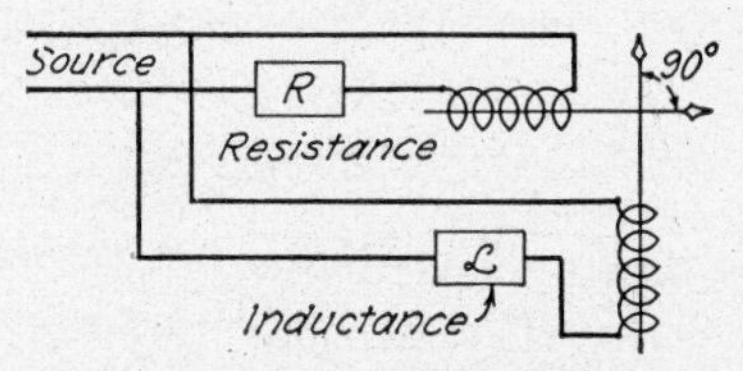

FIG. 3–3. Two coils in 90° space relationship, one containing high resistance, the other containing high inductance. The currents are in approximately 90° time relationship.

Figure 4–3a shows axes xx' and yy' as the axes of the coils in space relationship at 90°, and Fig. 4–3b shows the currents with respect to

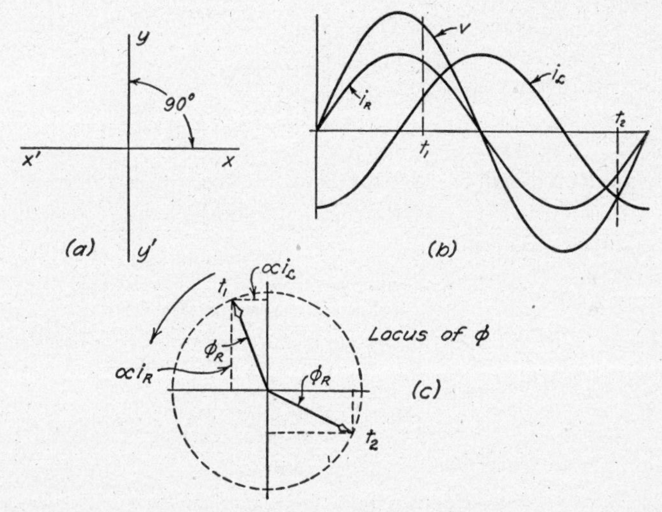

FIG. 4–3. A combination of space and time relationships: (a) space relationship of the flux; (b) time relationship of the current; (c) the resultant rotating field.

the reference voltage. The magnetomotive force equals $0.4\pi NI$ and the flux ϕ equals $\mathfrak{F}/\mathcal{R}$; therefore, the flux may be expressed by

$$0.4\frac{\pi}{\mathcal{R}} \times NI$$

or the flux, which is directly proportional to the current, will be in time relationship, or in "time phase" with the current. In Fig. 4–3c is shown the field resulting from the combination of coils arranged as shown in Fig. 3–3. It will be observed that, for every value of current in the two coils, there will be two independent magnetomotive forces produced by the coils respectively. However, one magnetic field cannot exist independent of other magnetic fields in a common magnetic circuit; therefore, these two magnetomotive forces will combine and form a common magnetic field, or a resultant which changes in position relative to time. This type of magnetic field is produced in the split-phase starting device for single-phase induction motors.

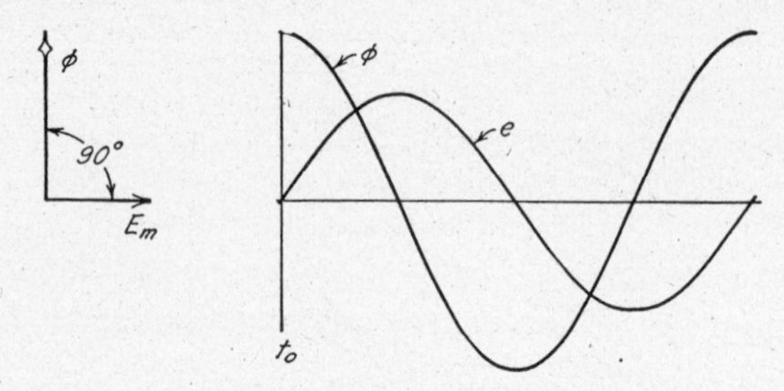

Fig. 5–3. Time-phase relationship between the flux wave and the induced voltage wave.

4. Phase Relationships of Flux and Induced Electromotive Force Waves. In the preceding article, the time-phase relationship between magnetomotive force and current was discussed. There is also a time-phase relationship between flux and induced electromotive force produced by the change of flux linkages. Assume, as shown in Fig. 5–3, that the flux is distributed in the air gap according to a sinusoidal law. The induced voltage e is equal to $-(Nd\phi/dt) \times 10^{-8}$ or the induced electromotive force is dependent on the slope of the flux wave. The slope of a sine wave will be a cosine wave, which is the first derivative $(d\phi/dt)$ of the given sine wave. When these sine and cosine waves are represented by vectors (Fig. 5–3) it will be seen that the flux leads the voltage it produces by 90° in time phase.

This relative phase displacement of the flux and the electromotive force induced is of primary importance in regard to the operation of transformers and rotating electrical machines. The analysis of the machine frequently requires definite time location of the flux when a definite induced electromotive force is being considered. An example of the use of these relationships occurs when the effect of leakage flux is considered as a reactance voltage.

5. Reactive Voltage Caused by Flux Linkages. To represent the linkages of flux as a voltage is impossible since flux linkage is a physical property of a magnetic circuit. However, applied voltage accounts for the voltage lost in the system (or machine) and, if this voltage must be used to overcome counterelectromotive forces produced by leakage flux or counterelectromotive forces produced by reactance, the source must supply potential at each instant of a kind and quantity to replace this loss. The leakage flux is a magnetic leakage present because a parallel air path serves to by-pass a considerable part of the total magnetic flux where it cannot be used.

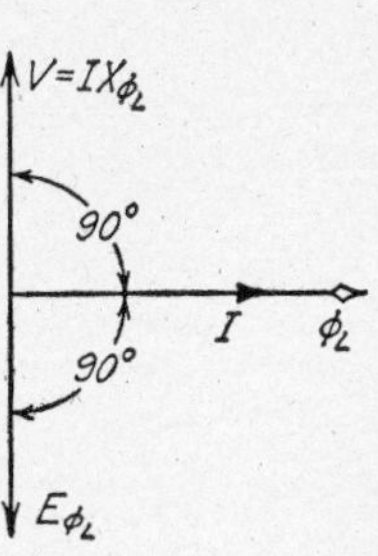

FIG. 6–3. Time-phase relationship between the current, flux linkages, induced electromotive force, and the component of the impressed voltage that overcomes the induced electromotive force produced by the linkages.

In Fig. 6–3 is shown the flux linkage ϕ_L with the induced electromotive force (E_{ϕ_L}) 90° behind the flux. If E_{ϕ_L} is the voltage produced by this flux, then the source must supply a voltage 180° in "time phase" with respect to this voltage loss. In the figure, this voltage is shown as V, which is 180° out of phase with E_{ϕ_L}. Therefore, V is 90° ahead of the flux ϕ. The current which produces ϕ has been shown to be in phase with the flux it produces; consequently, V and I, as shown by Fig. 6–3, are 90° in time relationship and V is 90° ahead of I. An impressed voltage which is 90° ahead of the current is of the nature of a pure inductive reactance drop and, for that reason, when referred to the source, the nature of the voltage used to overcome the induced voltage of a leakage flux is a voltage similar to that used to overcome the effect of reactance. It is possible in theoretical considerations to replace the leakage flux effects with reactance voltage drops. This simplifies the consideration of the operating characteristics of machines and will be utilized in the analysis of a-c apparatus.

6. Magnetomotive Forces of D-C Fields and Armatures. The magnetomotive force of the d-c fields of either an a-c or a d-c machine is produced by ampere-turns placed around the magnetic structure of the field. These ampere-turns produce a magnetomotive force as shown in Fig. 7–3 which shows both two-pole and multipole machine excitation. It is not essential that the poles in Fig. 7–3 be stationary. In the d-c machine it will be necessary to have stationary field poles, since commutation occurs simultaneously with armature rotation. In the a-c machine, the field may be either stationary or rotating and, except for synchronous converters and small machines, the field is usually the rotating element. The magnetomotive force produced by the ampere-turns wound on the field structure (windings in the electrical circuit in shunt, series, or a combination of both) produces the main field flux.

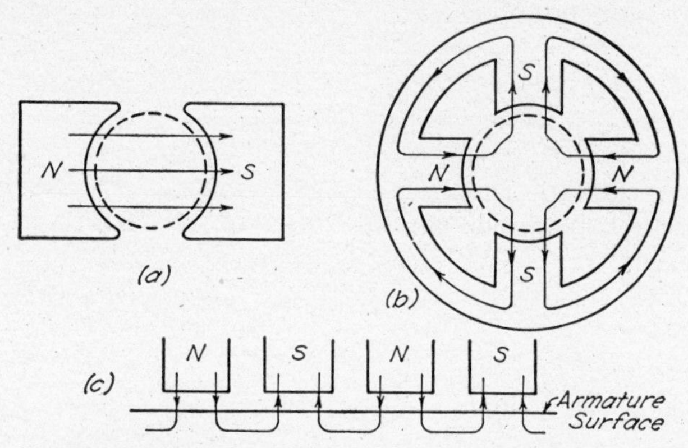

FIG. 7–3. Excitation of the main field in the d-c or a-c machine: (a) main field in a two-pole machine; (b) main field in a four-pole machine; (c) rectified four-pole machine showing the main field excitation.

Those magnetomotive forces which exist in the armature winding are called the armature reaction.

Figure 8–3 shows the armature reaction flux for a two-pole and a multipole d-c generator, whereas Fig. 9–3 shows the armature reaction flux

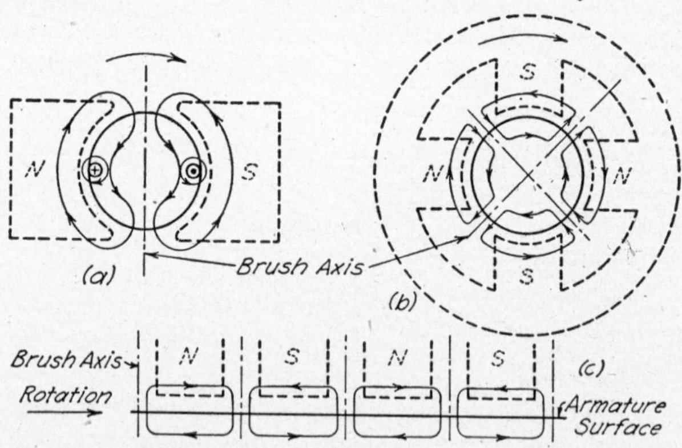

FIG. 8–3. Armature reaction flux in a d-c generator: (a) two-pole generator with clockwise rotation; (b) four-pole generator with clockwise rotation; (c) rectified drawing of a four-pole generator with clockwise rotation.

for a two-pole and a multipole d-c motor. The ampere-turns of the armature are produced by the current flowing in the armature conductors to satisfy the external load condition, which may be the result of an electrical or mechanical demand on the machine in the generator or motor, respectively.

The direction of the magnetomotive force in the d-c armature will be along the axis of the brushes, for it is through the brushes that the current enters and leaves the armature, thereby causing the current in each half of the winding of the two-pole machine to flow in such a direction as to form opposite polarities under the opposite poles. The same is true for the multipole machine. However, this does not cover as many mechanical degrees as the two-pole machine but, in both instances, the

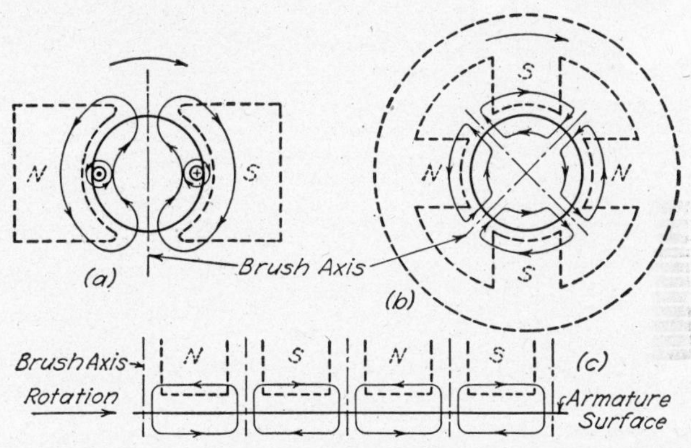

FIG. 9–3. Armature reaction flux in a d-c motor: (*a*) two-pole motor with clockwise rotation; (*b*) four-pole motor with clockwise rotation; (*c*) rectified four-pole motor with clockwise rotation.

same number (180) of electrical degrees are considered. It should be observed that with the same direction of rotation and the same relative polarity of the fields the armature reaction in the motor and generator are in opposite directions. This characteristic of similar theory and opposite direction when comparing motors and generators is always present. Therefore, by parallel study the operating characteristics of the two machines are fixed antitheses.

Magnetomotive forces can exist individually in a common magnetic path but fluxes cannot, however the main field magnetomotive force and the armature reaction magnetomotive force combine, as shown in Fig. 10–3, to form a resultant magnetomotive force. These magnetomotive forces can be analyzed by resolving the armature reaction magnetomotive force into two components: that portion which is in space phase with the main field, and that portion which is in quadrature with the main field. The portion which falls upon the main-field component (or the main-field component projected) either strengthens or weakens the main field, whereas that portion at quadrature to the main-field component causes distortion. It is possible, in the d-c machine, to analyze

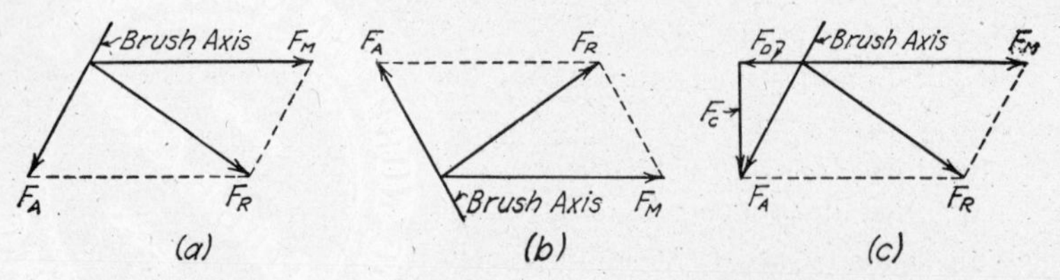

Fig. 10–3. F_M magnetomotive force of main field, F_A magnetomotive force of armature, F_R resultant magnetomotive force, F_D demagnetizing magnetomotive force or armature reaction, F_C cross-magnetizing magnetomotive force of armature reaction, when the direction of rotation is clockwise. (*a*) Resultant magnetomotive force in a generator. (*b*) Resultant magnetomotive force in a motor. (*c*) Resolution of armature reaction in a generator.

the number of ampere-turns on the armature that produce the two effects, demagnetizing and cross-magnetizing. Figure 11–3 shows the armature for a two-pole machine, indicating the cross-magnetizing and

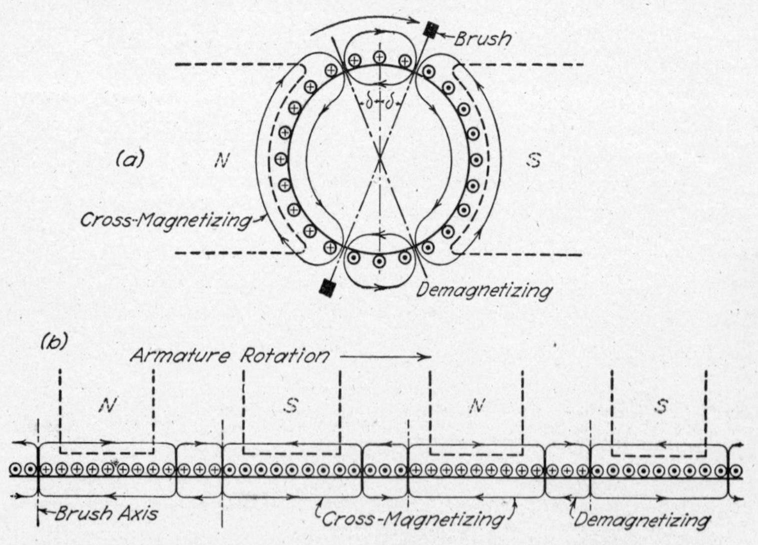

Fig. 11–3. (*a*) Demagnetizing and cross-magnetizing magnetomotive force in a two-pole d-c generator. (*b*) Demagnetizing and cross-magnetizing force in a four-pole d-c generator where the armature current has been rectified.

the demagnetizing ampere-turns. This division depends entirely upon the brush shift angle. The calculation of the cross-magnetizing and demagnetizing ampere-turns is more easily demonstrated by an example.

Example a. An eight-pole generator has a lap winding of 576 active conductors and carries a current of 100 amp. When it is necessary to advance the brushes 15 electrical degrees, how many demagnetizing and how many cross-magnetizing ampere-turns are present?

The number of conductors that will be affected per pole will be the conductors in twice the brush shift angle or the conductors in a 30° arc. There are actually eight poles and, therefore, 240 electrical degrees covered by the demagnetizing conductors.

The whole machine has 1440 electrical degrees; or the part of the armature that is influenced by 240° is in the ratio 240 to 1440. The turns that cause the demagnetizing effect are

$$\frac{2 \times 15^\circ \times 8}{360^\circ \times 4} \times 576 = 96 \text{ conductors}$$

which gives

$$\tfrac{96}{2} = 48 \text{ turns}$$

and the current per path will be

$$\tfrac{100}{8} = 12.5 \text{ amp}$$

since the eight-pole lap winding has eight paths in parallel.

The total number of ampere-turns causing a demagnetizing effect are

$$12.5 \times 48 = 600$$

Since the total number of ampere-turns will be

$$\tfrac{576}{2} \times 12.5 = 3600$$

the cross-magnetizing turns will be equal to 3000.

The same calculation can be made on a basis of ampere-turns per pole, and space degrees will be used:

$$\frac{15^\circ}{4} \text{ space degrees} = 3.75 \text{ degrees}$$

$$\text{Ampere-turns per pole} = \frac{\alpha}{360^\circ} \times Z \times \frac{I}{p}$$

where α = brush shift space degrees
Z = active conductors on armature
I = output current
p = path in winding

$$NI_D \text{ per pole} = \frac{3.75^\circ}{360^\circ} \times 576 \times \frac{100}{8}$$

$$= 75 \text{ ampere-turns per pole}$$

$$\text{Total demagnetizing ampere-turns } 75 \times 8 = 600$$

The scalar addition of ampere-turns is the method used by the designer in the analysis of the machine. When considering the armature reaction as the vector sum of the cross-magnetizing and demagnetizing components, it is necessary to multiply each of these magnetomotive forces by a space distribution correction coefficient if the result is to be quantitatively correct. The analysis of the armature reaction of the d-c machine is essentially a problem of space relationship, since the components of the magnetomotive forces are considered relative to each other in space, and it is assumed that the two groups act at right angles.

7. Magnetomotive Forces in the Field and Armature of Polyphase Machines. As stated in a previous paragraph, the main field of a polyphase synchronous machine is similar to the field of a d-c machine. It is necessary that a d-c supply, normally spoken of as field excitation, be available to produce these electromagnetic fields.

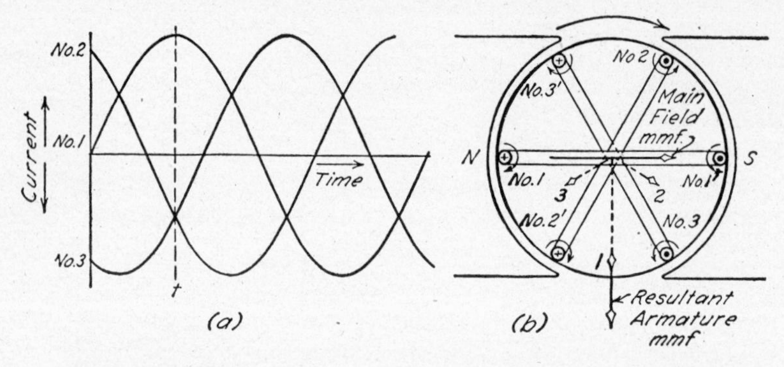

FIG. 12–3. A-c synchronous generator resultant armature magnetomotive force.

In the armature of an a-c synchronous generator or synchronous motor with balanced load (regardless of power factor), there is established with respect to the main-field magnetomotive force, in space relationship, a stationary magnetomotive force. This is produced by a rotating magnetomotive force whose frequency is dependent upon the frequency of the generating system, which is an armature reaction magnetomotive force. If the main field is revolving, this armature reaction magnetomotive force is stationary with respect to the rotating main magnetomotive force and displaced from it in proportion to the power factor and load. If the armature is the revolving member, the relative motion of the armature and the armature reaction field is such as to fix the resultant armature reaction field in space relationship with the stationary field, the angle of displacement being influenced by the power factor and load, as shown in Fig. 12–3.

Subsequent articles consider in detail the effect of power factor upon the armature magnetomotive force of the polyphase machine. Figure 12–3 gives an analysis of a balanced unity power-factor load. Consider time t (Fig. 12–3a) where the phase currents are 100 and 50 per cent respectively. Phases 1, 2, and 3 produce magnetomotive forces 1, 2, and 3 whose vector addition is the resultant armature magnetomotive force, having a fixed relationship to the resultant main-field magnetomotive force. If the current remains the same in the phases the resultant armature magnetomotive force vector will remain the same in length and direction. To establish this fact it is only necessary to select any other time in the cycle and determine the resultant magnetomotive force.

In the *asynchronous* (induction) machine, the rotating field is created by the armature current and its speed is determined by the number of poles and the frequency of the system (Fig. 13–3). This rotating field, which is an armature reaction field, is a controlling factor in the operation of the machine. In this type of machine, the excitation is supplied by the a-c system.

8. Rotating Magnetomotive Forces. In Fig. 13–3, parts b and c show a two- and a four-pole three-phase winding which is connected to a three-phase system indicated by the current waves in Fig. 13–3a. Since the phase currents and the magnetomotive forces in the windings are in "time phase," the curves show the relative values of the magnetic fields at the times t_0, t_1, and t_2. The convention of current flow with the change of time is shown in Fig. 13–3a. The three phases are numbered A, B, and C with the coil ends 1, 2, and 3 corresponding respectively. The coil ends 1′, 2′, and 3′ are the opposite ends of the same coils and, if current enters one side of the coil, it leaves the other side of the coil. These conventions permit the use of a diagrammatic presentation of the rotating field. Figure 13–3 shows the presence of a rotating field of the stator (three-phase wound) of a three-phase alternator or motor.

At time t_0 the current will be entering 1 and leaving 1′; in phase B the current is entering 2 and leaving 2′, but in phase C the current is leaving 3 and entering 3′. By the right-hand rule, it will be seen that the flux for the various coil sides will be added together to form a resultant field. In Figs. 13–3b and 13–3c, an analysis is made for the intervals of time, t_0, t_1, and t_2, with the resultant magnetomotive forces indicated by resultant vectors. By comparing the three diagrams, it will be seen that the resultant vector has rotated in a clockwise direction. If this analysis is made for every instant in the period covered by 360 electrical degrees, the resultant field in a two-pole machine has made one complete revolution. This same result will be obtained in the analysis of any polyphase system, but the discussion has been confined to the more common three-phase system. This phenomenon of rotating fields must be considered in the discussion of alternator armature reaction, in synchronous motor armature reaction, and in the induction motor.

9. Rotating Magnetomotive Force Constant in Magnitude. In the polyphase machine, the armature reaction or rotating field is constant

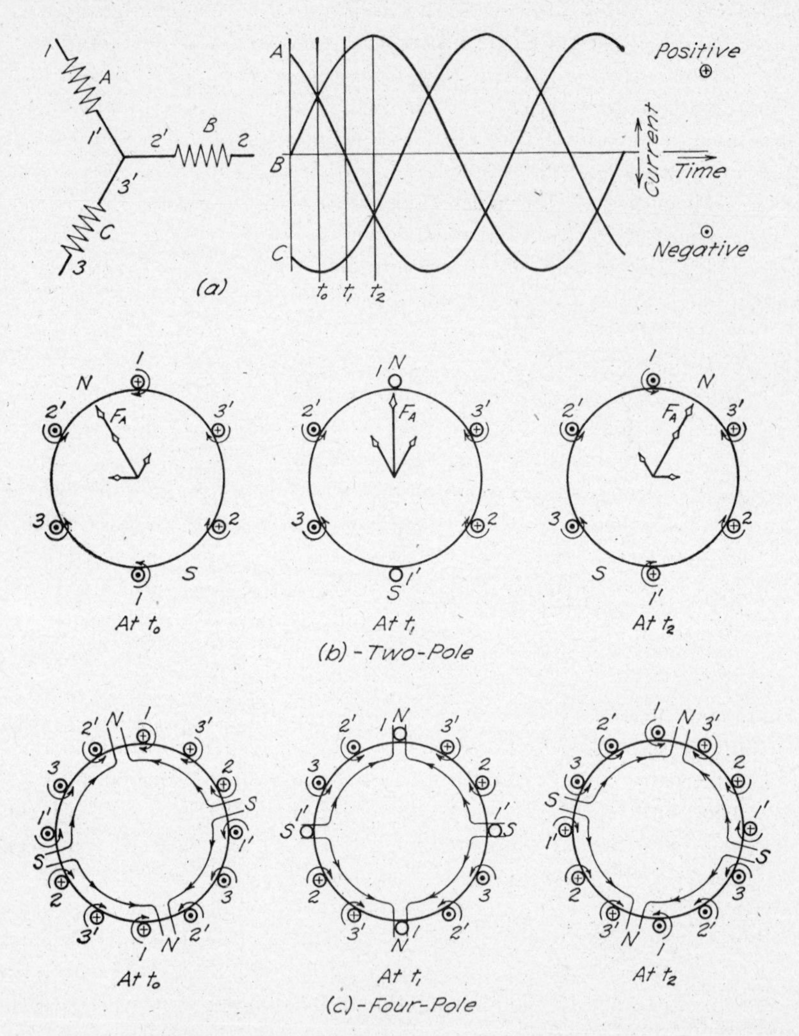

FIG. 13–3. Rotating field in a polyphase winding: (*a*) current waves for the current in the windings; (*b*) two-pole three-phase winding showing the position of the resultant magnetomotive force at the time periods t_0, t_1, t_2; (*c*) similar treatment of the four-pole three-phase winding at the time periods t_0, t_1, t_2.

in magnitude if the electrical system is balanced. In Fig. 13–3 the addition of the magnetomotive forces, with their proper vector sense, gives a resultant value which is 150 per cent of the maximum value in any one phase of the machine. The same convention has been used for the proper sign of the vector as was used in determining the direction of flow of current in the windings; that is, current entering the winding is positive and current leaving the winding is negative. These conventions are shown in Fig. 13–3*a*.

To summarize the results of the rotating field study, it may be stated that the three-phase winding produces a rotating field which is constant in magnitude and equals 150 per cent of the maximum for one phase.

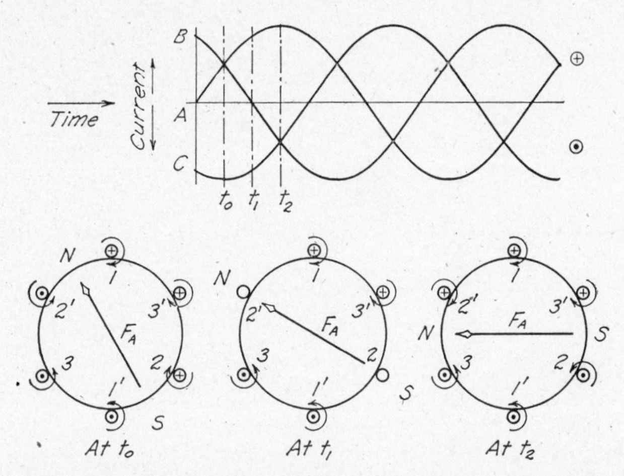

Fig. 14–3. Reversal of the rotating field by an interchange of two leads. Compare with field rotation shown for the three-phase winding, Fig. 13–3*b*.

10. Reversal of the Rotating Field. To reverse the direction of rotation of electrical equipment, it is necessary to reverse the rotation of the revolving field. This may be accomplished by the interchange of any two leads on a three-phase machine. Figure 14–3 shows the same winding as Fig. 13–3*b* but, in Fig. 14–3 the lines to phases *A* and *B* have been interchanged and the figure shows the analysis of the resultant fields at the time intervals, t_0, t_1, and t_2.

When the resultant rotation is compared with that shown in Fig. 13–3, it will be seen that the magnetomotive force moves in an opposite direction. To reverse the rotating field in a three-phase machine, it is only necessary to reverse any two leads, whereas in the two-phase machine, it is necessary to reverse the leads of one phase.

11. Armature Reaction in the Synchronous Machine. The magnitude of the rotating armature reaction magnetomotive force is determined by the load current and its relationship in "space phase" to the main-field magnetomotive force is determined by the load power factor. It is necessary to study the resultant effect of armature reaction for various power factor loads.

Figure 15–3 shows the three significant power factors. These power factors are (with respect to the induced voltage) unity, 90° lagging, and 90° leading. This analysis of the alternator is shown for both a two-

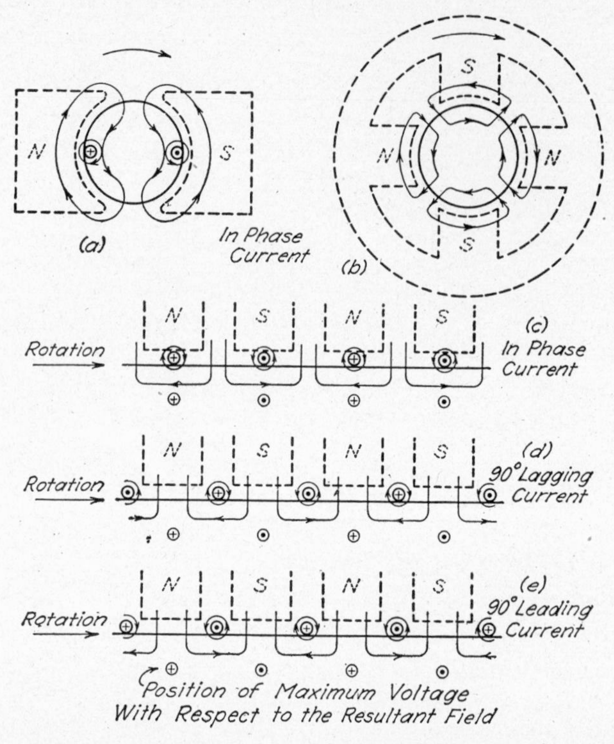

Fig. 15–3. Armature reaction flux for the synchronous generator: (*a*) armature reaction flux in the two-pole generator; (*b*) in the four-pole generator; (*c*, *d*, and *e*) showing the armature reaction flux in the four-pole generator at unity, lagging and leading 90° power factor.

pole and a multipole machine. In the use of the multipole study, the windings have been rectified to simplify the presentation.

When the system has a unity power factor the effect of armature reaction is cross-magnetizing, resulting in distortion, which, in turn, usually weakens the resultant field. When the current lags 90°, the tendency of the armature reaction is to weaken the field, whereas the effect of 90° leading power factor is to strengthen the field. Any combination of load conditions which does not cause an angle of lead (or lag) equal to 90° gives rise to a combined effect of cross-magnetizing and either magnetizing or demagnetizing effect. Figure 16–3 shows the resultant effect when the power factor of the current is leading (or lagging) by an angle θ.

Figure 17–3 shows the armature reaction effect in a synchronous motor when the machine has a unity power factor, a 90° leading, and a 90° lagging demand on the supply system. It will be observed that the syn-

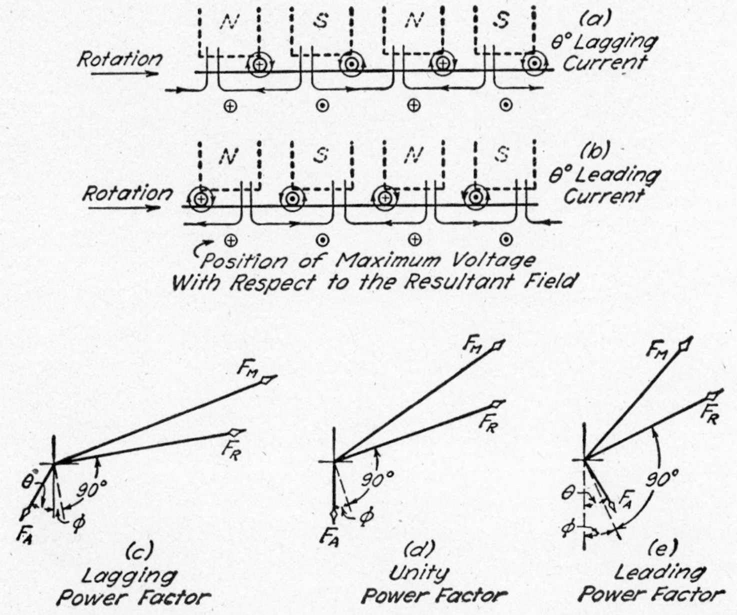

FIG. 16–3. Armature reaction, magnetomotive force, and flux in the four-pole synchronous generator: (*a* and *b*) current leads and lags by an angle θ; (*c*, *d*, and *e*) magnetomotive force diagrams with unity, leading and lagging power factor. ϕ is the angle between the terminal and induced voltage at load; θ is the power-factor angle of the load.

chronous motor has a reaction which is 180° to that of the alternator for the same power factor. As has been brought out in the discussion of d-c generators and motors, the effects in a generator and motor are opposite in every case.

If the armature reaction can be arranged so that it excites the main-field structure, it is possible to remove all the field excitation and cause the motor action to take place without external d-c excitation. This particular phenomenon has been utilized in the small synchronous motors used in clocks and controlled timing. Here, the main structure has an a-c winding which produces the effect of d-c excitation in the rotating iron element, forming a motor with synchronous motor characteristics.

12. Armature Magnetomotive Force in Single-Phase Machines. In the single-phase machine, as compared with the polyphase machine, there does not exist a constant resultant rotating magnetomotive force.

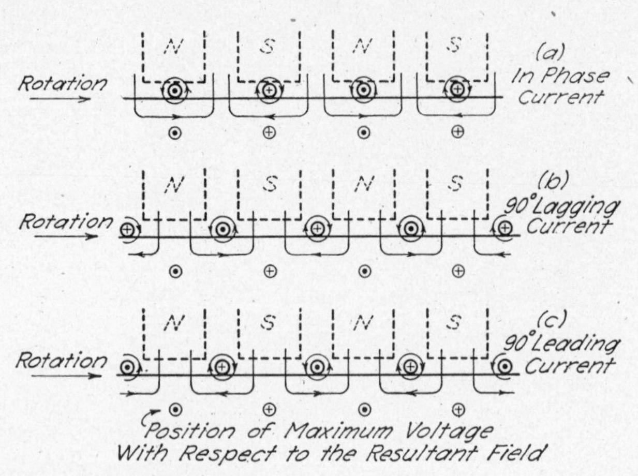

FIG. 17–3. Armature reaction flux of the synchronous motor: (a, b, and c) armature reaction flux in the three-phase synchronous motor with unity, 90° lagging and 90° leading power factor.

The magnetomotive force varies from a maximum to a minimum and is essentially fixed in space with respect to the armature. This pulsating magnetomotive force produces a field revolving relative to the poles but essentially fixed in space relationship with the armature.

Figure 18–3 shows the magnetomotive force in a single-phase generator for two types of load: first, where the current is in phase with the

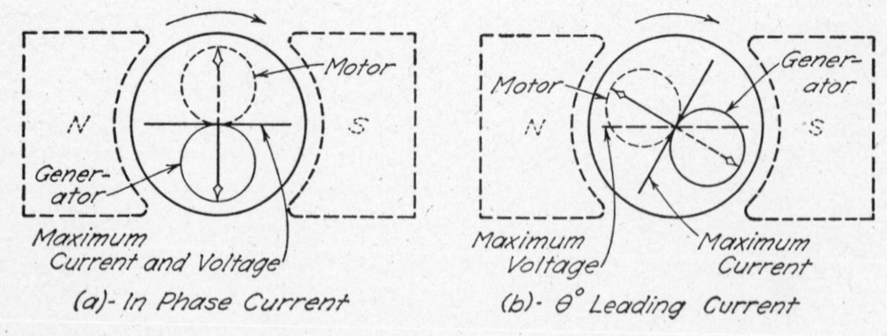

FIG. 18–3. Armature reaction in a single-phase machine and the locus of magnetomotive forces.

induced electromotive force, and, second, where the current leads the induced electromotive force by an angle θ. This magnetomotive force will be a double frequency pulsating magnetomotive force which produces harmonics in the induced voltage. If the power factor is other than unity, the relative position of the resultant magnetomotive force will be changed, but the characteristics of the magnetomotive force will be the same as in the case of unity power factor. This type of armature reaction is of minor importance in the a-c supply and need not be considered in the more important power equipment.

13. Resolving a Pulsating Magnetomotive Force into Two Oppositely Rotating Magnetomotive Forces. Frequently in the analysis of single-phase generator armature reaction and single-phase motor operation,

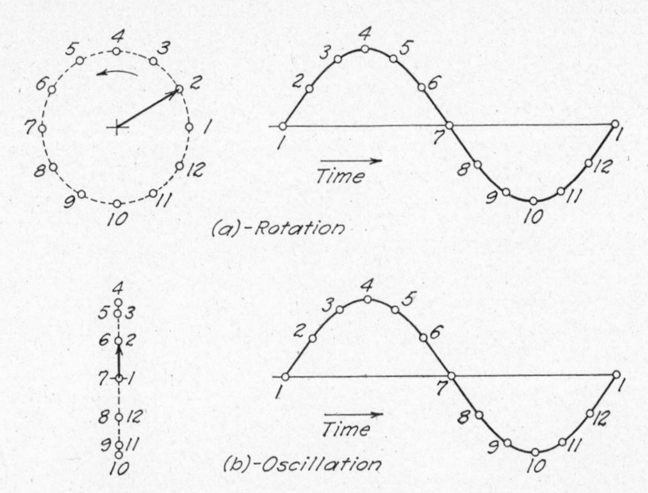

FIG. 19–3. Production of sinusoidal waves: (*a*) by a rotating vector, where the angular velocity is uniform; (*b*) by the movement of a vector in a straight line following an oscillatory motion.

the simple oscillating field, varying according to the sine law, will be replaced by two opposite and equal rotating magnetomotive forces, the maximum value of each of these rotating magnetomotive forces being one-half the resultant. A different conception of variation according to a sine law will be observed in studying the two diagrams shown in Fig. 19–3; part (*a*) is a variation caused by a revolving vector and part (*b*) is the variation caused by the oscillation along a single axis, both sine waves being plotted with respect to time.

The resultant of the two revolving vectors will lie along a vertical axis and will be equal in magnitude to the actual magnetomotive force at every instant. Figure 20–3*a* shows the direction of the two vectors and the resultant field which is sinusoidal and stationary in space. Contrast this figure with Fig. 19–3*a* where the revolving vector produces a sine wave through an angular change in space.

In the final analysis, these two revolving magnetomotive forces are considered as acting independently on the armature of the machine. Since this change occurs in the machine at synchronous speed with respect to the armature, the effect will be that one of the magnetomotive forces rotates in the same direction as the main-field magnetomotive force while the other will rotate in an opposite direction. The first component will be stationary with respect to the rotating element; the other will have a double frequency.

This method of analysis is often used in explaining the operation of single-phase induction motors but is lacking in true physical analysis

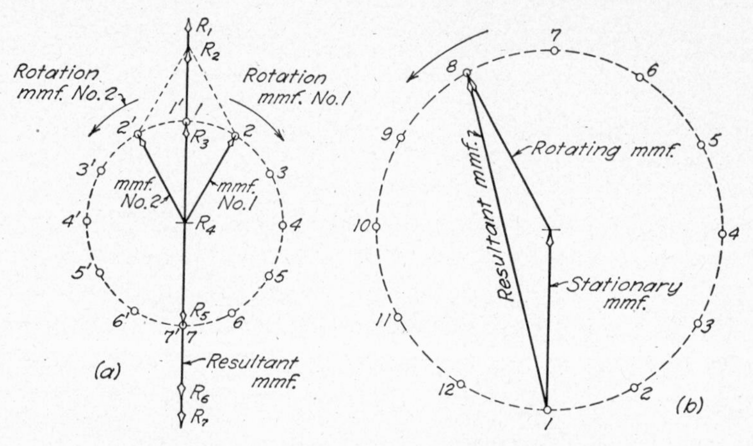

FIG. 20–3. (*a*) Replacement of an oscillating magnetomotive force by two oppositely rotating magnetomotive forces. (*b*) The resultant magnetomotive force for one stationary and one rotating magnetomotive force.

and is open to criticism in that it is not rigorous. However, it is one of the methods of approach in dealing with the complicated problems of magnetomotive forces created by armature currents in electrical machines.

Figure 20–3*b* shows the locus of the resultant magnetomotive force when a stationary magnetomotive force is combined with a rotating magnetomotive force, so that the resultant follows a circle. This method is used in the analysis of the armature reaction of a single-phase generator.

14. Summary. To summarize the factors in armature reaction, it is well to note the similarity between d-c and a-c machines. In the d-c machine, the fields are stationary in space and, even though the armature revolves, the armature reaction is stationary in relationship to the main-field magnetomotive force and bears a definite space relationship to it for every brush position. In the polyphase a-c machine, either the armature or the field revolves and, regardless of which type of machine is being considered, the armature reaction always bears a definite space relationship to the main-field magnetomotive force, this relationship being influenced by the power factor of the load.

In either a d-c machine or an a-c machine of the polyphase type, the armature reaction for a given load is constant in magnitude. Armature reaction bears a definite space-phase relationship to the main-field magnetomotive force which depends upon brush position in the d-c machines or power factor of the load in the a-c machines, respectively. In the final analysis, the study of armature reaction in either of these two machines is a study of a phenomenon of the same nature.

These relationships hold for both d-c motors and a-c synchronous motors and the effect of the phenomenon is reversed from that of the generator. In considering armature reaction, the resultant phenomena may be clearly set forth in the statement that the magnitude and directional effect of armature reaction are controlled by the magnitude of the load and the brush position or power factor, depending upon the type of equipment being considered.

Armature reaction is the most important electromagnetic characteristic determining the performance of a machine; and it influences the voltage parameters for the equivalent electrical circuit because it changes the resultant magnetic field upon which the induced electromotive force depends.

PROBLEMS

1–3. Two coils, of 100 turns each, are wound on a common iron core. The parameters of the circuit are such that two sine wave generators of the same frequency (50 cycles) and equal voltage produce equal magnetomotive force in the cores. The generator voltages are phased at 90° with a maximum current of 100 amp. Give the expression for the resultant magnetomotive force when $t = 0.01$ sec and $F_1 = F_m \sin \omega t$ with $F_2 = F_m \sin [\omega t + (\pi/2)]$.

2–3. Two identical coils on cores, space-phased at 90°, are supplied from the same single-phase source. If the current in each is $i = I_m \sin \omega t$, what is the expression for the resultant magnetomotive force in the air gap?

3–3. Two identical coils on iron cores space-phased 90°, with currents $i_1 = I_{m_1} \sin \omega t$ and $i_2 = I_{m_2} \sin [\omega t + (\pi/2)]$ produce an air-gap flux. What is the expression for the resultant magnetomotive force?

4–3. A 3-phase supply, with fundamental sine wave variation, is connected to coils displaced by 120°. The flux density in the three phases, 1, 2, and 3, have maximum values of β_1, β_2, and β_3, in space-phase at the axis of the coils. Give the equation for and draw the resultant diagram for the flux density at any point α from the time when phase 1 is passing through zero in a positive direction. What would be the expression for the flux density if $\alpha = \omega t$?

5–3. Determine the resultant field in a 3-phase balanced stator winding if β_m is 6×10^4 lines per square inch (*a*) at any time interval, (*b*) when $t = 0.01$ sec and $\omega t = \alpha$, (*c*) when $\omega t = 377t$ and $\alpha = 30°$.

6–3. An air-cored coil has an area of 10 sq cm and a magnetic circuit length of 10 cm. The coil is wound with 500 turns of wire and a current $i = 20 \sin [377t + (\pi/6)]$ is flowing. Determine (*a*) the expression for the instantaneous impressed voltage, (*b*) the value of this voltage at the time 0.01 sec.

7–3. Determine the demagnetizing and cross-magnetizing ampere-turns for a 4-pole, simplex wave-wound 520 conductor d-c armature carrying a 100-amp armature current, if the brush shift for good commutation is 18 space degrees.

8–3. In Prob. 7 consider the machine a simplex lap-wound machine and determine (*a*) demagnetizing and (*b*) cross-magnetizing ampere-turns.

9–3. Using Fig. 10–3*c*, the magnetomotive force diagram for a generator, for a study of demagnetizing effect, assume an 8-pole, 480 conductor, simplex lap-wound d-c armature carrying 500 amp with a brush shift of 48 electrical degrees. From the magnetomotive force diagram $F_D = F_A \sin \alpha$, where F_D is a function of $\sin \alpha$, the brush shift angle. Determine if the relationship in the expression is true. Prove the conclusions reached.

10–3. In a 4-pole synchronous generator the magnetomotive force of the armature is 200 gilberts and that for the resultant field is 2000 gilberts, at unity power-factor load. If the generated voltage leads the terminal voltage by 15° determine the magnetomotive force of the main field and the phase displacement with respect to the terminal voltage.

11–3. In Prob. 10 consider the machine a synchronous motor with a 15° lagging power factor, the induced and terminal voltage having a 180° phase relationship. What will be (*a*) the main-field magnetomotive force, (*b*) the phase relationship with respect to the terminal voltage?

12–3. The phase densities in the air gap for a 3-phase field are $\beta_{i_1} = \beta_m \sin \omega t$, $\beta_{i_2} = \beta_m \sin [\omega t + (2\pi/3)]$, and $\beta_{i_3} = \beta_m \sin [\omega t - (2\pi/3)]$, determine the resultant flux density if $\beta_m = 8 \times 10^4$ maxwells per square inch.

13–3. Two magnetomotive force vectors, each of 100 gilberts, are rotating at uniform velocity in opposite directions. If the frequency of the system is 30 cycles what is the maximum magnetomotive force in the system?

14–3. A 25-cycle oscillating system has a maximum amplitude of 10 units. Express the resultant sine wave magnetomotive force, of displacement versus time, in three forms.

15–3. Determine the stationary and revolving vector components to produce sine wave characteristics for $x^2 + y^2 = 2ay$, where a is 25 and the system is one of 25 cycles. Write the expressions for the waves in both rectilinear and polar form.

CHAPTER 4

TRANSFORMERS

1. Definition and Purpose. "A transformer is an electric device, without continuously moving parts, which by electro-magnetic induction transforms electric energy from one or more circuits to one or more other circuits at the same frequency, usually with changed values of voltage and current." *

Because of its simplicity of construction and its widespread use in power transmission, the transformer is the first piece of electrical apparatus to be discussed. For long distance transmission, transformers are used to furnish the high voltage at the sending end and to reduce the voltage at the receiving end where the energy is utilized by motors, lamps, or other electrical equipment.

2. Induced Voltage. It was shown in Chapter 2 of Volume I that the induced voltage in any coil of N turns depended upon the number of turns and the rate of change of the flux ϕ, with respect to time, which link the turns.

$$e = -N\frac{d\phi}{dt} \times 10^{-8}$$

Since this induced voltage depends upon a change in flux linkages, the relationship is true for a coil moving or rotating in a field and for a coil in a field of varying flux. The first commonly occurs in a generator and the second in a transformer. For both, the induced voltage by Lenz's Law causes a current to flow in such a direction as to oppose the cause which produces the change in flux linkages.

If the flux (ϕ) is varied according to a sinusoidal function, the expression for induced voltage can be written as

$$e = -N\frac{d\phi}{dt} 10^{-8}$$

and

$$\phi = \phi_m \sin \omega t$$

* American standard definitions of electrical terms—American Institute of Electrical Engineers (15.20.010).

Then,

$$e = -\frac{1}{10^8} N \frac{d}{dt} \phi_m \sin \omega t$$

or

$$e = -\omega \frac{1}{10^8} N\phi_m \cos \omega t \qquad (a\text{–}4)$$

Since the general expression for a sinusoidal voltage is

$$e = E_m \sin \omega t$$

the expression (a–4) may be written as

$$e = \frac{1}{10^8} \omega N \phi_m \sin (\omega t - 90°)$$

The induced voltage, therefore, lags the flux ϕ in time phase by 90°. The maximum voltage E_m is

$$E_m = \omega N \phi_m 10^{-8}$$

$$E_m = 2\pi f N \phi_m 10^{-8}$$

and the effective value (or voltmeter reading) is

$$E = \frac{E_m}{\sqrt{2}} = \frac{2\pi f}{\sqrt{2}} N\phi_m 10^{-8}$$

$$E = \sqrt{2}\pi N f \phi_m 10^{-8}$$

$$E = 4.44 N f \phi_m 10^{-8}$$

The total flux change per cycle is $4\phi_m$ and the form factor (E/E_{av}) for a sine wave is 1.11.

3. Ideal Transformer. Figure 1–4 shows a coil (resistance negligible) connected to a source of alternating voltage V, having an alternating current flowing in the coil, which creates a magnetomotive force. This varying magnetomotive force causes a flux change which, in turn, produces an induced voltage E, opposing the terminal voltage V. This induced voltage, E, is equal to V in magnitude and opposite in direction.

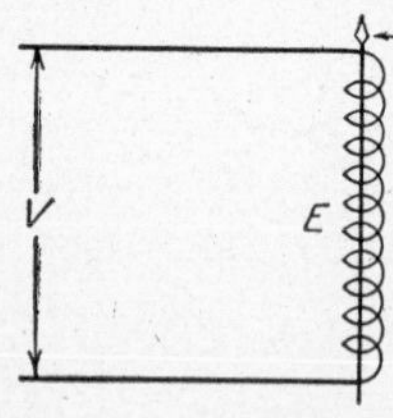

Fig. 1–4. Simple inductance coil.

Kirchhoff's Law may be written for this circuit as

$$\overline{V} + \overline{E} = 0$$

Figure 2–4 shows the phase relationship between the impressed voltage V, the current I, and the induced voltage E for the circuit of Fig. 1–4.

If other coils are placed so that the turns link the flux of this coil, the induced voltage will be proportional to the rate of change of the flux linkages. If perfect linkages are assumed (coupling coefficient $K = 1$),

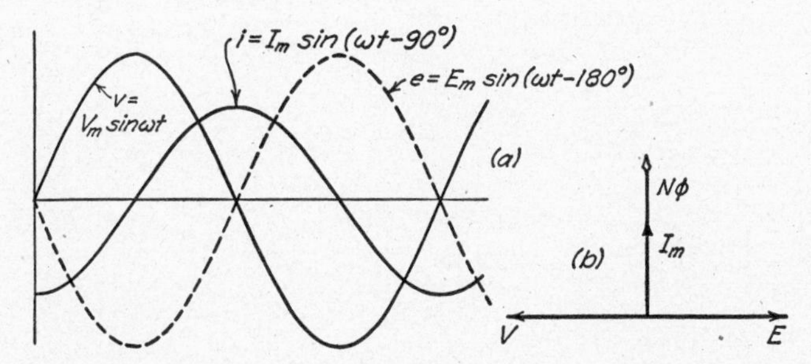

FIG. 2–4. (a) Relationship between the sinusoidal waves of terminal voltage, current, and induced voltage. (b) Vector diagram for these relationships.

the induced voltages will be directly proportional to the number of turns in the coils.

In Fig. 3–4*a*, the induced voltage in each coil, the flux ϕ being assumed to be the same for all coils, is

$$E = -N \frac{d\phi}{dt} 10^{-8} \qquad E_1 = -N_1 \frac{d\phi}{dt} 10^{-8} \qquad E_2 = -N_2 \frac{d\phi}{dt} 10^{-8}$$

$$E_3 = -N_3 \frac{d\phi}{dt} 10^{-8}$$

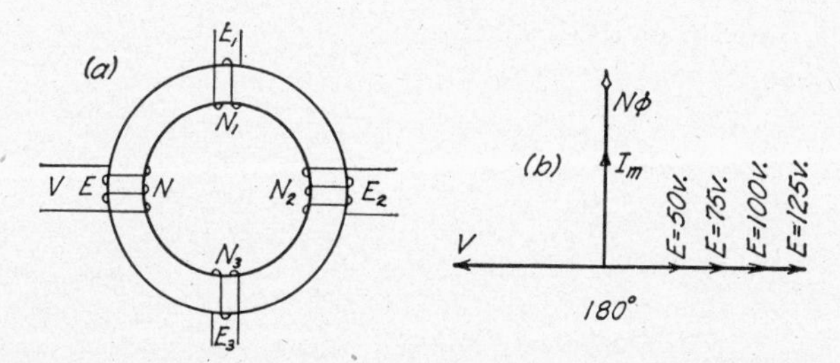

FIG. 3–4. Induced voltages in coils on the same magnetic circuit.

Since the flux is the same for all coils, the induced voltage per turn for all coils is the same and the total induced voltage per coil depends upon the number of turns in the coil. It follows, then, that

$$\frac{E}{N} = \frac{E_1}{N_1} = \frac{E_2}{N_2} = \frac{E_3}{N_3}$$

Example a. Assume (in Fig. 3–4a) that the values of N, N_1, N_2, and N_3, are 100, 50, 75, and 125 turns, respectively. Determine the voltage induced in each coil if 100 volts alternating current are impressed upon the coil having 100 turns. Draw the vector diagram.

$$E_{100} = V = 100 \text{ volts}$$

Therefore, $E_{100}/N_{100} = 1$ volt, the induced voltage per turn. Also, $E_{50} = 50$ volts; $E_{75} = 75$ volts; $E_{125} = 125$ volts.

The vector diagram is shown in Fig. 3–4b and the induced voltage for the different coils are all in time phase with each other.

4. The Transformer. The previous discussion has been of an ideal transformer, where losses are not considered. In the transformer, the magnetic system consists of a closed iron circuit. This magnetic circuit

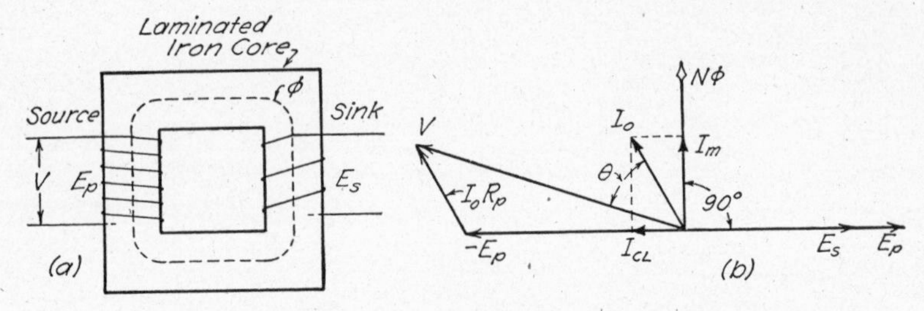

FIG. 4–4. The transformer and transformer vector diagram at no load.

is a core, built up of laminated steel stampings bolted (or clamped) together. The two coils (primary and secondary) are securely fastened on this iron core. The input side of the transformer is called the primary and the output side the secondary.

Figure 4–4a shows the construction principle of the transformer with the primary winding connected to an a-c source of voltage. The transformer differs from the ideal in that there are losses in the core and windings. For this reason, the input current at no load cannot lag the impressed voltage by 90°, as shown in Fig. 3–4b.

In Fig. 4–4a, the induced voltages in the primary and secondary windings (E_p and E_s) are caused by the flux ϕ of the magnetic circuit. This flux is produced by a current which is 90° ahead of the voltages E_p and E_s. The presence of the varying flux ϕ in the iron of the magnetic circuit causes hysteresis and eddy current losses in the iron. Therefore, a component of the input current must be an energy component to supply these losses.

The input current to the primary at no load consists of two components: (1) a magnetization component which is in quadrature with and leading the induced voltage and (2) an energy component, in phase with the component of impressed voltage to balance the induced voltage, which supplies the iron losses and a negligible amount of copper loss in the primary.

The transformer at no load acts in the same way as an iron-cored reactance coil with an additional winding on the magnetic circuit. The vector diagram for the transformer under no-load condition is shown in Fig. 4–4*b*. The voltages in the primary must satisfy Kirchhoff's voltage equation, which may be written

$$\bar{V} = -\bar{E}_p + \bar{I}_0\bar{Z}_p$$

where I_0 is the no-load (or exciting) current and Z_p is the impedance which in this case is R_p, the resistance of the primary circuit.

The exciting current I_0 is composed of two components I_m, the magnetizing (or excitation) component, and I_{cl}, the current component compensating for the loss in power in the iron of the magnetic circuit and the copper loss in the winding. The copper loss is usually negligible as compared to the iron loss under no-load conditions.

5. Loading the Transformer. Figure 5–4 shows a transformer, its primary and secondary windings, and the instantaneous directions of currents in the windings at a specific time. When the secondary winding

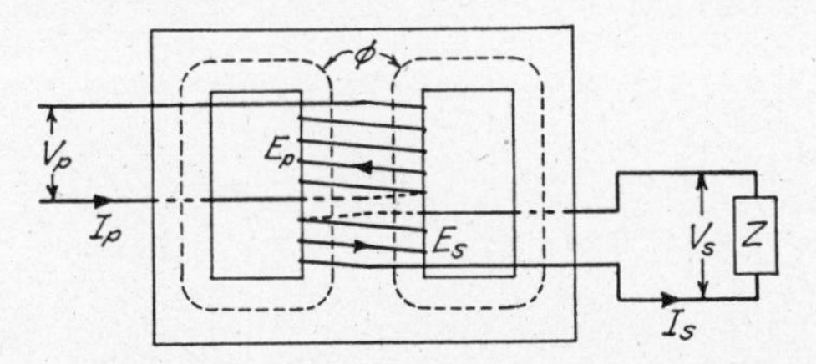

FIG. 5–4. Instantaneous directions of currents in a transformer.

is open-circuited, the current in the primary is just sufficient to establish the flux ϕ in the iron. If the secondary is connected to an impedance Z, a current I_s will flow with a magnitude depending upon the values of E_s and Z. The current in the secondary winding, in accordance with Lenz's Law, will be in such a direction as to establish at every instant a magnetomotive force in opposition to the main magnetomotive force. The reaction of two opposing magnetomotive forces is to give a resultant magnetomotive force in the magnetic circuit which is momentarily less than the original. If the resultant magnetomotive force is momentarily reduced, the induced voltages E_s and E_p will be reduced. With the value of the primary induced voltage E_p reduced, the primary current will increase until equilibrium is established in the magnetic circuit. This means that the resultant magnetomotive force is returned to approximately its original value, and that the new primary current under load differs from the no-load primary current by an amount sufficient to maintain the resultant magnetomotive force approximately constant. The increase above no-load condition in magnetomotive force on the primary must balance the opposing magnetomotive force caused by the secondary load current. This is the sequence of phenomena which follow the loading of the secondary of a transformer.

The change in the induced voltages of the windings of a transformer from no load to full load is usually less than 2 per cent. This means that the net flux in the transformer iron remains practically constant for all conditions of load, and the resultant magnetomotive force acting on the magnetic circuit under all loads is also practically constant and will be equal to the magnetomotive force at no load. Any loading on the secondary, causing secondary ampere turns in opposition to the no-load primary ampere turns, is balanced by an increased primary current sufficient to compensate for the effect of the secondary current.

The no-load (or exciting) current is a small percentage of the rated primary current of the transformer (usually less than 5 per cent) and it does not materially change the primary current value under loading. The following relationship of primary and secondary ampere turns is approximately true of all loads.

$$I_pN_p = I_sN_s$$

$$\frac{I_p}{I_s} = \frac{N_s}{N_p}$$

where I_p = primary current
I_s = secondary current
N_p = primary turns
N_s = secondary turns.

The ratio of primary to secondary currents varies inversely as the turns of the respective windings.

If the effects of the resistance and the reactance are neglected and the magnetic circuit of the transformer is considered perfect, the volt-ampere input to the transformer equals the volt-ampere output.

$$V_pI_p = V_sI_s$$

and

$$\frac{V_p}{V_s} = \frac{I_s}{I_p} = \frac{N_p}{N_s}$$

The ratio of primary to secondary terminal voltages varies directly as the turns of the respective windings.

6. Leakage Reactance. In the discussion of the transformer, up to this time, it has been assumed that the flux that links both the primary and secondary is the same at all times. Actually, it is impossible to obtain this condition, regardless of the care in placing the windings together and in the design of the magnetic circuit. The flux of the transformer magnetic circuit may be considered to consist of three parts: (*a*) the mutual flux, which links both the primary and secondary windings, (*b*) the flux, which links only the primary winding, and (*c*) the flux, which links only the secondary winding.

The part of the flux that links only the primary winding is called the primary leakage flux ϕ_p and the part of the flux that links only the secondary winding is called the secondary leakage flux ϕ_s.

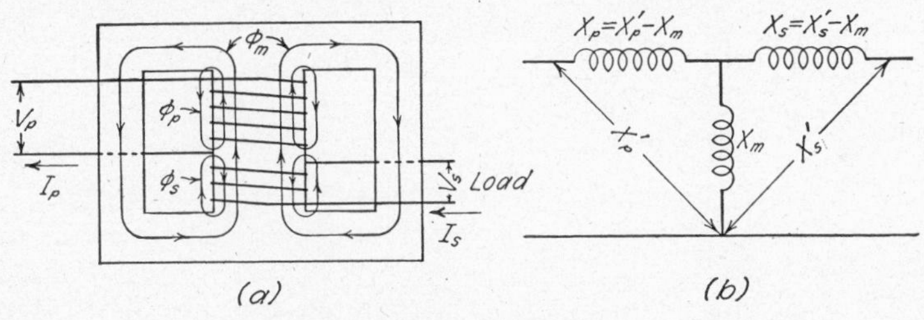

FIG. 6–4. (*a*) Flux in a transformer core. (*b*) Simple electric circuit of a 1:1 ratio transformer showing mutual effect.

Figure 6–4*a* shows the transformer with the three parts of the total flux in the magnetic circuit.

The primary leakage flux ϕ_p is dependent upon both the primary winding and the primary current and it induces an electromotive force in the primary, but not in the secondary winding. The voltage induced by ϕ_p will lag the primary current I_p by 90° and the component of the impressed voltage V, which balances this induced voltage, must, therefore, lead the current I_p by 90°. The induced voltages produced by the flux ϕ_p lags the current I_p by 90° and affects the circuit in the same manner as an inductive reactance in series. The effect of the primary leakage flux is identically the same as that of an inductive reactance and, as a result, this leakage flux may be replaced (without altering the electric circuit analysis) by a hypothetical reactance called the primary leakage reactance. The symbol for this factor is X_p. This method of substitution has been discussed in Chapter 3.

In the same manner, it can be shown that the secondary leakage flux ϕ_s is dependent upon the secondary current I_s. This leakage flux induces a voltage only in the secondary winding, which lags the secondary current by 90° and, therefore, a component of induced voltage, equal and opposite, must be supplied by the winding if electrical equilibrium is to be maintained. As in the primary, this leakage flux is dependent upon the secondary current I_s and, therefore, its induced voltage can be replaced by a hypothetical inductive reactance acting with the current I_s. For the secondary circuit, the term secondary leakage reactance is used and the symbol is X_s.

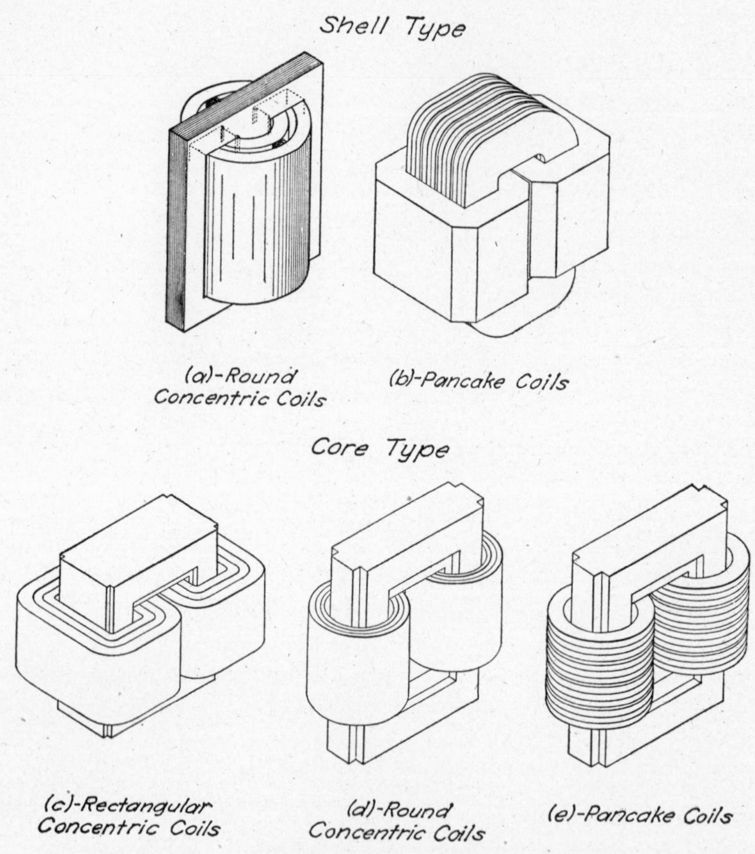

FIG. 7–4. Various types of coil and core assembly.

The various fluxes ϕ_m, ϕ_p, and ϕ_s do not exist separately in the transformer core, but only a resultant flux is present. This division is made in order to simplify the discussion of the reactions within a transformer.

It should be noted that the leakage reactances X_p and X_s are not reactances caused by the self-inductances of the primary and secondary windings respectively. The primary and secondary windings are connected electrically by the mutual inductance of the transformer. In

Chapter 4 of Volume I it was shown that an induced voltage in one coil could be obtained because of a current change in a second coil linked to the first one by mutual coupling. Figure 6–4*b* shows the simple electric circuit diagram of an equivalent 1:1 ratio transformer. The effects of resistance have been omitted in order to simplify the diagram. It can be seen from the diagram that primary leakage reactance X_p will differ from the reactance of self-induction X'_p by the effects of the mutual linkages. In a like manner X_s differs from X'_s. For close-coupled circuits where the coupling coefficient is practically one, the resistance and leakage reactance are small, and the ratio of terminal voltages under load is practically equal to the turn ratio. Some transformers, such as audio transformers, are loose-coupled. These transformers, therefore, have a low coupling coefficient and large resistance and leakage reactance. The ratio of terminal voltages under load is considerably less than the turn ratio.

The existence of leakage fluxes is an undesirable condition in a transformer since a loss in voltage always reflects on the performance of the transformer. As a result, the windings are placed as closely together as is possible in order to reduce these leakage fluxes. There are conditions, however, in which use is made of the transformer leakage reactance in order to get a definite performance. The constant current transformer is an example, and will be discussed later. Figure 7–4 shows several ways of assembling the windings of transformers for both the core and shell type of magnetic circuits. Two types of coil arrangement are shown: (1) layer (or pancake) windings for both primary and secondary, and (2) concentric windings. The coils which constitute the primary winding are connected together, and the coils which constitute the secondary winding are connected together. The coils of a respective winding may be in series or parallel, depending upon what is necessary to give the proper voltage and current rating.

7. Transformer Vector Diagram Under Load Conditions. When a load is connected to the secondary terminals, a current flows which is dependent upon the magnitude of the secondary terminal voltage and the impedance of the load. If the transformer is to supply this demand, the input to the transformer through its primary must be capable of meeting the requirements of the load and the losses that exist in the transformer. In order to simplify the construction, relative to the lengths of the various vectors, a 1:1 ratio transformer is considered. Also, the lengths of the vectors representing the component voltages, caused by the resistances and reactances, are increased relative to terminal and induced voltages to magnify their effects upon the transformer terminal conditions.

Figure 8–4 shows the vector diagrams for a 1:1 ratio transformer with three loads of different power factor connected to the secondary output terminals.

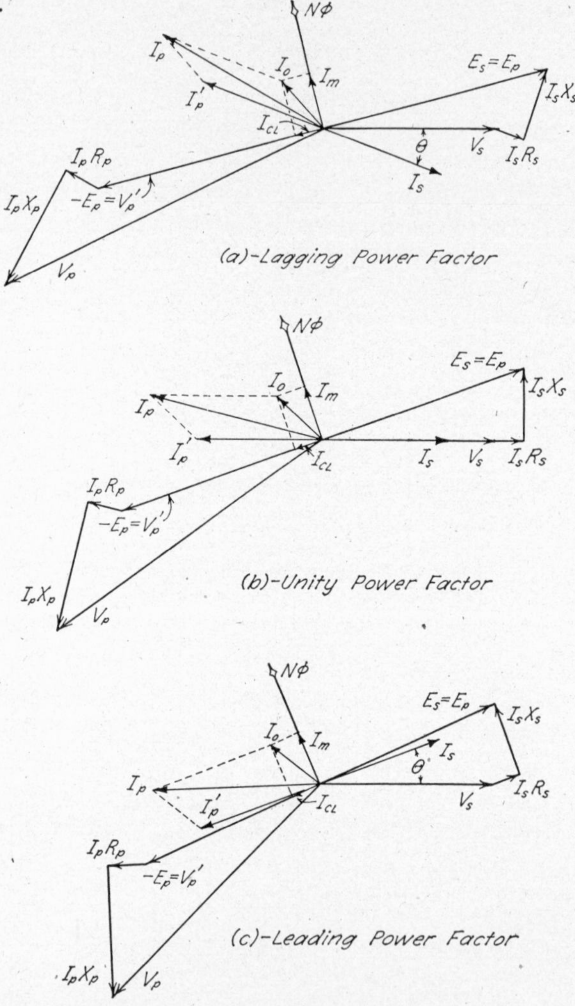

Fig. 8–4. Transformer vector diagrams for different power factors.

The secondary current I_s is drawn relative to the secondary terminal voltage V_s depending upon the load power factor. The secondary-induced voltage E_s will differ from V_s by an amount equal to the resistance voltage component I_sR_s and reactance voltage component I_sX_s in the secondary winding.

$$\overline{E}_s = \overline{V}_s + \overline{I}_s\overline{R}_s + \overline{I}_s\overline{X}_s \qquad \overline{E}_s = \overline{V}_s + \overline{I}_s(R_s + jX_s)$$

The magnitude and direction of E_s can be determined, and the induced voltage in the primary winding will always be in the same direction and equal to $E_s(N_p/N_s)$. The magnetomotive force and the magnetizing current I_m, which maintains this magnetomotive force, are at 90° to the induced voltages E_s and E_p and leading in time phase. The core loss component I_{cl} is a power component only, and will be at 90° to I_m, and in phase with the component of input voltage, $-E_p$, to balance the induced voltage in the primary winding. The vector sum of I_m and I_{cl} is I_0, the no-load primary (or exciting) current.

The total primary current under load was increased by an amount sufficient to supply additional primary magnetomotive force to oppose that of the secondary. The net balance remaining was the amount that is required under all conditions; it is supplied by I_0. The load component of primary current I_p' is opposite in time phase to I_s and is equal in magnitude to $I_s(N_s/N_p)$. If $N_p/N_s = a$, then $\bar{I}_p' = -\bar{I}_s(1/a)$. The total primary current is I_p and is the vector sum of I_p' and I_0.

$$\bar{I}_p = \bar{I}_p' + \bar{I}_0 \qquad \bar{I}_p = -\bar{I}_s\left(\frac{1}{a}\right) + \bar{I}_0$$

To determine the primary impressed voltage, the voltages necessary to balance the voltage components caused by the primary resistance and reactance and the induced voltage E_p must be added vectorially. Referring to Fig. 1–4, the phase relation between the induced voltage in a coil and the impressed voltage on the coil is 180°. The impressed voltage V_p can be found from the voltage expression

$$\bar{V}_p = -\bar{E}_p + \bar{I}_p\bar{R}_p + \bar{I}_p\bar{X}_p \qquad \bar{V}_p = -\bar{E}_p + \bar{I}_p(R_p + jX_p)$$

The power factor of the secondary is the load power factor and that of the primary is practically the same as the secondary in the ordinary transformer. The change in phase angle, caused by the transformer resistances and reactances, is negligible.

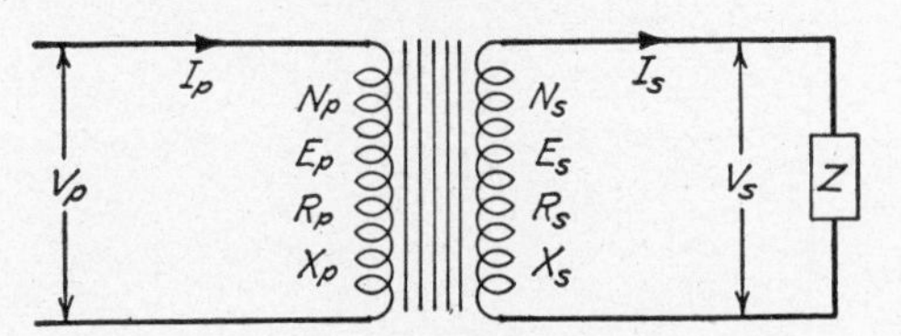

FIG. 9–4. Circuit diagram of a transformer.

8. Equivalent Circuit of a Transformer. Figure 9–4 shows the circuit diagram of a transformer with a secondary load. The transformer has a primary of N_p turns and a secondary of N_s turns.

From the previous discussion, the voltage relationship is

$$\bar{E}_s = \bar{V}_s + \bar{I}_s(R_s + jX_s)$$

It is possible to make substitutions and convert both the secondary and primary values so that the final result is a voltage expression containing all the transformer and load constants. From this relationship a simple electrical circuit can be drawn that will satisfy the circuit parameters. In this way, the transformer can be reduced to an equivalent electric circuit for analytical work. This reduction can be made as follows.

Using the equation indicated and continuing,

$$\bar{E}_s = \bar{V}_s + \bar{I}_s(R_s + jX_s) = \bar{I}_s\bar{Z} + \bar{I}_s(R_s + jX_s)$$

$$\bar{E}_p = \bar{E}_s\left(\frac{N_p}{N_s}\right)$$

Substituting,

$$\bar{E}_p = \left(\frac{N_p}{N_s}\right)[\bar{I}_s\bar{Z} + \bar{I}_s(R_s + jX_s)]$$

From the vector diagram (Fig. 8–4),

$$\bar{V}_p = -\bar{E}_p + \bar{I}_p(R_p + jX_p)$$

and, when N_p and N_s are not equal,

$$\bar{I}_p = \bar{I}_p' + \bar{I}_0 = -\bar{I}_s\left(\frac{N_s}{N_p}\right) + \bar{I}_0 \qquad -\bar{I}_s = \bar{I}_p'\left(\frac{N_p}{N_s}\right)$$

Therefore,

$$\bar{V}_p = -\left\{\left(\frac{N_p}{N_s}\right)[\bar{I}_s\bar{Z} + \bar{I}_s(R_s + jX_s)]\right\} + \bar{I}_p(R_p + jX_p)$$

Substituting for I_s and reducing,

$$\bar{V}_p = \left(\frac{N_p}{N_s}\right)^2\bar{I}_p'\bar{Z} + \left(\frac{N_p}{N_s}\right)^2\bar{I}_p'(R_s + jX_s) + \bar{I}_p(R_p + jX_p)$$

$$\bar{V}_p = \bar{I}_p'\left[\left(\frac{N_p}{N_s}\right)^2\bar{Z}\right] + \bar{I}_p'\left[\left(\frac{N_p}{N_s}\right)^2(R_s + jX_s)\right] + \bar{I}_p(R_p + jX_p)$$

If $(N_p/N_s) = a$, then $(N_p/N_s)^2 = a^2$ and

$$\bar{V}_p = \bar{I}_p'a^2\bar{Z} + \bar{I}_p'a^2(R_s + jX_s) + \bar{I}_p(R_p + jX_p)$$

and, substituting for I_p its equivalent,

$$\bar{V}_p = \bar{I}_p'a^2\bar{Z} + \bar{I}_p'a^2(R_s + jX_s) + (\bar{I}_p' + \bar{I}_0)(R_p + jX_p)$$

From this voltage equation, it may be seen that a simple electrical circuit can exist which will satisfy the equation and that this circuit may be considered the *exact* equivalent of the transformer.

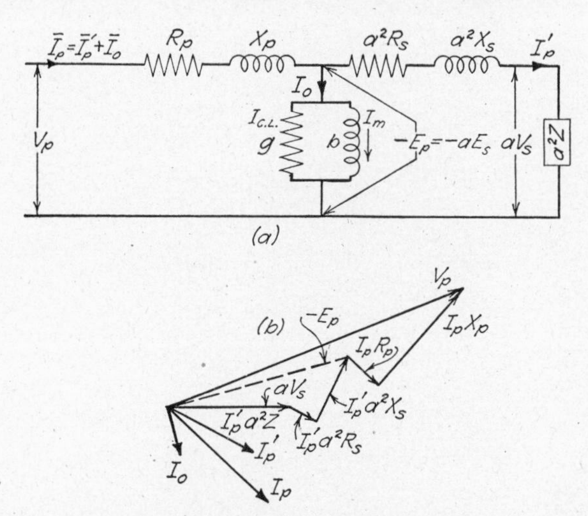

FIG. 10–4. Exact equivalent circuit of a transformer and vector diagram.

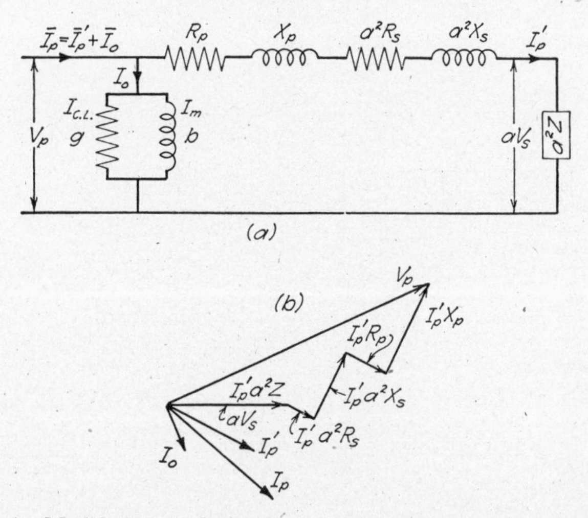

FIG. 11–4. Modified equivalent circuit of a transformer and vector diagram.

Figure 10–4 shows this exact circuit and a vector diagram for an assumed load. The exciting current I_0 consists of two components: one, a power component, which can be represented by a conductance and the other, a magnetizing component, which can be represented by a susceptance. These components of the exciting current are equivalent values which will give the exact components of I_0 and they can, therefore, be considered a part of the equivalent transformer circuit.

The exciting current of a transformer is small compared to the load component of current and is at, approximately, a 90° power-factor angle. The total current, therefore, does not differ materially from the load

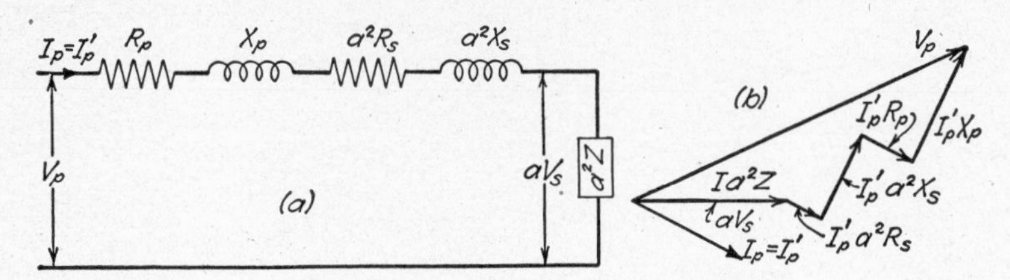

FIG. 12–4. Simplified equivalent circuit of a transformer and vector diagram.

current and, for this reason, the exciting current effects are generally omitted in transformer circuit calculations.

Figure 11–4 shows the modified circuit diagram and a vector diagram for this circuit. The change in position of the parallel branch makes it possible to combine the two winding impedance constants.

Figure 12–4 shows a vector diagram for an assumed load and the simplified equivalent transformer circuit, where the effect of the exciting current is omitted entirely from the circuit calculations.

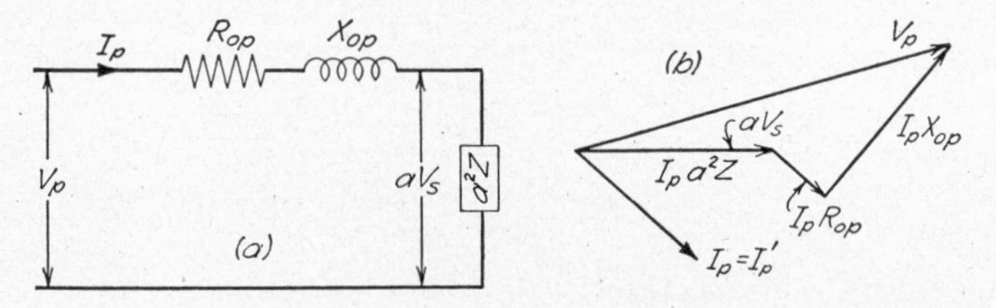

FIG. 13–4. Simplified transformer circuit diagram and vector diagram.

It is possible to combine the winding impedances in Fig. 12–4 and represent the simplified circuit as indicated in Fig. 13–4, where

$$R_{op} = R_p + a^2R_s$$

$$X_{op} = X_p + a^2X_s$$

Thus far, the equivalent circuit has been considered from the primary side (or the side of impressed voltage) of the transformer. Since the loaded side of the transformer is the secondary, it is often desirable to express the values in terms of secondary conditions. An expression for this is obtained from a consideration of the voltage equation for the conditions of Fig. 12–4.

$$\bar{V}_p = \bar{I}_p'(R_p + jX_p) + \bar{I}_p'a^2(R_s + jX_s) + \bar{I}_p'a^2\bar{Z}$$

but

$$I_p' = \frac{1}{a} I_s \quad \text{and} \quad V_{ps} = \frac{1}{a} V_p$$

When equivalent values in terms of the secondary base are substituted for I_p' and V_p, the expression for the transformer equivalent circuit, in terms of the secondary, becomes

$$\bar{V}_{ps} = \bar{I}_s \frac{1}{a^2}(R_p + jX_p) + \bar{I}_s(R_s + jX_s) + \bar{I}_s\bar{Z}$$

The simplified circuit referred to the secondary (or load) side of a transformer would be as shown in Fig. 14–4.

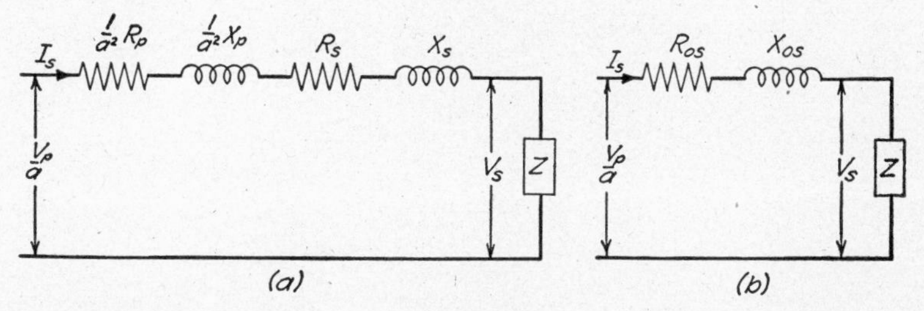

FIG. 14–4. Simplified equivalent circuit diagram of a transformer referred to the secondary.

It is possible, as has been shown, to reduce the transformer to a simple equivalent circuit with the constants referred to either the primary or secondary side as a basis for the circuit construction. These equivalent values can always be expressed, when referred to the primary side, as

$$R_{op} = R_p + a^2R_s$$

$$X_{op} = X_p + a^2X_s$$

when referred to the secondary side, as

$$R_{os} = R_s + \frac{1}{a^2}R_p$$

$$X_{os} = X_s + \frac{1}{a^2}X_p$$

where

$$a = \frac{N_p}{N_s}$$

and

$$R_{op} = a^2 R_{os}$$

$$X_{op} = a^2 X_{os}$$

$$R_{os} = \frac{1}{a^2} R_{op}$$

$$X_{os} = \frac{1}{a^2} X_{op}$$

Example b. A transformer, having a value of 10 for a has a primary resistance and reactance of 0.1 ohm and 1.0 ohm, respectively. The resistance and reactance of the secondary are 0.002 ohm and 0.02 ohm, respectively. Express the equivalent resistance and reactance values referred to the primary side and secondary side.

$$a = 10$$

$$R_{op} = 0.1 + 100(0.002) = 0.3 \text{ ohm} \qquad R_{os} = 0.002 + \tfrac{1}{100}(0.1) = 0.003 \text{ ohm}$$

$$X_{op} = 1.0 + 100(0.02) = 3 \text{ ohms} \qquad X_{os} = 0.02 + \tfrac{1}{100}(1.0) = 0.03 \text{ ohm}$$

9. Percentage Values for Transformer Constants. The practice, at present, is to give the value of the transformer constants in per cent of the transformer rating. The transformer rating is in volt-amperes and is always the output of the transformer. The values of resistance, reactance, and impedance are given in percentage of secondary terminal voltage under full-load current. This means that the values I_sR_{os}, I_sX_{os}, and I_sZ_{os} are given as percentage of V_s when I_s is at rated value. The value of the exciting current can be given in the same manner: I_{os} in percentage of I_s at full-load value. The real advantage in giving these constants in percentage is the ease with which the voltage regulation and efficiency can be calculated.

The percentage method has been used in Chapter 14 of Volume I to express voltage drops in conductors. The same method will be used in determining voltage regulation (which will be discussed in the next section) and also in determining the transformer efficiency (which will be discussed in Chapter 11).

Example c. A 2300-volt/230-volt, 10-kva transformer has the following constants: 1 per cent resistance; 10 per cent reactance; 5 per cent exciting current. Find the equivalent resistance, reactance, and exciting current referred to both the low voltage and high voltage sides.

Low voltage side:

$$\text{Full-load current } \frac{10{,}000}{230} = 43.5 \text{ amp}$$

$$IR_{OL} = 230 \times 0.01 = 2.3 \text{ volts} \qquad R_{OL} = \frac{2.3}{43.5} = 0.0528 \text{ ohm}$$

$$IX_{OL} = 230 \times 0.1 = 23 \text{ volts} \qquad X_{OL} = \frac{23}{43.5} = 0.528 \text{ ohm}$$

$$I_{OL} = 43.5 \times 0.05 = 2.175 \text{ amp}$$

High voltage side:

$$\text{Full-load current} = \frac{10{,}000}{2300} = 4.35 \text{ amp}$$

$$IR_{OH} = 2300 \times 0.01 = 23 \text{ volts} \qquad R_{OH} = \frac{23}{4.35} = 5.28 \text{ ohms}$$

$$IX_{OH} = 2300 \times 0.1 = 230 \text{ volts} \qquad X_{OH} = \frac{230}{4.35} = 52.8 \text{ ohms}$$

$$I_{OH} = 4.35 \times 0.05 = 0.2175 \text{ amp}$$

10. Voltage Regulation of a Transformer. "The regulation of a constant-potential transformer is the change in secondary voltage, expressed in per cent of rated secondary voltage, which occurs when rated kva output at a specific power factor is reduced to zero, with the primary impressed terminal voltage maintained constant." †

The voltage regulation of a transformer may be considered a measure of the ability of the transformer to maintain its output voltage. This ability is judged on the basis that the lower the percentage of regulation, the better the ability to maintain voltage.

The voltage regulation in per cent may be expressed as

$$\text{Percentage voltage regulation} = \frac{V_{NL} - V_{FL}}{V_{FL}} \times 100$$

where V_{NL} = no-load secondary terminal voltage
V_{FL} = full-load secondary terminal voltage.

Since the primary voltage is constant regardless of the secondary load, the value of V_{NL} will be equal to $V_p(1/a)$. If the transformer ratio is 1 to 1, $V_p = V_s$ at no load.

† Article 15.20.235, American standard definitions of electrical terms. American Institute of Electrical Engineers, August, 1932.

The voltage regulation can be determined for any power factor once the transformer rating and constants are known. In most instances, the transformer constants are given on the name plate, along with the capacity and voltage ratio. These values, as has been stated, are given as percentage values and, for this reason, the regulation is easily determined when these values and the load power factor are known.

Example d. Determine the voltage regulation of the transformer given in Example *c* for load-power factors of unity, 80 per cent lag, and 80 per cent lead. Draw a vector diagram for these three cases.

Unity power factor:

$$V_{NL} = \sqrt{(100 + 1)^2 + (10)^2} = 101.4 \text{ per cent}$$

$$\text{Percentage regulation } 101.4 - 100 = 1.4 \text{ per cent}$$

80 per cent lagging power factor:

$$V_{NL} = \sqrt{(100 \times 0.8 + 1)^2 + (100 \times 0.6 + 10)^2}$$

$$= \sqrt{(81)^2 + (70)^2} = 107 \text{ per cent}$$

$$\text{Percentage regulation } 107 - 100 = 7 \text{ per cent}$$

80 per cent leading power factor:

$$V_{NL} = \sqrt{(100 \times 0.8 + 1)^2 + (100 \times 0.6 - 10)^2} = \sqrt{(81)^2 + (50)^2}$$

$$= 95.2 \text{ per cent}$$

$$\text{Percentage regulation } 95.2 - 100 = -4.8 \text{ per cent}$$

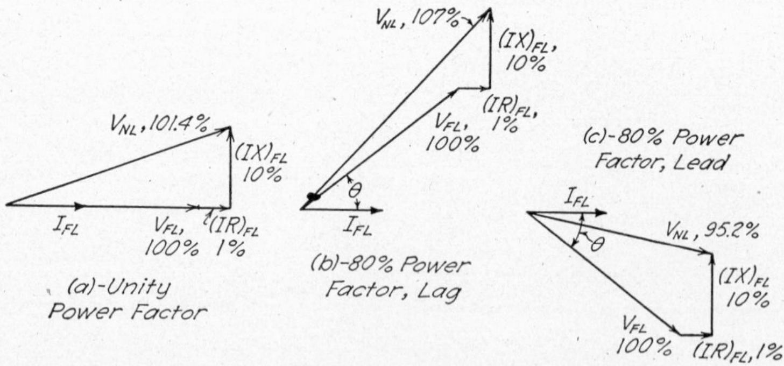

FIG. 15–4. Vector diagrams at full-load and different power factors for the simplified transformer circuit.

Negative regulation means that the terminal voltage increases as load is applied. The vector diagrams for these three loads at different power factors are shown in Fig. 15–4.

If the transformer constants are not given in percentage, the solution can be obtained, all values being used as voltage components. Therefore, the solution of the example just given can be changed to voltage values by multiplying each percentage value by the rated voltage value of the base, which is 230 volts if the low side is used as a base or 2300 volts if the high side is used as a base.

If the ohmic (or percentage) values of the constants are not known, they must be determined by test. The exciting current at rated voltage and frequency can be determined by measurement of the input current to the transformer when the secondary side is on open circuit; this is the no-load test. The resistance and reactance values, however, must

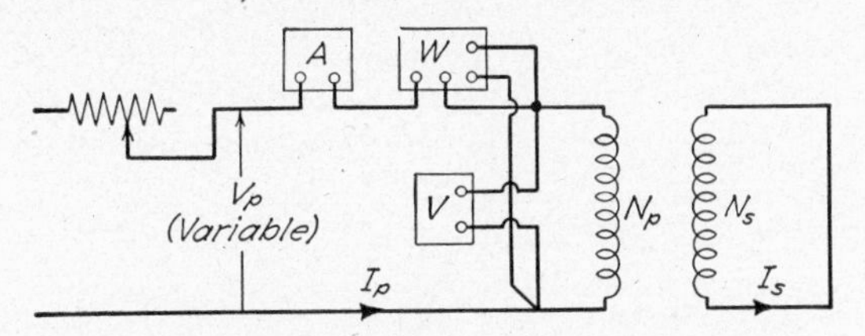

FIG. 16–4. Circuit diagram for short-circuit test.

be obtained from a short-circuit test. Figure 16–4 shows the circuit diagram of the test circuit with the necessary instruments, voltmeter, ammeter, and wattmeter, connected. For this test, it is necessary to short-circuit the secondary and apply a voltage on the primary (usually about 5 to 10 per cent of the primary rated voltage) of an amount to cause full-load current to flow in the primary winding. If I_p is at rated value, I_s is also at rated value $[I_s = I_p(N_p/N_s)]$.

The power input to the transformer for this test supplies (1) core loss, (2) primary copper loss, and (3) secondary copper loss. Since a small percentage of rated voltage is used, a small percentage of rated flux exists in the magnetic circuit and the iron loss is a negligible amount, as compared to the copper loss. The power input for this test may, therefore, be considered as all copper loss. Then

$$W = I_p^2 R_p + I_s^2 R_s = I_p^2 R_{op} = I_s^2 R_{os}$$

$$R_{op} = \frac{W}{I_p^2} \qquad R_{os} = \frac{1}{a^2} R_{op}$$

From these relationships, it is possible to determine the equivalent resistance referred to either the high side or low side winding.

Since the transformer is short-circuited, the values of input voltage and current can be used to determine the equivalent impedance of the transformer, referred to the input side. The output voltage V_s is zero and all the input voltage is used to overcome the impedances of the windings. Figure 17–4 shows the vector diagram. Then, under short circuit, the following relationships exist:

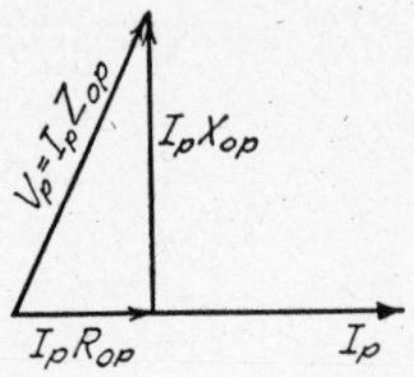

$$V_p = I_p Z_{op} \qquad Z_{op} = \frac{V_p}{I_p}$$

FIG. 17–4. Vector diagram for short-circuit test.

After the values of Z_{op} and R_{op} are determined, the value of X_{op} is easily obtained from the relationship

$$X_{op} = \sqrt{(Z_{op})^2 - (R_{op})^2}$$

When the transformer constants have been determined, the voltage regulation can be calculated, either by using the percentage method or by using all components as voltage components.

Example e. From a short-circuit test on a 5-kva, 1000/100-volt, 60-cycle transformer, the following data were obtained (the high voltage side was used as the primary): $V_p = 75$ volts, $I_p = 5$ amp, $W = 50$ watts.

(Note: The wattmeter reading has been corrected for potential coil loss.) Find the values of R_{op}, R_{os}, X_{op}, X_{os}, and the voltage regulation for a unity power-factor load.

$$R_{op} = \frac{50}{(5)^2} = 2 \text{ ohms} \qquad R_{os} = 0.02 \text{ ohm}$$

$$Z_{op} = \tfrac{75}{5} = 15 \text{ ohms} \qquad Z_{os} = 0.15 \text{ ohm}$$

$$X_{op} = \sqrt{(15)^2 - (2)^2} = 14.86 \text{ ohms} \qquad X_{os} = 0.1486 \text{ ohm}$$

Using the secondary side,

$$V_{NL} = \sqrt{(V_s + I_s R_{os})^2 + (I_s X_{os})^2} = \sqrt{[100 + 50(0.02)]^2 + (50 \times 0.1486)^2}$$

$$V_{NL} = \sqrt{(100 + 1)^2 + (7.43)^2} = \sqrt{10255.2}$$

$$V_{NL} = 101.3 \text{ volts}$$

$$\text{Percentage regulation} = \frac{101.3 - 100}{100} \times 100 = 1.3 \text{ per cent}$$

11. Autotransformer. The transformers previously discussed were those in which the primary and secondary windings are separate and electrically insulated from each other. There is, however, another type of transformer which has only one winding, a part of which serves as both primary and secondary. This type of transformer is called the autotransformer or compensator.

Figures 18–4*a* and 18–4*b* show the circuit diagrams of the autotransformer used as a step-down and as a step-up transformer, respectively. If it is used as a step-down transformer, all the winding between 1 and 3 is the primary and the part between 2 and 3 will serve also as a secondary winding. If it is used as a step-up transformer, the winding between 2 and 3 is the primary and the winding between 1 and 3 is the secondary. Part of the winding always serves both the primary and secondary sides in the autotransformer.

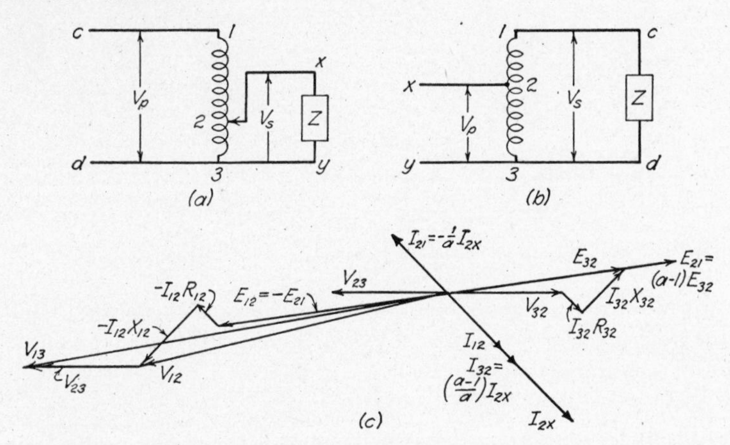

FIG. 18–4. Circuit diagrams and vector diagram of an autotransformer.

All the autotransformer winding links the same mutual flux; therefore, the induced voltage in each turn will be the same. If N_{13} and N_{23} are the turns in the primary and secondary respectively (Fig. 18–4*a*), the transformation ratio becomes

$$\frac{N_p}{N_s} = \frac{N_{13}}{N_{23}} = a$$

When a load is connected to the secondary, a current I_{2x} is supplied by the transformer. The current is supplied by the windings N_{32} and N_{12}.

$$\bar{I}_{2x} = \bar{I}_{12} + \bar{I}_{32}$$

The currents I_{12} and I_{32} will be in phase with respect to the load but in opposition with respect to the magnetic action on the transformer core. For the standard transformer it was shown that the primary and the secondary ampere-turns (exciting current neglected) were equal. Neglecting the exciting current in the autotransformer under load conditions, the ampere-turns caused by I_{12} and I_{32} must be equal. Therefore,

$$I_{12}N_{12} = I_{32}N_{32}$$

and

$$\frac{I_{32}}{I_{12}} = \frac{N_{12}}{N_{32}} = \frac{N_{31} - N_{32}}{N_{32}} = a - 1$$

or

$$I_{32} = (a - 1)I_{12}$$

In the same manner, it can be shown that the ratio of the induced voltages

$$\frac{E_{12}}{E_{23}} = \frac{N_{13} - N_{23}}{N_{23}} = a - 1$$

or

$$E_{12} = (a - 1)E_{23}$$

Figure 18–4*c* shows the vector diagram of an autotransformer supplying power to a load having a lagging power factor. The exciting current has been neglected in this analysis. The vector diagram is similar in most respects to that for the standard transformer. If a step-up autotransformer is considered, the same method of analysis is used, and the vector diagram will be similar in every respect to the one given. The ratio of transformation will change the relative lengths of the voltage and current vectors.

Autotransformers are used chiefly as motor-starting compensators, where it is not necessary for the transformer primary and secondary windings to be electrically insulated from each other. At the present time, only a few autotransformers are in use in transmission systems, because it is usually desirable to isolate electrically the various sections of a large system. Since a single winding is used for both primary and secondary circuits, the total copper required is reduced and the transformer efficiency is slightly improved.

12. Constant Current Transformer. Although most electrical systems are operated as constant potential systems, there are instances in which a constant current system offers advantages. The series street lighting circuit is an example of this constant current system. The lamps are connected in series, and the system voltage is adjusted until the desired current is obtained in the circuit.

A constant current transformer operates upon the principle of increase in secondary voltage as the power output increases, the secondary current remaining practically constant. To accomplish this, the leakage reactance should be very high so that, between the limit of short circuit ($V_s = 0$) and some value along the drooping part of the external voltage characteristic curve, the current would remain practically constant. Figure 19–4 shows a schematic diagram and operating voltage curve for a constant current transformer. The transformer is usually operated between x and y on the curve. If the change in leakage reactance can be controlled automatically, the current can be held constant throughout

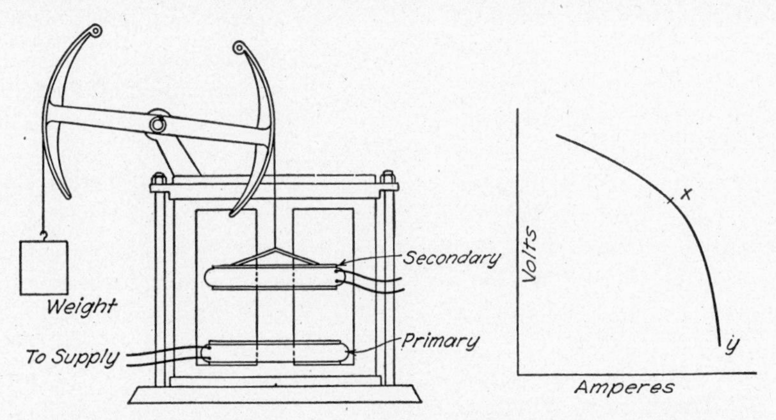

FIG. 19–4. Schematic diagram and operating voltage curve for a constant current transformer.

a wide range of secondary voltage. This is accomplished by having one coil movable on the iron core. Because of the repulsion produced between the two windings by their respective currents, the two coils are

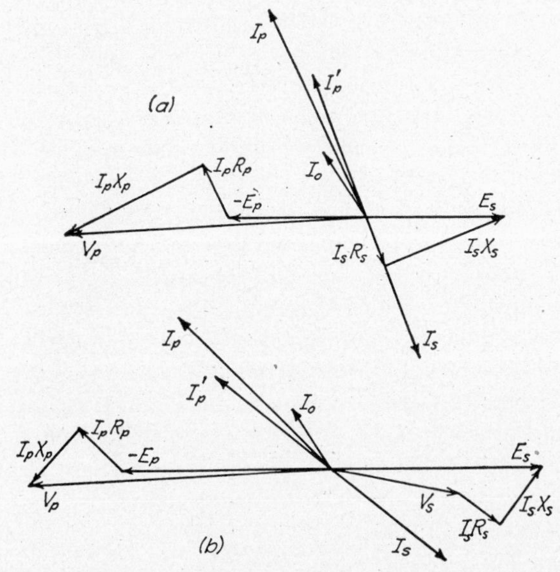

FIG. 20–4. Vector diagrams of a constant current transformer for short-circuit and load conditions.

separated from each other until part of the weight of the moving part is balanced, the remainder being balanced by counterweights. If the impedance of the secondary load circuit is decreased, the secondary current will increase momentarily, causing the coils to move farther apart. This will cause the leakage reactance to increase and the load current to decrease. Figure 20–4 shows the vector diagrams for the two loads of short circuit and a load such as that indicated by the points y and x on the curve of Fig. 19–4.

In loading a constant current transformer, it is necessary first to separate the coils and short-circuit the secondary. After the primary is energized, the removal of the short circuit places the desired secondary load on the transformer, allowing the secondary winding to assume its position nearer the primary coils so that the applied load may be properly carried. The reaction between the primary and secondary balances the weight of the moving coil and the counterweights.

13. Transformer Winding Connections. Most transformer primary and secondary windings consist of several coils, and it is necessary to "phase" or connect these coils so that their individual voltages combine properly to give the desired primary or secondary voltage. Usually, the coils are placed symmetrically on the iron core and the end connections are brought out in a definite way. These are indicated on the name plate of the transformer so that connections can be properly made.

It is possible in most cases to determine the high and low voltage sides of the transformer and, after this has been done, to use the rated voltage per coil to excite the transformer. With the transformer excited from rated voltage, rated induced voltage per coil is produced and, by properly adding these voltages vectorially, coils may be connected in parallel or series.

As an example, assume that a transformer having two primary and two secondary coils is to be connected as a 1:2 ratio transformer. The rated voltage per coil is 100 volts and the rated current is 10 amperes. Figure 21–4 shows the circuit diagram of this transformer. In Fig. 21–4a, the coils are indicated and an induced voltage of 100 volts per coil exists. To parallel coils 1 and 2, the induced voltages must oppose each other and, if end b is connected to a, the voltage indicated between b' and a' must be zero. If the voltage is zero, b' and a' may be connected together and no current will flow in the coils because of the lack of voltage in the closed circuit. The secondary coils must be connected in series in order to obtain 200 volts. This can be done by again connecting one end of coil 3 to one end of coil 4 and measuring the difference of potential between the free ends. If the voltage is zero, the voltages oppose and, if it is 200 volts, the voltages add. The latter is a series connection. It follows, then, that to connect the coils for this 1:2 ratio, it is necessary to

(Primary) Connect *a* to *b*, *a′* to *b′*, and the source between *a* and *a′*.
(Secondary) Connect *c′* to *d* and obtain output voltage between *c* and *d′*.

In order to designate the internal relationship of the primary and secondary windings, it is common practice to mark the transformer leads. This means that any designation will apply to the relative instantaneous directions of currents in the leads. Primary and secondary leads will be marked the same polarity when, at a given instant, current

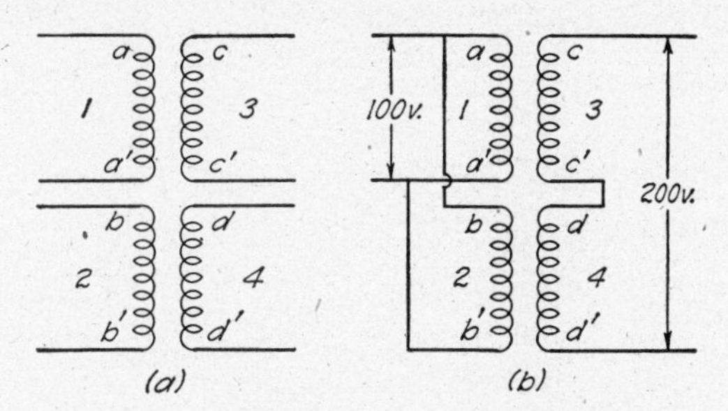

FIG. 21–4. Transformer coils and connections.

is entering the transformer at the primary lead designated and at the same instant current is leaving the transformer at the secondary lead designated. The direction of current flow will be the same as if the two transformer leads were connected together in the transformer to form a continuous electric circuit.

The polarity of a single-phase transformer can be designated as either additive or subtractive. If two adjacent leads from the primary and secondary are connected together and voltage is applied to the primary winding then

a. The transformer polarity is additive if the voltage across the remaining primary and secondary leads is greater than the voltage of the high voltage winding alone.

b. The transformer polarity is subtractive if the voltage across the remaining primary and secondary leads is less than the voltage of the high voltage winding alone.

Figure 22–4 shows the schematic circuit diagram of a 2:1 ratio transformer supplied from the high voltage side. For the connection as shown, if $V > V_p$, the transformer is connected additive; if $V < V_p$, the transformer is connected subtractive.

The terms additive and subtractive are seldom used with instrument transformers although it is apparent that the windings will be one connection or the other. The terminals of instrument transformers are marked H_1 for primary and X_1 for secondary leads to indicate leads of the same polarity.

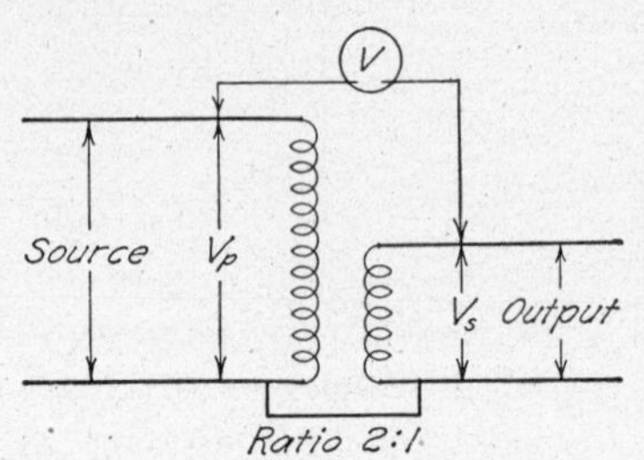

FIG. 22–4. Transformer schematic diagram for polarity check.

14. Polyphase Transformer Connections. The connections for primary and secondary coils of a bank of transformers determine the kind of transformer connection. There are in use today the following three-phase transformer connections:

	PRIMARY WINDINGS	SECONDARY WINDINGS
(a)	Delta	Delta
(b)	Wye	Wye
(c)	Delta	Wye
(d)	Wye	Delta

There are also some special transformer connections, which will be discussed in the next article.

For these four classifications three similar transformers are used in a bank and the primary and secondary windings are connected in one of the ways listed. The primary windings can always be connected in delta or wye and the bank can be energized. The secondary windings, however, must always be properly phased together in the desired type of connection. If the transformers are exactly alike, it may be possible that each secondary winding will be symmetrical with reference to its primary winding, and the terminals of each transformer secondary may be connected together in the same way in which the primaries are connected. Figure 23–4 shows circuit diagrams of the four kinds of transformer connections.

No difficulty will be experienced in loading an individual transformer of any bank if the primary winding of the transformer is connected to a source that does not depend upon some other transformer primary being energized. This means that if a three-phase four-wire supply is used for all wye-connected primaries, any transformer secondary winding can be loaded individually. By attempting to load a secondary of a wye-wye bank (line to neutral), this can be shown. If the primary side does not have the neutral connected, the primary current of the loaded transformer is limited by the impedance of the two unloaded transformers and the current flow is approximately the exciting current value. This condition is sometimes called a "shifting" neutral. If the neutral is connected to the source on the primary side, this shifting is prevented and no trouble is experienced. Another objection to the wye-wye bank without neutral connection is the third harmonic present in secondary

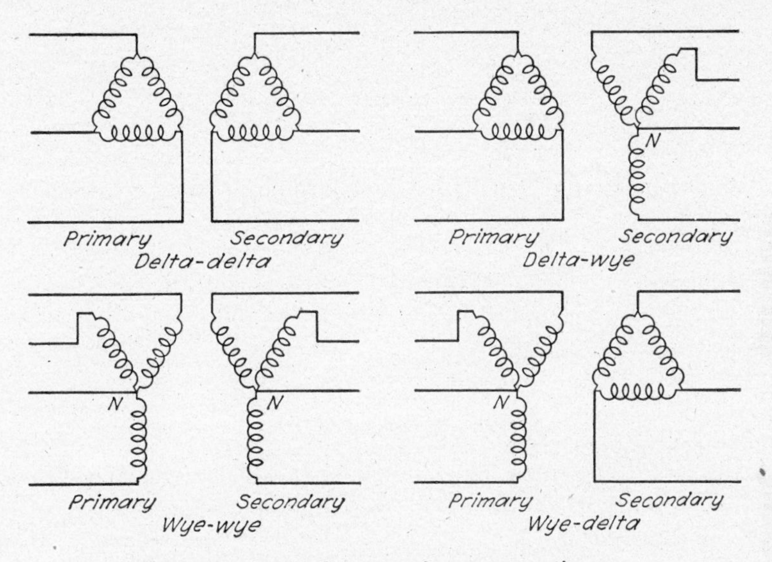

FIG. 23-4. Polyphase transformer connections.

voltage. This third harmonic component of voltage causes interference in any telephone system which may be influenced by the magnetic field of the transmission system.

A study of the four types of transformer connections shows that, in addition to the normal transformation ratio, a factor of $\sqrt{3}$ is present in the transformer banks which do not have the primary and secondary windings connected alike.

In Chapter 12 of Volume I it was shown that a 30° displacement existed between line values of currents or voltages when a wye system and a delta system were compared. Hence, the approximately 180° displacement between primary and secondary line values of currents and voltages will not exist if the primary and secondary windings of the transformer bank are not connected alike. This 30° displacement angle will cause a shift between the line values.

The following table gives the value of the secondary line voltage in terms of the primary line voltage for these various transformer bank connections, in which the individual transformer ratio (N_p/N_s) is a:

Transformer Bank Connection	Secondary Line Voltage
Delta-delta	$\frac{1}{a} V_p$
Wye-wye	$\frac{1}{a} V_p$
Delta-wye	$\frac{\sqrt{3}}{a} V_p$
Wye-delta	$\frac{1}{a\sqrt{3}} V_p$

15. Harmonics in Transformer Magnetizing Currents. To produce a voltage having a sine wave, the rate of change in the magnetic flux of a transformer must also be a sine wave. Since the permeability of the iron changes at different flux densities, the magnetizing current producing a sine wave of magnetic flux cannot itself be a sine wave. It has been found by analysis that the magnetizing current of a transformer producing a sine wave of induced voltage, primary and secondary, has a considerable third harmonic component in it. It also contains some higher odd harmonics but to a lesser degree. However, the magnetizing current of a transformer does not contain any even harmonics since the plus and minus half-waves of a complete cycle of magnetizing current are the same. Only odd harmonics can satisfy this condition. If the magnetizing current does not contain all the harmonics necessary to produce a sine wave of induced voltage, the voltage will contain those harmonics which the magnetizing current lacks, and sometimes more. As an example, if the magnetizing current does not contain the necessary third harmonic component, the induced voltages will contain a third harmonic component. In practically all transformer banks used in transmission, the proper components of exciting current are supplied. In this event large harmonic voltages are not developed in the windings. In some instances it is not possible to supply the proper magnetizing current and, as a result, higher harmonic voltages will be induced in the transformer windings.

One of the most common methods of connecting transformers is delta on the secondary side and wye or star on the primary side. Assume that the magnetizing currents for each transformer contain, in addition to the fundamental, a third harmonic component. Since the transformers are connected in three-phase relationship, their voltages are 120° apart and, therefore, their magnetizing currents are 120° apart. The three leads supplying the bank carry these magnetizing currents and their resultant must at all times be zero. An analysis of the magnetizing current waves for the transformers shows that the resultant is not zero; therefore all the transformer magnetizing current cannot be supplied through the three primary leads from the power source.

Figure 24–4 shows the star-delta connection with the arrows indicating the instantaneous directions in which the third harmonic currents should flow in the star side. The third harmonic currents of all three phases are in phase with each other and, having no return path in the star side, they cannot flow. Therefore third harmonic voltages will be generated because of the absence of the third harmonic component currents. These voltages are all in the same direction since their components of the magnetizing currents are all in the same direction.

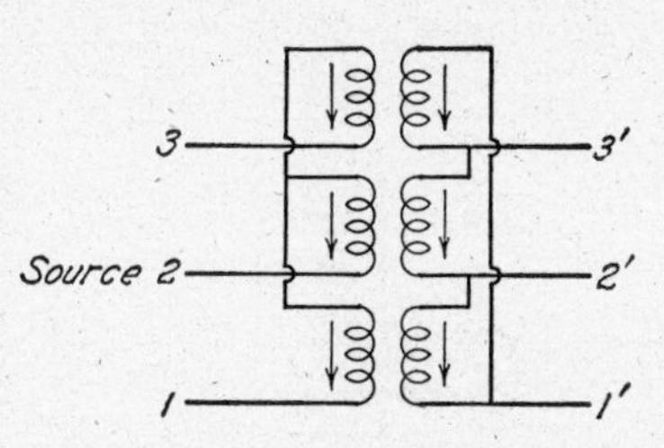

Fig. 24–4. The instantaneous direction of the harmonic currents in the star-connected primary of a transformer bank.

The third harmonic voltages are induced in both the primary and secondary but the delta-connected secondary is a closed local circuit for its third harmonic voltage. This voltage will produce a third harmonic current which will circulate around the closed delta and produce a third harmonic magnetic flux, which in turn will cut both the primary and secondary windings. This flux will generate in both windings a third harmonic voltage approximately equal and opposite to the voltages caused by the lack of third harmonic current in the primary. The third harmonic component of the magnetizing current for a bank of transformers connected in star-delta is supplied by a circulating current in the closed delta winding.

If the star-delta bank is fed by a star-connected generator with the neutral connected as shown in Fig. 25–4, there is a path for the third harmonic components to flow in the neutral and, if the generator contains a third harmonic voltage, this voltage will cause an additional third harmonic current to circulate in the transformer and generator windings. The magnetizing current for this type of connection will be supplied in the same manner as when the source of supply is a bank of transformers with their secondaries connected in star, with both neutrals grounded.

The third harmonic voltages from the generator are all in the same direction since the generator voltages of fundamental frequency are 120°

apart, and the third harmonic voltages are three times the fundamental. When these voltages are impressed on the primaries of the transformers, there will be induced third harmonic voltages in the delta secondary, and consequently a third harmonic current will circulate. The magnitude of this circulating third harmonic current is determined by the total third harmonic voltages of the generator and the combined impedances of the transformer bank and generator. This current may be of considerable magnitude for certain conditions.

If the transformer bank is connected in delta-delta, the magnetizing currents are supplied in a similar manner, except that a part of the third

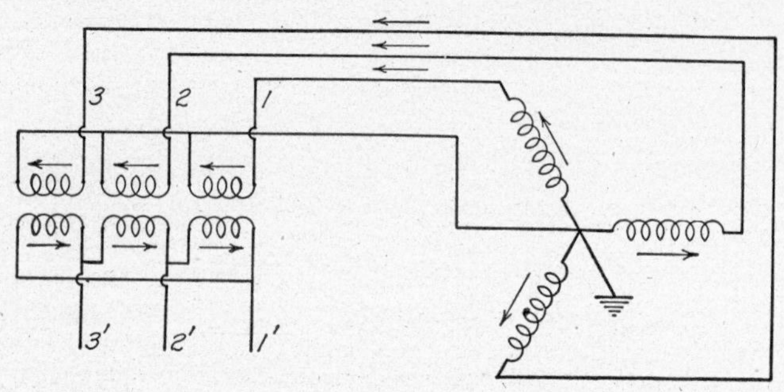

Fig. 25–4. Schematic diagram showing the third harmonic path if the star primary is supplied from a star-connected alternator with the neutral connected.

harmonic current will circulate in the primary local circuit and a part in the secondary, the magnitudes being in inverse proportion to the equivalent impedances of the two windings. When the bank is connected in delta-star, all the third harmonic magnetizing current will circulate in the primary local circuit.

When the transformer bank is connected in star-star the third harmonic component current cannot flow, since it cannot come from the line and there is no closed local circuit in which it can circulate. Consequently, a third harmonic voltage will appear in both primary and secondary windings between the lines and transformer neutral. The third harmonic voltages in the star-star bank can be eliminated by providing a small winding in each phase and connecting these windings in delta. This winding, called a tertiary, carries the harmonic currents only. The third harmonic magnetizing current can circulate in this winding in the same manner as in the secondary of a star-delta-connected bank. It is possible to have the tertiary supply the third harmonic current components for more than one bank of transformers. The tertiary supply can also be used as a regular transformer winding as in a three-winding transformer.

16. *V* or Open Delta Connection. If one transformer is removed from a delta-delta bank, an open delta or *V* bank is still in operation furnishing a three-phase supply. This is true, because the removal of one transformer does not disturb seriously the voltage relationship of the system. The voltage balance under load may, of course, be disturbed but, if the three-phase secondary load is balanced, the unbalance of secondary voltage is usually less than 5 per cent.

It would appear that the capacity of a bank, when one transformer is removed, would be decreased 33⅓ per cent and that the bank would

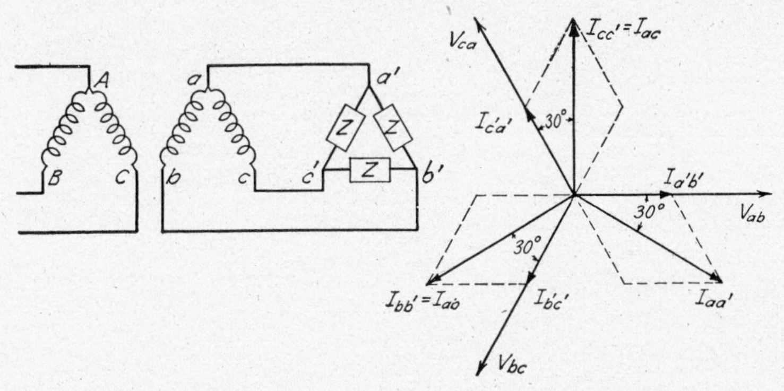

FIG. 26–4. Circuit diagram of open delta transformer connections at unity power factor.

have 66⅔ per cent of its original capacity. This would be true if conditions remained the same for both instances, but they do not. For the open delta connection, the line and coil currents become the same, and the power factor of the transformer current for closed delta and open delta is different. The line current and coil currents of a transformer under a load differ by 30° in time phase with respect to their voltages for balanced delta conditions. This same condition also holds for the open delta transformer bank. Consequently the actual rating is reduced to 86.6 per cent (cosine 30°) of the normal rating of the transformers. Therefore, the rating of an open delta transformer bank becomes

$$66\tfrac{2}{3} \times 0.866 = 58 \text{ per cent}$$

Figure 26–4 shows the transformers connected in open delta and a vector diagram for a three-phase connected load. The rating of the open delta bank in terms of the delta bank can be determined by considering the power ratings directly.

$$\frac{P_V}{P_\Delta} = \frac{\sqrt{3}VI}{3VI} = \frac{1}{\sqrt{3}} = 0.58 \text{ or } 58 \text{ per cent}$$

It has been common practice to install two transformers in open delta and, as the power demand increases, to install the third transformer, making a closed delta bank. The addition of the third transformer is an increase of 50 per cent in transformer cost corresponding to an increase of (100 − 58)/58 or 72.5 per cent in terms of original transformer capacity.

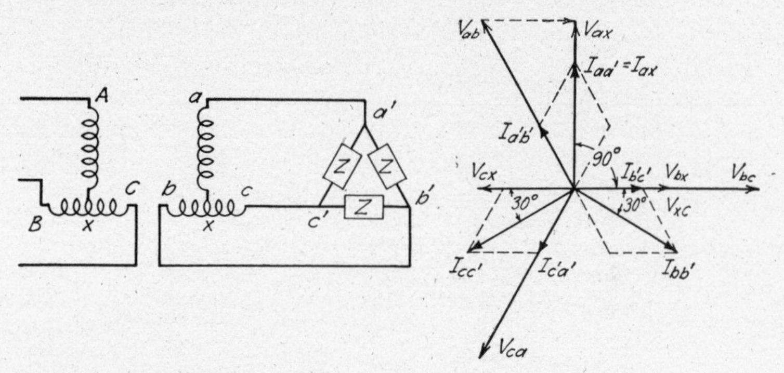

FIG. 27–4. Tee transformer connection diagram and vector diagram.

17. Tee and Scott Connection. Instead of connecting two transformers in open delta for three-phase transformation, the two transformers may be connected in tee. Figure 27–4 shows the circuit diagram and a vector diagram for this type of connection. The vector diagram is for a unity power-factor load; it shows the currents and voltages for the

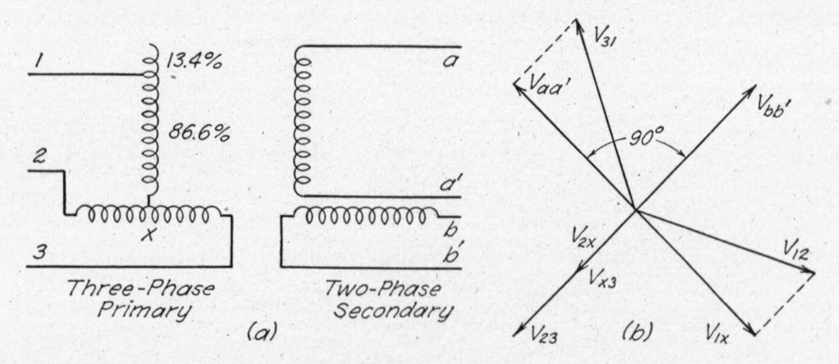

FIG. 28–4. Circuit diagram for the Scott transformer bank connection and vector diagram of voltages.

individual transformers. The tee connection requires a midtap on the windings of one transformer so that the connections can be made. For balanced voltages, the teaser transformer operates at 86.6 per cent of its normal voltage rating and, as in the open delta bank, the full kilovolt-amperes of the transformer bank cannot be used.

If the secondary windings are not connected, the voltages in the windings, which are displaced 90°, can be used for a two-phase supply. This makes it possible to connect a three-phase and two-phase system, provided, of course, that the proper tap is used on the teaser transformer. For three-phase to three-phase transformation, it is not important, but for use with a two-phase system, the 86.6 per cent tap must be available on the primary of the teaser if the primary and secondary line voltages are to be balanced. This is called the Scott tap on the transformer.

Where two-phase systems are still in use, many Scott banks are used to obtain an interconnection with the standard three-phase systems. Figure 28–4 shows the circuit diagram of a Scott bank and the voltage vector diagram for a 1:1 ratio transformer bank.

18. Instrument Transformers. It is not considered safe practice to connect measuring instruments directly to high voltage circuits. Unless

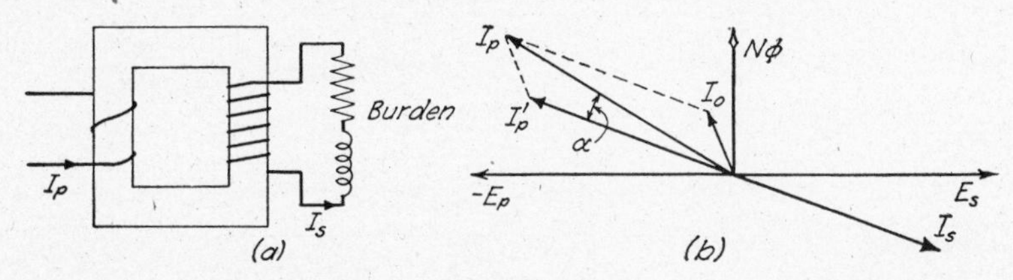

FIG. 29–4. Circuit diagram and vector diagram of a current transformer.

the high voltage circuit is grounded at the measuring instrument, it may be subject to undesirable voltage stresses. This makes the instrument circuit dangerous to use in obtaining meter indications. To eliminate this danger, instrument transformers are used. By means of these transformers, it is possible to insulate the circuits containing the measuring instruments from the circuits being measured. The ratio and phase angle errors of these instrument transformers are determined so that correction factors may be used to give correct values for the circuits being measured. The secondary values of these transformers are all reasonable values which can be measured on standard meters. These values are 100 volts for potential transformer secondary and 5 amperes for a current transformer secondary (rated conditions).

a. Current Transformer. A current transformer is one which is used to deliver a definite fraction of the line current of the electrical circuit to an electrical measuring device. Because the rated current on the secondary side of a current transformer is limited in most commercial transformers to 5 amperes, the secondary turns are usually greater in number than the primary turns. Figure 29–4 shows a vector diagram, and a circuit diagram of a current transformer. The primary current varies with the load current, and the secondary must be short-circuited at all times, through a meter coil or low impedance, to keep the magnetization of the iron at a safe value and to prevent excessive voltages on the secondary side. The current transformer is low in volt-ampere capacity and must not be overloaded if the ratio of primary to secondary current is to be constant at all times. The secondary circuit of a current transformer is always short-circuited through a low impedance path if it is not in use with measuring instruments. If the secondary is opened, all the primary current becomes magnetizing current, and this results in the iron being highly saturated. Another result, because of the turn ratio, is a high secondary terminal voltage which may damage the insulation of the transformer. It is necessary to demagnetize a trans-

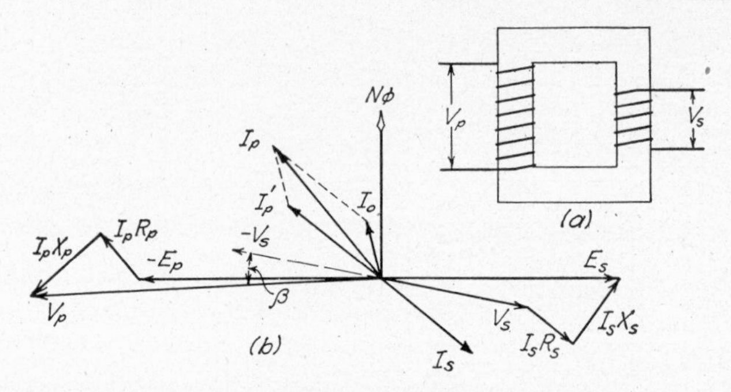

FIG. 30–4. Circuit diagram and vector diagram of a potential transformer.

former completely if this happens, in order to restore correct ratio and phase angle. Angle α (Fig. 29–4b) should be as small as possible in order to insure correct secondary current. The magnitudes of α are called the phase angle errors. The angle may be positive or negative with reference to I_p, depending upon the accuracy of the transformer. The magnitude of angle α is usually less than one degree.

b. Potential Transformer. A potential instrument transformer is similar to the standard transformer in principles of operation. It is designed, however, to give a high degree of accuracy in its transformer ratio and to have a constant phase relationship between the primary and the secondary voltage for the capacity of the transformer. The capacity of the transformer is only a few volt-amperes in most instances, since they are used with voltmeters, wattmeters, and protective relays. Figure 30–4 shows a circuit and vector diagram of a potential transformer. The primary and secondary terminal voltages are nearly 180° apart for all loads, and the impedance drop in the transformer is very small, giving a constant transformation ratio for all load conditions.

Angle β (Fig. 30–4*b*) shows the phase angle shift of the secondary voltage with respect to a 180° shift in direction of voltages. As in the current transformer this angle is of the order of minutes and is not important unless a comparison of voltages is being made.

c. Uses for Instrument Transformers. When the ratio and phase angle errors of the current and potential transformers have been determined, corrections can be made and the voltage, current, and power of a high voltage circuit accurately measured. These transformers make it possible to measure, at any place in the electrical system, the electrical quantities to be determined.

Potential transformers are built with voltage ratios such that the rated secondary voltage is nominally 110 volts. Current transformers

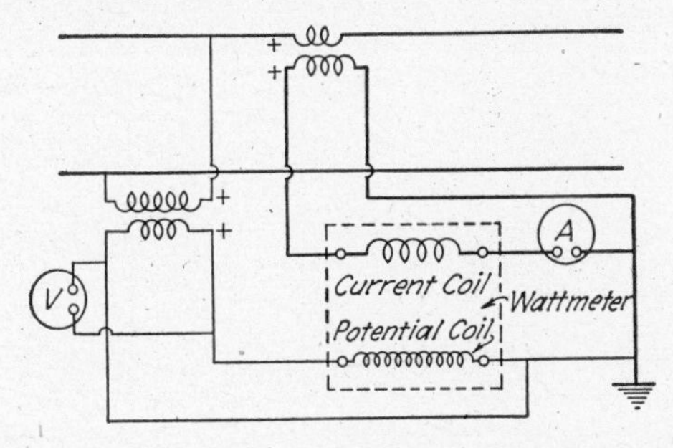

FIG. 31–4. Instrument transformer connections used with a voltmeter, ammeter, and wattmeter.

are built to have a rated secondary current of 5 amperes. These ratings make it possible to use standard ranges in voltmeters, ammeters, and wattmeters.

The polarity markings are an aid in making connections wherever instantaneous directions are important (for instance, in wattmeter or directional relay operation).

Figure 31–4 shows a typical circuit diagram, having potential and current transformers used with voltmeter, ammeter, and wattmeter. In all instrument-transformer secondary circuits, one side is connected to ground to give added protection to the meter circuit. Instrument transformers with accurate ratios and small phase angle errors are very desirable for power or energy-measuring circuits. The cost of these transformers per kilovolt-ampere is high when compared to the standard transformer.

Transformers of lower grade can be used for protective relay operating circuits, since the relay setting can be adjusted to correct for the ratio and phase angle errors.

19. Commercial Transformers. The figures show how the commercial transformers are assembled and insulated. The windings and core are mounted together and placed in oil-tight steel tanks provided with moisture-tight covers. After the windings and core are fastened into the case, the case is filled with a high grade insulating oil. The oil not only gives additional insulation between the windings but also acts as a conductor to the case for the heat generated by the iron loss and copper loss of the transformer. The primary and secondary leads are brought out of the case through insulated bushings, which are constructed to distribute the electrical stresses over their surface and prevent breakdown of the bushing, and to allow an arc-over from the lead to the transformer case.

FIG. 32–4. Assembled core and coils for a 60-cycle, 7.5-kva, 6900/11,950 wye to 115/230-volt distribution transformer. (Courtesy of General Electric Co.)

Figure 32–4 shows the assembled core and coils of a small distribution transformer. The control on the right of the transformer is a tap-changing contact, which provides a small change in transformer ratio to compensate for line voltage drop whenever the transformer is installed at the end of a long line. The low voltage terminals are shown at the left, and the high voltage terminals are protected by the porcelain holders.

Figure 33–4 shows the windings and core of an oil immersed self-cooling transformer with its insulating bushings. The individual coils which make up the primary and secondary windings are separated from each other enough to allow the oil to circulate freely. The connections to the outside of the transformer case are made through the insulated bushings.

Figure 34–4 shows the core and the coils of a transformer designed to supply power to an electric furnace. The windings are on a shell-type core. The low voltage side, because of the large current capacity, consists of a group of heavy copper bars. The pancake coils and spacing strips can be seen in the figure. The iron core is held together with reinforced plates and heavy bolts.

Figure 35–4 shows the assembled core and coils for a three-phase power transformer. Each phase is on a separate leg of the iron core,

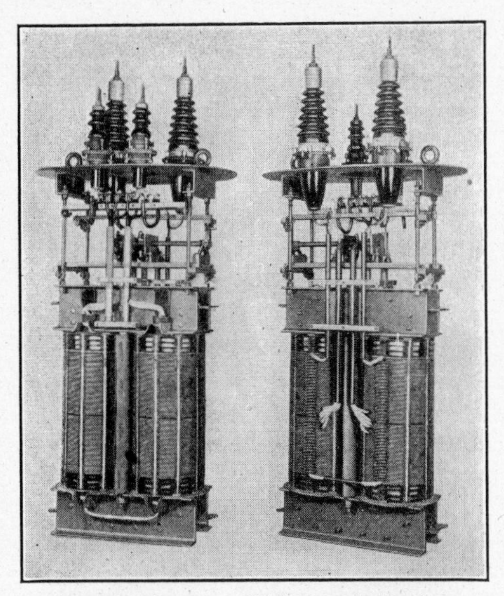

Fig. 33–4. A 667-kva, single-phase, 45,000/2400/7200-volt outdoor type transformer. (Courtesy of Allis-Chalmers Mfg. Co.)

Fig. 34–4. The core and coils of a single-phase furnace transformer. The transformer rating is 5000-kva, 25 cycles, 13,200/130–160 volts. (Courtesy of Allis-Chalmers Mfg. Co.)

Fig. 35–4. Assembled core and coils for a three-phase power transformer. Transformer rating is 30,000-kva, 60 cycles, 132,000/14,800 wye volts. (Courtesy of General Electric Co.)

Fig. 36–4. Phantom view of a 5-kva, 60-cycle, 2400/120/240-volt distribution transformer. (Courtesy of General Electric Co.)

and the terminals of the primaries and secondaries are shown entering the insulating tubes which go to the insulated bushings on the top of the transformer case. The coils are spaced to allow the oil to circulate. The three-phase transformers are being used more each year, especially in large power installations.

Figure 36–4 shows the phantom view of a transformer core and coils in the metal case. This transformer is similar to the one shown in Figure 32–4. The bushing terminal connections are made to the transformer. The transformer case is filled with oil before the transformer is placed in operation.

PROBLEMS

1–4. The maximum value of the flux in the core of a transformer is 10^6 lines when connected to a 60-cycle system. What is the voltage induced in the secondary of 500 turns? Assume sinusoidal voltages.

2–4. A 60-cycle, 220/110-volt transformer is wound with 150 turns on the high voltage side. If the maximum flux density is 7×10^4 lines per square inch, what is the cross-sectional area of the iron core?

3–4. The high voltage side of a 25-kva, 2300/230/115-volt, 60-cycle transformer consists of 425 turns of No. 8 copper conductor. Determine the current ratings of all the windings. Wire of what size should be used in the secondary to give the same current density as used in the primary? (Use standard A.W.G. size.)

4–4. A 150-kva, 13,800/2300-volt, 60-cycle transformer has the following primary and secondary constants: resistance of the primary, 11 ohms; reactance of the primary, 30 ohms; resistance of the secondary, 0.3 ohm; and reactance of the secondary, 0.9 ohm. Draw the simplified circuit diagram of this transformer, referring all values to the secondary side.

5–4. A 100-kva, 2300/230-volt, 60-cycle transformer takes 400 watts and 0.6 ampere at no load when rated primary voltage is applied. Determine (*a*) core loss current, (*b*) magnetizing current, (*c*) no-load power factor, (*d*) per cent of exciting current. Neglect the primary copper loss caused by the exciting current.

6–4. A 75-kva, 2300/230-volt, 60-cycle transformer has 0.75 per cent core loss, 1 per cent resistance, 5 per cent reactance, and 5 per cent exciting current. Calculate (*a*) core loss in watts, (*b*) copper loss at full load in watts, and (*c*) the resistance and reactance in ohms referred to the primary side.

7–4. Determine the voltage regulation for the transformer of Prob. 6 at unity, 80 per cent lagging, and 80 per cent leading power factor.

8–4. An autotransformer is used to step down an input voltage of 230 volts to 40 per cent input voltage. If the output current is 100 amp at unity power factor, determine the current and voltage in each part of the transformer. How much power is transformed and how much is transferred?

9–4. A 150-hp, 2300-volt, 60-cycle, 3-phase induction motor is operating at full load. The motor efficiency is 91.5 per cent and the power factor is 90 per cent. The power is supplied by a 12-kv, 3-phase line through a wye-delta transformer bank. Determine the transformer rating and line currents in all parts of the system.

10–4. A balanced 3-phase synchronous motor load of 200-kw at unity power factor is supplied from an open delta bank of transformers. The motor voltage is 460 volts

3-phase and the primary supply to the transformers is 2300 volts 3-phase. Determine the primary and secondary line currents and the kilowatt load on each transformer.

11–4. A 3-phase, 100-volt, 12-kw load at 100 per cent power factor is supplied power from a 200-volt 3-phase supply by two like transformers connected in "T." Determine the kilowatt load on each transformer.

12–4. The following data were obtained on a 15-kva, 2400/240-volt transformer.

Open-Circuit Test	Short-Circuit Test (Low voltage side short-circuited)
$V = 240$ volts	$V = 120$ volts
$I = 9$ amp	$I =$ full load
$W = 115$ watts	$W = 225$ watts

Determine the transformer efficiency at rated kilovolt-ampere output and power factors of 1.0, 0.8, and 0.6. What are the per cent resistance and reactance of this transformer?

13–4. A 150-kva, 3-phase load at 1500 volts is supplied power from a 2400-volt supply by means of three autotransformers connected in wye. Draw the diagram of connections and determine all currents.

14–4. An open delta bank of transformers is to supply a 130-kva, 3-phase balanced lighting load. At some future date a third transformer will be added to make a closed delta bank capable of supplying an increase in load of 70 per cent. The primary voltage is 2300 volts and the secondary is 230/115 volts. Transformers of what size should be installed?

15–4. A 75-kva, 0.8 power-factor lagging load is supplied power at 230 volts by two transformers operating in parallel from a 2300-volt primary supply. Transformer 1 is 50 kva and has 0.75 per cent resistance and 4 per cent reactance. Transformer 2 is 25 kva and has 1 per cent resistance and 5 per cent reactance. What is the kilovolt-ampere output of each transformer?

CHAPTER 5

THE DYNAMO

The term dynamo is becoming obsolete in the vocabulary of the electrical engineer. It appeared frequently in the earlier textbooks, because the writers, as well as the engineers concerned with design and application problems, recognized the need for a term that classified all types of rotating electrical machinery, especially since their operation is based upon principles common to all. When the engineer began to specialize, because of the extensive expansion in the use of electrical rotating machinery, his vision of the whole field was narrowed and certain specific principles were developed which did not emphasize the general and fundamental laws.

This chapter will consider only the fundamental principles involved in electrical rotating machinery. The generator must produce a voltage and maintain this voltage, to a reasonable degree, up to full load, whereas the motor must develop a starting torque and be capable of taking load up to its rated capacity. These are the fundamental requirements of the dynamo. How it performs under load will be considered in the succeeding chapters (7, 8, 9, 10, 12, and 13) in a study of the specific applications and the characteristic principles of the machines in general use.

The dynamo is a machine which develops electromotive force by means of conductors cutting lines of induction. It delivers either mechanical or electrical energy dependent upon and in proportion to the vector relationship and magnitude of its induced voltage, with respect to its terminal voltage. Even the acyclic machine (homopolar machine) obeys this fundamental principle in the generation of direct current. In this machine, the generated electromotive force is a d-c voltage. All other machines, whether of the d-c or a-c type, have a-c electromotive forces generated. All obey the same fundamental principles.

In the generator, mechanical energy is converted into electrical energy at a speed and torque which is determined by the prime mover and the electrical load. In the motor, electrical energy is supplied to the terminals to satisfy the mechanical energy requirements at the shaft. The important characteristics of the motor are the changes of speed and torque corresponding to the variation in the mechanical load. The same dynamo may be used as a motor or as a generator if the basic requirements for the specific task are established and maintained during the operation.

Since a motor consists of conductors moving relative to a magnetic field, the motor at all times performs the dual function of generator and motor and, for resultant motor action, energy must flow into the machine. It is possible for a generator operating in parallel with other generating machines to change from generator to motor action without exhibiting any outward evidence of change. However, the change may be disclosed by the indicating meters connected to the machines involved.

1. Fundamental Dynamo Principles. For the proper torque characteristics to be developed in the dynamo:

1. The machine must have two elements, each one able to provide its own component of magnetic field.
2. One element must be free to move with respect to the other.
3. The two magnetic fields must have components in space quadrature.
4. The two magnetic fields must have components in time phase.
5. For *motor torque* to be developed, the electromotive force caused by the motion of the moving element with respect to the magnetic field of the other and the current flowing in the moving element must have components of electromotive force and current in time-phase opposition.

In the *generator*, the electromotive force and current must have components in time phase.

Only in the fifth item do the motor and generator differ in their general principles, and this difference corresponds to the difference in power flow in the two machines.

2. Generator Principle. If a conductor, which is a part of a closed circuit, is moved at right angles to a magnetic field, the induced voltage will cause a current to flow which tends to oppose the force causing the motion. Figure 1–5 shows the principle of a simple generator using a single conductor and two magnetic poles. These poles may be produced either by a permanent magnet or by electromagnets. The conductor, if carrying current, is surrounded by a magnetic field caused by this current, and the simplest explanation of generator action involves the relationship of this field to the main field and the relationship of the induced voltage and current.

Since the magnetic field produced by the current in the wire surrounds the wire, it is necessarily in the direction of the main magnetic field on one side of the wire and opposed to this field on the other side. An analysis of the resultant field distribution shows a crowding of lines on one side of the conductor. This crowding of the lines of force tends to cause the conductor to move at right angles to the main field and in a direction opposite to the direction of the force applied in producing the motion. Figure 1–5*b* shows the effect of reversing the direction of movement of the conductor.

The generator is a machine that transforms mechanical energy into electrical energy. The simple generator described above would perform

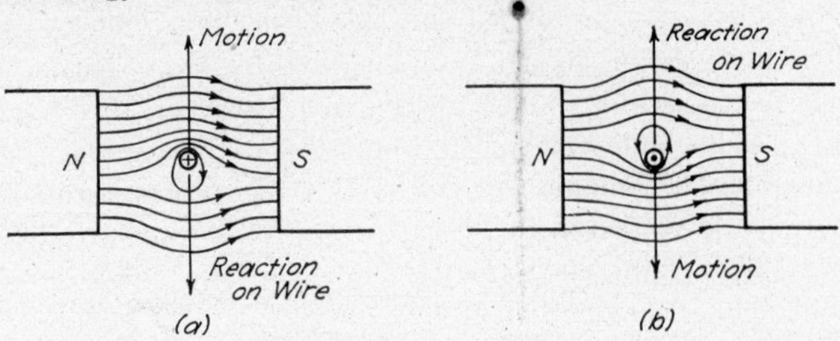

FIG. 1–5. Generator action showing the direction of current flow produced by the induced electromotive force.

this function. For efficient operation, two conductors are placed in the main magnetic field so that they are approximately a pole pitch apart and are able to rotate about an axis in such a manner that they cut the main field at right angles. This result may be obtained by using a loop of wire on the rotating element. The resultant effect is the formation of a force couple which opposes the rotation of the coil. The coil has an induced electromotive force of opposite polarity in the two sides and is,

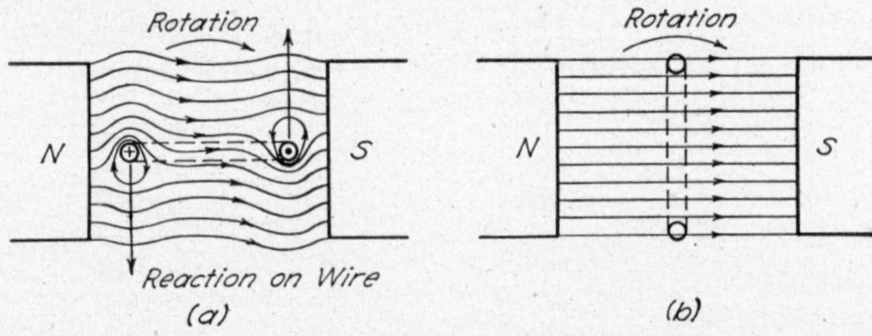

FIG. 2–5. Generator action when the current and voltage are in phase.

therefore, additive in the closed loop. Figure 2–5 shows a simple single-coil generator with proper movement, voltage, and current relationship.

3. Generator Induced Electromotive Force. The electromotive force produced in a generator depends upon the rate of change of flux linkages, which may be expressed as

$$e = -\frac{d(N\phi)}{dt} \times 10^{-8}$$

$$e = -\frac{d\lambda}{dt} \times 10^{-8}$$

whereas the type of electricity (whether alternating current or direct current) depends upon the method of delivery to the external circuit. The current is inversely proportional to the external equivalent impedance, and its influence within the machine is governed by brush position in the d-c machine and by the power factor in the a-c machine.

Direct-current generators and synchronous generators are the most important types of generators. Both will be examined to see if they

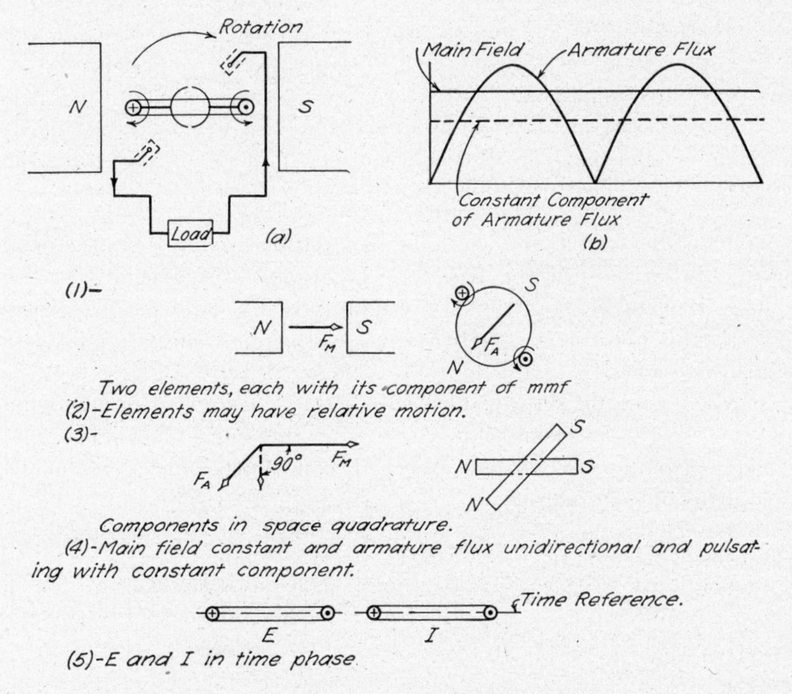

FIG. 3–5. Illustrating that the five basic fundamental requirements are present in a simple d-c generator.

satisfy the requirements listed under the five items in the first article of this chapter.

4. The D-C Generator. Figure 3–5*a* shows a schematic diagram of a d-c generator. The main field is obtained from some magnetic source, and the single moving coil is attached to a commutator for making the connection reversals at the proper time. The brushes are assumed to be in the neutral axis during load conditions to eliminate confusing influences.

An analysis of the machine considering the five basic fundamentals shows that:

1. There are two separate elements tending to produce separate components of the magnetic field—the magnetomotive force of the main field and the magnetomotive force of the armature. The magnetic axis of the armature winding coincides with the brush axis.
2. The armature is free to turn relative to the main field.
3. The axis of the magnetic field caused by the armature (determined by brush position) is out of space phase with the axis of the main-field flux.
4. The main-field flux and the armature flux have components acting at the same time, for the main-field flux is constant and the armature flux is unidirectional (Fig. 3–5*b*).
5. An investigation of the induced electromotive force and the current in the moving element shows these two to be in phase and satisfying the conditions for generator action.

Though this simple unit will give a pulsating wave of unidirectional nature, it satisfies all the required conditions for a generator. The voltage is made constant by a multiplicity of coils which add voltage in series and are so spaced that they reduce the pulsations to a relatively small value compared with the total voltage.

5. A-C Generator. Figure 4–5 shows the schematic diagram of an a-c generator. This simple machine is of the single-phase type, and the single coil has its two ends attached to slip rings which conduct the current to the external circuit.

If the machine is considered as a generator, it will be found that:

1. There are two elements (the main field and the armature), each tending to provide its own component of magnetic field.
2. These two elements are free to move with respect to each other.
3. The axis of the armature magnetic field and the axis of the main-field flux are out of space phase and have quadrature components.
4. Since the main field is constant in value and the armature field is pulsating but it has a unidirectional component, there are components of the magnetic fields acting together.
5. Regardless of the power factor, if the machine is to supply electrical energy, there will always be components of induced voltage and armature current in phase, because I cannot lead or lag E by more than 90°.

When this analysis is carried to the polyphase machine, the constant field caused by the current in the armature winding is fixed in space relative to the main field. The armature magnetomotive force does not pulsate and components of the two elements will be acting together.

6. Summary for Generators. The facts set forth in the two preceding articles covered the two important types of generators, which may be classed definitely as having common fundamental principles. The same principles will apply to special types of generators, such as induction and acyclic generators. These requirements apply to machines

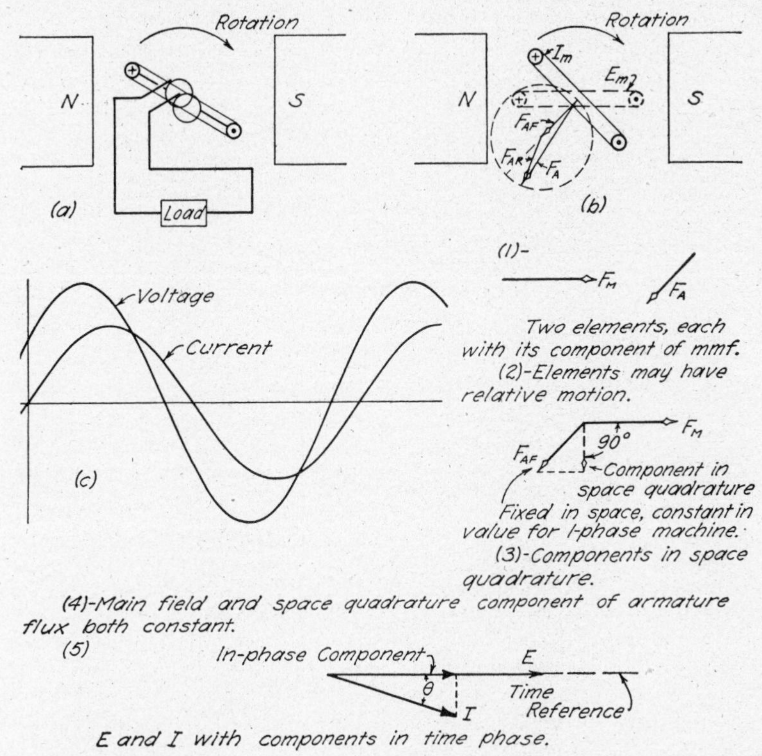

FIG. 4–5. Illustrating the five basic and fundamental requirements that are present in the single-phase a-c generator. The generator is shown with lagging power factor load.

which deliver electrical energy to an external circuit and, to a reasonable degree, maintain their respective terminal potentials; or, in short, the machine must develop useful torque to oppose the prime mover.

Single-coil generators of both d-c and a-c types are the same in their operation, and the various steps applied to the analysis give similar results. The shift of the brushes in the d-c machine may be such that there will be no useful torque, and the power factor in an a-c machine may be such that there will be no useful torque.

7. Motor Principle. If a conductor is carrying an electric current in the presence of a magnetic field, there will be a resultant torque as long as the conductor has a space component of current in a plane at right angles to the main magnetic field. Figure 5–5 shows the principle of the simple motor using a single conductor and two magnetic poles. A linear motion will seldom satisfactorily fulfill the requirements for energy conversion, but rotation caused by forces forming a couple will meet the usual requirements. This result may be secured by placing a coil of wire in a magnetic field so that it is free to rotate about an axis at right angles to the field. Since the motor requirements and characteristics

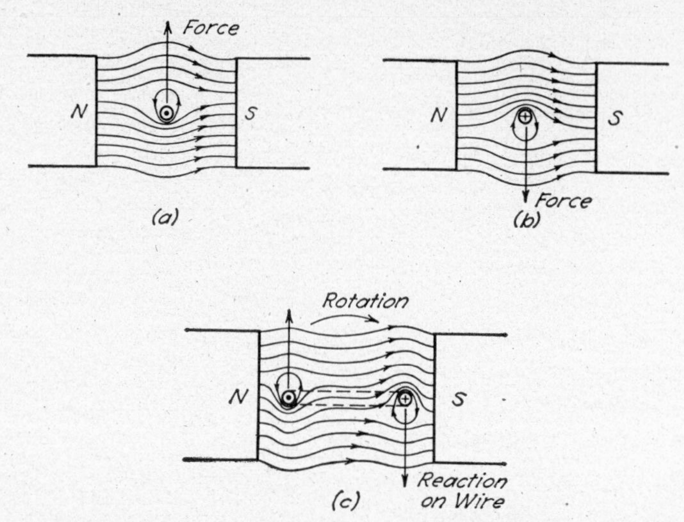

FIG. 5–5. (*a, b*) Motor action when a wire carries current in the presence of a magnetic field. (*c*) Rotational torque in the motor winding because of a force couple.

are numerous, the fundamental principles which apply to all classes of motors, either alternating or direct current, will be considered first.

In the d-c machine, there is the flux of the main-field structure. The resultant flux is called the air-gap flux; the flux of the rotating element is called the armature flux. The magnetic axis of the armature winding in the d-c motor coincides with the brush axis, considered in the study of armature reaction. If the brush axis is moved so that the armature axis coincides with the main-field axis, the torque becomes zero.

In the a-c motor, the secondary element may be the stator or the rotor, depending upon the construction of the motor. The study of the fundamental principles will be confined to the more common types of d-c and a-c motors: the three types of d-c motors, the synchronous motor, and the asynchronous polyphase induction motor. The basic principles of the machines of small capacity (single-phase motors) will be discussed in Chapter 8.

Figures 7–5, 9–5, and 10–5 show the relationships of the motor in the same manner that Figs. 3–5 and 4–5 did for the generator, and the same five major principles that were listed as the fundamental dynamo principles apply. Of these principles, the last three are the most difficult to apply. These are (*a*) that the axis of the magnetic field caused by the armature must not be in space phase with the axis of the main-field flux, (*b*) that the average torque or induced voltage will be zero unless the armature current and the main-field flux have components in time phase, and (*c*) that the electromotive force induced by motion in one element must have a component in time opposition with the current in that same element if motor torque is to be developed.

Figure 5–5 shows the simple structure of a single-coil motor element and indicates the forces upon the two coil sides which will produce a couple or motor action. In the general diagram shown, either element may be the moving element and the machine may be either a d-c or an a-c machine, since only the applications and not the fundamentals are different in the analyses of the two types. The fields produced by the elements are such that they have components in space quadrature. In the a-c machine, the explanation of the time-phase relationship between main-field flux and armature flux depends upon the established reference. In the a-c motor analysis, the armature is used as the reference; consequently, the coil moves with respect to the main field even when the armature flux is stationary with respect to the main field. The current will have a component in time phase with the main-field flux if the field produced by the armature or rotating element produces, in turn, a field that reacts with the main field as shown in Fig. 5–5. The coil, being supported on bearings, will be free to move. The two fields are produced by two independent magnetomotive forces, and the current and induced voltage of the armature element are in time opposition. These conditions meet the requirements of the fundamental principles of motor action.

To pass the critical points, which occur when a single coil is used, an additional element must be added to the motor to reverse the current in the single coil, so that the torque will always be in the same direction and produce rotation. Obtaining such unidirectional torque is accomplished by different means in various classes of motors.

The explanation of the motion of the coil in the magnetic field developed by the force on the conductor (this force having been established through the "tension" caused by the lines of force being crowded to one side of the conductor, as shown in Fig. 5–5), and by the tendency of the field to reduce to a minimum length, is an aid in understanding motor action but does not compare in value with the analysis of the presence of the five fundamental principles just outlined.

8. Motor Torque. Oersted (1820) observed that a wire carrying current, when in the presence of a magnetic field, was acted upon by a force, which depended upon the flux density, the current in the conductor, the length of the wire, and the angle which the wire made with respect to the direction of the field. This may be expressed by the following equation.

$$F = \frac{\mathcal{B} l I \sin \gamma}{10}$$

where the force F is in dynes, $\mathcal{B}$ is the flux density in lines per square centimeter, l is the length of the conductor in centimeters, I is the current in amperes, and γ is the inclination of the conductor to the field flux in degrees. If the conductor is at right angles to the field flux, the force is a maximum, for when $\gamma = 90°$ the value of $\sin \gamma = 1$.

Example a. Determine the force in pounds upon each side of a coil of 40 turns carrying a current of 15 amp if the axial length of the coil is 10 in. and the flux density is 20,000 lines per square inch. The conductors are at right angles to the flux. There are 4.448×10^5 dynes in a pound.

$$\mathcal{B} = \frac{20{,}000}{(2.54)^2} \text{ lines per square centimeter}$$

$$l = 10 \times 2.54 = 25.4 \text{ cm}$$

$$F = \frac{20{,}000 \times 10 \times 2.54 \times 15 \times 40}{(2.54)^2 \times 10 \times 4.448 \times 10^5} = 10.6 \text{ lb}$$

on each side of the coil.

Since an actual machine consists of many coils, a large number of conductors have force exerted upon them at the same time, and the total force will be the summation (Σf) of the individual forces. The physical constant for any specific machine is determined by the length of the conductors, armature radius, number of poles, flux per pole, and the paths through the winding. The torque, therefore, for a specific machine will be

$$T_{\max} = K_1 I \phi$$

where K_1 represents the constant factors of design, I the armature current per path, and ϕ the flux per pole, with I and ϕ in *space phase.* This ideal condition assumes that there is a complete reaction between the field produced by the armature current per path (I) and the flux per pole (ϕ), and that γ is an angle of 90°. If the armature field has only a component in quadrature with the air-gap flux, the effective field for motor action is a function of the angle, which is the space angle between I and ϕ. The effective value of ϕ is expressed by $\phi_m \cos \alpha$. When the field does not act as a whole but as a component, the maximum torque will not be obtained, for the torque will be expressed by

$$T = T_{\max} \cos \alpha$$

where α is the space-phase angle between the armature flux and the component at quadrature with the air-gap flux, and $T_{\max}$ is the torque when I and ϕ are in space phase (Fig. 6–5).

In the d-c machine, the angle α approaches zero and the maximum torque is the normal torque; but, in the a-c machine, where the dis-

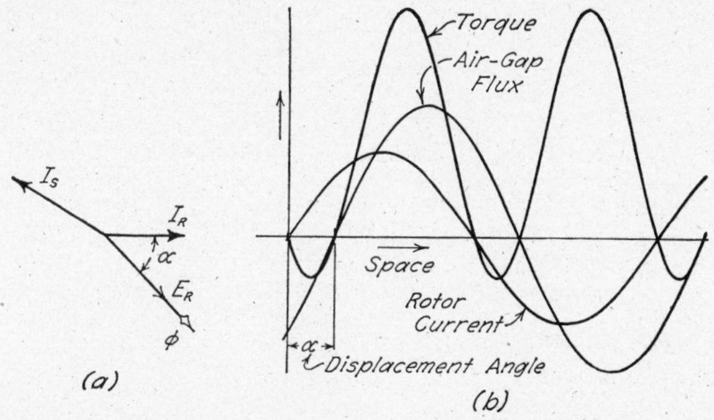

FIG. 6–5. Not time but space diagrams: (a) $\imath$ displaced in space α degrees from E which occurs at position of maximum flux (if E and I both occur at position of maximum flux $T = T_{\max} = KI\phi$); (b) space phase of current, flux, and torque when I and ϕ are not in space phase.

placement may be appreciable, the actual torque may be only a percentage of the maximum which is determined by the parameters of the machine.

9. Motor Horsepower and Torque. In any machine, the effect of a force depends not only upon its magnitude but also upon the length of the lever arm. The torque is measured by the product of the force and the radial distance to the line of action. If the torque and speed of the rotating element are known, it is possible to determine the output of a motor in foot-pounds per unit time. Horsepower is expressed as

$$\text{Horsepower} = K_2TN$$

where the torque T is the force in pounds times the radius of the lever arm in feet. N is the speed in revolutions per minute, and

$$K_2 = \frac{2\pi}{33{,}000}$$

or

$$\text{Horsepower} = 0.00019TN$$

Since there are 746 watts in a horsepower, it is possible to convert horsepower into electrical units. This permits an analysis of the electrical requirements from the mechanical rating of the motor. Frequently, in the study of motor characteristics and operation, this relationship is useful.

10. Counterelectromotive Force. As has been stated before, each motor, by the nature of its construction and operation, is also a generator. It is necessary that the generator action remain less than the motor effect in order that the machine may absorb power from the system. When the conductors move relative to a magnetic field, the voltage induced in them is

$$e = -N \frac{d\phi}{dt} \times 10^{-8}$$

Since one element in a motor has conductors and for motor action there must be an independent magnetic field separate from the field set up by the conductors, the conductors must cut this independent flux. The relative motion of conductors and flux gives simple generator action.

The voltage induced in the armature winding of a motor, according to Lenz's Law, would produce a current that would tend to establish conditions opposing the motion causing it and, therefore, would react against the impressed voltage. Since the applied voltage causes the current that produces torque to flow in the armature, the induced voltage tends to establish a current that would flow in the opposite direction; therefore, the induced voltage must have a component opposite to the impressed voltage. This generated voltage in the motor is known as the counterelectromotive force. In general, it may be stated that the sum of the complex voltages for the impressed and countervoltages determines the current flow in the winding, which, in turn, determines the torque. In the d-c machine, this sum is an algebraic relationship since all components either add or oppose directly.

The counterelectromotive force may be expressed in terms of the constants of the machine, the speed, and the resultant field, or

$$E_c = K_3\phi N$$

where K_3 is a coefficient for the specific machine, ϕ is the flux per pole, and N is the relative speed between the conductors and the flux in revolutions per minute.

There are two essential requirements for successful motor operation: the motor must have (1) the ability to deliver load and (2) a starting torque, applied externally or inherent in the machine itself. In some machines, starting torque results without special design; in others, it is produced by various means which will be discussed later.

11. The D-C Motor. The d-c motor is constructed in the same manner as the d-c generator, having an armature equipped with a commutator and a field structure on which the brushes are supported. If a potential difference of suitable magnitude is applied between the terminals of the motor, regardless of whether the field and armature are in series or parallel, a torque will be developed (as explained in Art. 7) and the armature will rotate.

Figure 7–5 shows the parallel and series connections of the field circuits and also four positions of an armature in the main-field flux.

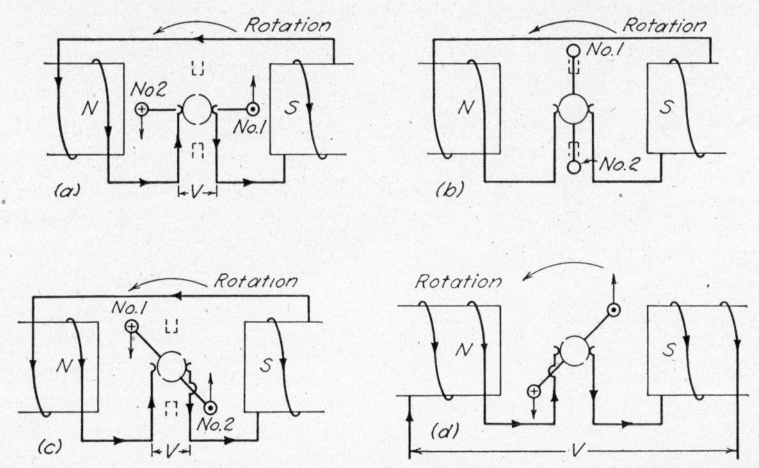

FIG. 7–5. Schematic diagrams of d-c motors: (*a*, *b*, *c*) various positions of the armature coils, in a shunt motor, show the torque continuous in one direction even when the current is reversed; (*d*) the series motor.

In Fig. 7–5*a*, the brushes deliver the current to the armature to develop the torque in the direction shown. In Fig. 7–5*b*, the coil has moved to a position of zero torque, since the coil is undergoing commutation and is without current while being short-circuited by the brushes. In Fig. 7–5*c*, the coil has passed the point of zero torque, and the brushes conduct the current to the coil so that the torque is in the same direction as before the commutation period. The torque produced on the coil before and after the zero point (commutation period) act in the same direction because the current as well as the coil position relative to the poles has been reversed. In order to have available forces acting upon the armature to carry it through the zero point of one coil, additional coils are placed upon the armature so that some coils will be active while others pass through the zero point.

The d-c machine will develop a torque proportional to the air-gap flux and armature current and will start from a stationary position.

The two magnetic field components are independent, being produced by two independent windings connected in parallel (shunt machine) with one free to move with respect to the other. These two magnetomotive forces have components in space quadrature and time phase, with the current and induced voltage of the rotating element in time-phase opposition. Figure 7–5*d* represents the connection for a series motor. Though the elements are connected differently from the elements in the shunt machine, there is no change in the fundamental principles discussed for the parallel connection of the motor elements, and the space and time relationships are still those required for motor action.

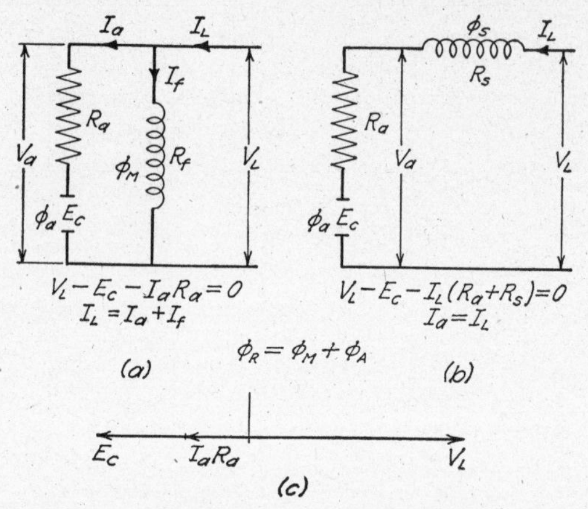

FIG. 8–5. Equivalent circuit diagrams for (*a*) a shunt and for (*b*) a series d-c motor. (*c*) The relationship between the voltage impressed across the armature, the counter voltage, and the armature voltage component.

To supply the increased torque ($T = K_1\phi_m I \cos \alpha$) when a greater load is applied to the shaft, it is necessary that one (or both) magnetic fields increase. This increase must not produce a marked angular change in the space or time relationship of the fields, currents, or induced electromotive forces. If there is a marked angular or time displacement (so that the useful components are not adequate to meet the requirements of the load), the demands for additional torque cannot be met and the machine will either stop or demand excessive current from the source. In both instances, the motor will burn up unless there is proper overload protection for such emergencies.

In the shunt machine, the main-field flux cannot change appreciably because the field winding is across the line but, in the series machine, the main-field flux may change. With both types of connections, the current in the armature increases with addition of load. The initial effect of applying load is to decrease the speed of the machine and this, in turn, decreases the counterelectromotive force, which depends upon speed for its magnitude ($E_c = K\phi_R N$). The general expression for the equivalent circuit of a d-c motor ($V_L - E_C - I_a R_a = 0$, Fig. 8–5) must hold; and, since the counterelectromotive force (E_c) is reduced and the terminal voltage remains constant, $I_a R_a$ must increase to satisfy the conditions expressed by the equation. Since R_a is essentially constant, the armature current I_a will increase. This increase in current will increase the fields of either the armature or main field, or both; this means additional torque, since $T = K_1 \phi I$. The decrease of armature speed with load will continue until equilibrium (external and internal torque balance) is again established. A d-c motor, therefore, is capable of satisfying the requirements of a shaft load.

With speed as the important characteristic, it is necessary to consider what factors affect the speed. These may be studied with respect to the counterelectromotive force equation ($E_c = K_3 \phi_R N$).

$$N = K_3' \frac{E_c}{\phi_R}$$

where $E_c = V_L - I_a R_a$. With a change of air-gap flux, there will be a change in speed, whereas, in a machine where the value of ϕ remains constant, the speed change will depend upon the influence exerted by the $I_a R_a$ component.

In Chapter 3 it was shown that the armature reaction, which establishes the armature flux, can be changed in position with respect to the main field by shifting the brushes. This shift of brush position changes the component of armature magnetomotive force that can react with the main-field magnetomotive force; and, if this component is changed without a change of shaft load, the speed of the motor will be altered. This may be the change of air-gap flux produced by the cross-magnetizing and demagnetizing effect upon the main field as affecting the expression $N = K_3'(E_c/\phi_R)$, because a change of resultant flux has an inverse effect on speed.

12. The Synchronous Motor. The synchronous motor has a d-c field and an a-c armature. In general, the relationships (Fig. 4–5) given for the synchronous generator are applicable to the synchronous motor. The proper application of the fifth principle, and consequent reversal of the direction of the current flow in the armature conductors for the specific rotation shown, is the only change that is necessary in the figure. As previously stated concerning motors, the electromotive force caused by motion of one element with respect to the magnetic field of the other and the current which flows in the first element must have components in time opposition.

The direction of current in the armature is reversing rapidly at standstill, that is, before the rotating element can attain speed in any one direction. Since the torque is reversed as the current reverses, the rotor remains stationary. The synchronous motor will not start without the use of auxiliary devices or equipment, because the inertia of its parts keeps it from following the reversing torque which is caused by the rapidly changing magnetomotive force of the armature.

If the rotor is driven at the proper speed in the required direction so that the reversal of armature current occurs when the coil is in the proper space position, the torque will always be in the same direction and the motor will continue to operate. When the machine is running at synchronous speed, the condition which places the two component magnetic fields at space quadrature and in time phase (shown in Fig. 4–5) may be satisfied.

The ability of the synchronous motor to take load depends upon the counterelectromotive force, as does that of the d-c machine. The difference lies in the fact that, since the machine must operate at a constant speed, the value of the counterelectromotive force cannot change magnitude as the load is applied, except as armature current affects the air-gap flux. The average speed must remain the same at all times for, even if only a small portion of a revolution were lost per minute, at the end of a short interval of time the two component magnetic fields would not have components in space quadrature and there would be no torque for continued operation. In the single-phase motor, this condition exists when the coil flux reduces to zero, but this critical point is passed by using the energy stored in the moving parts. In the polyphase motor, this zero point is eliminated because the various phases pass through zero at different times.

It is possible for the counterelectromotive force to change phase relationship with the impressed voltage, changing the available voltage with which to cause a current to flow in the armature. Figure 9–5*b* shows the vector diagram of a synchronous motor under a light load (E_c) and of the same machine with increased load (E_c'). The additional current demanded, resulting from the change in the phase relationship between the impressed and induced voltages, supplies the added torque required to counteract the load applied to the shaft.

The principle of load transmission without a speed change has a simple analogy in a mechanical system. If two shafts are coupled by a spring, they will operate at the same average speed, but the driven shaft will lag behind the driver by an angle depending upon the magnitude of the load. By referring to Fig. 9–5*b* it will be seen that a similar relationship occurs in the synchronous motor as load is added. The countervoltage changes from angle α to angle α' and only momentarily does the shaft change its speed (that is, during the period the countervoltage changes from position E_c to E_c'). The diagram shown in Fig. 9–5*b* should be considered as revolving at synchronous speed and the shift as being relative to a reference moving with the diagram.

The shift through the angle $\Delta\alpha$ causes the armature magnetomotive force to move so that the component in quadrature with the main-field

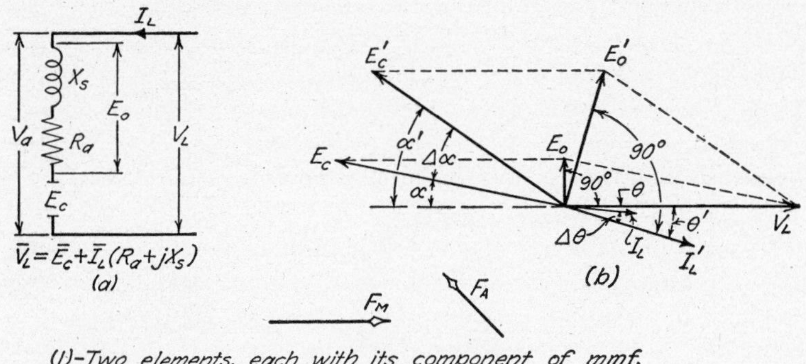

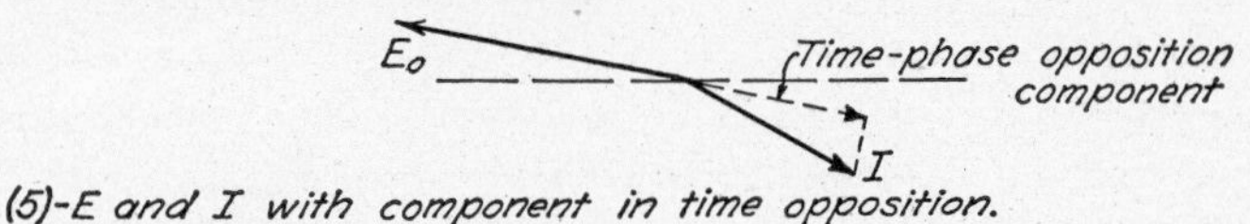

FIG. 9–5. (*a*) Equivalent circuit diagram of a polyphase synchronous motor. (*b*) Vector diagram of a polyphase synchronous motor at two load values, I_L and T_L'. Diagrams drawn per phase.

magnetomotive force is changed and frequently decreased, making it a smaller portion of the total magnetomotive force. However, the increase in armature current increases the total armature magnetomotive force. The machine is capable of taking additional load up to the point where the increase of shaft load causes the in-phase component of current to decrease. At this time, the machine ceases to operate at synchronous speed, falls out of step, and stops.

In the d-c machine, the shift of the brushes influences the armature reaction and affects the characteristic motor action. In the synchronous motor, there is a corresponding effect when the operation of the machine causes a power-factor change; that is, when the power-factor angle changes from θ to θ' (shown on the diagram in Fig. 9–5*b*). If this angular change is brought about by a change of the counterelectromotive force through a change of excitation at constant load, the motor will maintain a constant energy component of current with respect to the generated voltage with an increase or decrease in the quadrature component of current. This change in current value causes a reaction between the main-field flux and armature flux, which, though it cannot cause the speed to change, does influence the operating characteristics of the motor.

13. The Asynchronous Motor. For the present, the discussion of the asynchronous motor will be confined to the polyphase induction motor, which occupies a place in the electrical engineering field of greater prominence than the d-c and synchronous motors.

As explained in Chapter 3, there is a revolving magnetic field of constant magnitude established by a three-phase or polyphase winding of an a-c machine. In the induction motor, a short-circuited secondary winding is placed in the region of this revolving field and, if free to rotate, will revolve at a speed slightly below that of the revolving field, which rotates at synchronous speed. In Fig. 10–5 are diagrams showing the interaction between the secondary conductors and this revolving field.

The rotating magnetic field in an induction motor corresponds to the armature reaction of an alternator. This field is constant in magnitude, as previously demonstrated, when considered with respect to the stator winding but, with respect to a rotor coil, the linkages vary. The rotating field turns at synchronous speed, but the rotor speed is a few per cent less and a rotor coil (viewed from any point in the rotating field) will, with time, fall slowly behind the rotating field until it has dropped back one pair of poles and is again in the original electrical position with respect to the rotating field. This relative motion of the rotor and the synchronous revolving field is the slip.

The vector diagram of a blocked rotor induction motor will be the same as the vector diagram of a short-circuited transformer, because the mutual flux between the rotor and stator of the induction motor bears the same relationship to the motor windings as the mutual flux in a transformer bears to the primary and secondary windings. At any other load, the induction motor is the equivalent of a transformer with the secondary loaded by a resistance which replaces the mechanical load, this being equivalent to a non-inductive resistance in an electrical circuit, and where the variation of the mutual flux is the same as the flux variation in the secondary of a transformer. As the secondary of the motor revolves, the induced electromotive force is produced by an approximately constant magnetic field.

As the revolving field rotates around the stationary short-circuited rotor coils, a voltage is induced in the rotor winding, which, being a closed circuit, permits a current to flow. This current is in such a direction that the field around the conductors causes the closed rotor winding to follow in the direction of the rotating field. The current in the short-circuited winding produces a magnetic field with a component in space

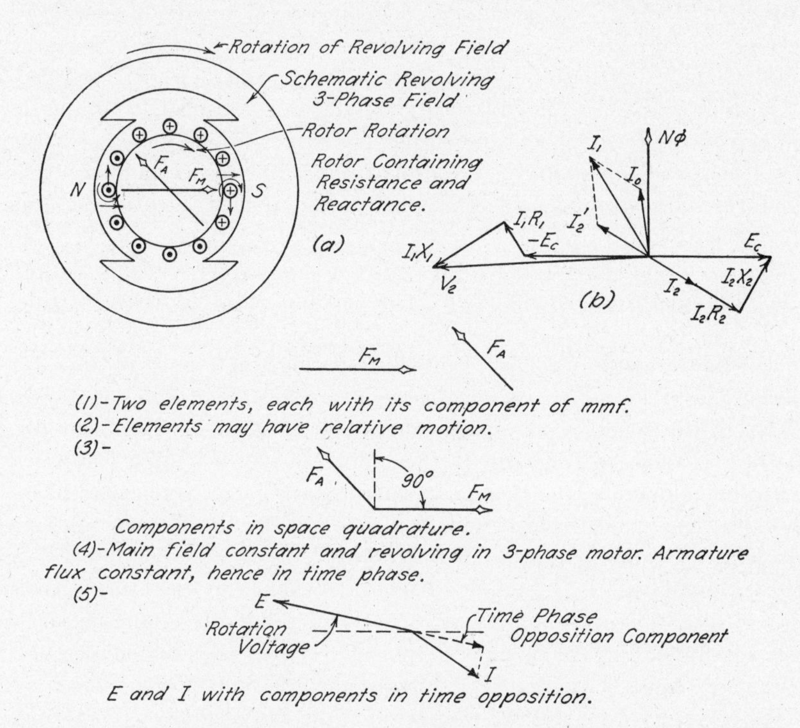

Fig. 10–5. (*a*) A schematic diagram of a polyphase induction motor. (*b*) The vector diagram of one phase of the polyphase induction motor.

quadrature and a component in time phase with the main field. The axis of the rotor magnetic field will be in space quadrature with the rotating field if the winding is free from inductive reactance; if not, a component of the rotor field will be in space quadrature with the rotating field. Therefore, polyphase induction motors will have starting torque. This torque will increase up to a maximum as the rotor speed increases, then it decreases, and vanishes at synchronous speed, as explained in Chapter 8. The rotor will reach a speed which causes equilibrium to exist between opposing mechanical torque and the electrical torque developed by the two magnetic fields.

When load is applied to the shaft, the rotor will lose speed and there will be a corresponding increase in countervoltage in the rotor, since the relative speed between the short-circuited coils and the revolving field will increase. This increase in countervoltage will cause more current to flow in the short-circuited winding, thus increasing the rotor field. If the machine is analyzed by equivalent transformer action, it will be seen that this increase of ampere turns in the secondary momentarily reduces the ampere turns in the primary (because it tends to reduce the mutual flux) and that equilibrium is reestablished by an increased flow of current from the source because it produces an equivalent number of ampere turns to overcome the secondary action. This increase in the rotor field and the ability of the primary or stator to take added power from the source provides the additional torque to meet the load increase. The shaft load can increase until the component of the rotor field, in time phase and space quadrature with the main field, will not supply the additional torque demanded. The machine will then cease to function if the load is further increased.

The power factor of the rotor influences the characteristics of the rotor performance through effect on the armature reaction, as do the power factor of the synchronous motor and the brush shift of the d-c motor. If the resistance of the rotor in the induction motor is high compared with the inductance, the current in the rotor will be nearly in time phase with the main field, which will have a marked effect on the starting characteristics and operation of the motor.

14. Summary. In fundamental consideration, the operating principles of both the motor and generator are the same except for the phase relationship of the induced electromotive force, in the moving element, with respect to the current component which flows in this element.

These basic principles, which consider the initial ability to produce torque and voltage and also the ability to take load, are the fundamentals. It is through the characteristics of the machine under load conditions that applications to specific tasks and equipment are made. The generator and motor characteristics will be developed in detail in the following chapters.

PROBLEMS

1–5. A 2-pole, 800-rpm generator, with 200 turns, cuts a flux. The change is expressed by the law $\phi_i = 4 \times 10^6 \cos \omega t$. Determine the voltage generated.

2–5. A conductor 10 in. long and moving at a rate of 100 ft per sec cuts a field with a flux density of 10^4 maxwells per square inch. What average voltage is generated?

3–5. Determine the average voltage generated by a 500-turn coil in one-fourth revolution if its speed is 20 rps and the field strength is 8×10^5 lines.

4-5. A 4-pole, d-c, simplex lap-wound generator of 300 active conductors revolves at a speed of 1800 rpm in a field density of 7×10^4 lines per square inch delivered by poles measuring 8 in. by 8 in. What will be the average voltage between the brushes?

5-5. A 6-pole, simplex-wound armature with 200 turns generates an average voltage of 200 volts at a speed of 1200 rpm. Determine the flux per pole.

6-5. (*a*) Determine the force on a wire which is at 90° to a flux density of 10^4 lines per square inch. The wire is 10 in. long and carries 100 amp. (*b*) If the same conductor is placed so that the angle with the field is 15° what will be the force?

7-5. A coil of 200 turns, 10 in. long and carrying 10 amp in a field with a flux density of 18×10^3 lines per square inch has how many pounds of force exerted upon it?

8-5. A shunt motor has its armature blocked and a current of 25 amp flows through the armature to produce torque. If the line voltage remains constant and the resistance in the armature circuit is adjusted to increase the current to 50 amp, neglecting the effect of armature demagnetizing flux, determine the change in torque.

9-5. A series motor has an armature current of 25 amp. When the line resistance is changed to allow 50 amp to flow through the armature, what happens to the torque? (Consider the magnetic change linear and neglect the demagnetizing effect of the armature current.)

10-5. When a prony brake with a 24-in. arm is being used, the force on a scale measures 35 lb. (*a*) If the machine is running at 900 rpm and draws rated current through the armature what is the horsepower delivered? (*b*) If the line voltage is 220 volts d-c and the efficiency is 80 per cent what is the line current?

11-5. An armature carrying 100 amp develops a torque of 120 lb-ft. A reduction of the field strength by 25 per cent is followed by an armature current increase to 160 amp. What per cent of the original torque is now developed?

12-5. If the machine in Prob. 4 is to be used as a d-c motor, what is the locked armature torque when 50 amp flow in the armature?

13-5. A 1800-rpm shunt motor has a rated voltage of 220 volts. The line current is 52 amp and the field current is 2 amp. If the armature resistance is 0.3 ohms what is (*a*) the horsepower output (if the windage and friction are neglected) and (*b*) what is the torque?

14-5. A 1000-rpm motor has its field weakened by 10 per cent while the armature current is held the same. Neglecting the effect of armature reaction, find the new speed.

15-5. A 4-pole, 60-cycle, induction motor has a rated speed of 1750 rpm. (*a*) What is the rotor frequency at full load? (*b*) What is the ratio of the generated voltage in the rotor at starting and full load, if the flux is assumed to be constant?

CHAPTER 6

COMMUTATION

The process of rectification, discussed in Chapter 2 of Volume I, will always require a time period equivalent to 360 electrical degrees. Rectification applies to the process of changing alternating current into direct current. The process of commutation, which may occur in any commutating machine whether alternating current or direct current, is accomplished by means of a commutator (reversing switch), the process occurring in a very few electrical degrees. Commutation takes place at each set of brushes placed on the machine. These two processes are frequently confused because both imply a change of condition.

The study of commutation refers particularly to d-c machines, and is an important factor in the design of the machine; although some a-c machines have commutators, the design problems are more complicated than those of the d-c machines. The commutator has played an important part in the problem of speed control of heavy duty a-c motors.

As discussed in Chapter 3, the armature reaction is such an important consideration in commutation that it is difficult to consider one without the other. The axis of armature reaction in the d-c machine follows the brush axis and a shift of the brush axis influences the effect of armature reaction upon the main field. It is also true that the magnitude of the armature reaction determines the position of the brush for the best operation of the machine for proper commutation. As the question of commutation is discussed, frequent reference must be made to the armature reaction phenomenon.

The commutator and commutation have limited the ability of d-c systems to compete with a-c systems in the distribution of power. The commutating machine is limited in magnitude of voltage, because the commutator is constructed of segments separated by thin sheets of mica which are not sufficient insulation against high induced voltages caused by self-induction. Therefore, the voltage is usually limited to an approximate maximum of 750 volts because of the necessary limitation of commutator construction. Higher voltages can be obtained by placing two or more machines in series and insulating all but the first machine from ground. For d-c services, particularly those requiring speed control, the commutation machine cannot be surpassed and has held its position in this field against any extensive replacement by a-c machines. It is not unusual to deliver energy to a motor generator set as alternating current, converting the alternating to direct current for supplying motors to operate equipment.

1. Basic Principles in Commutation. Figure 1–6 shows a set of coils on the armature of a machine passing through the period of commutation. In Fig. 1–6*a*, the coil *c* is shown approaching the brush position and the neutral axis while the coil *b* has just passed by the axis. The current in coil *b* is in an opposite direction from that in coil *c*. though

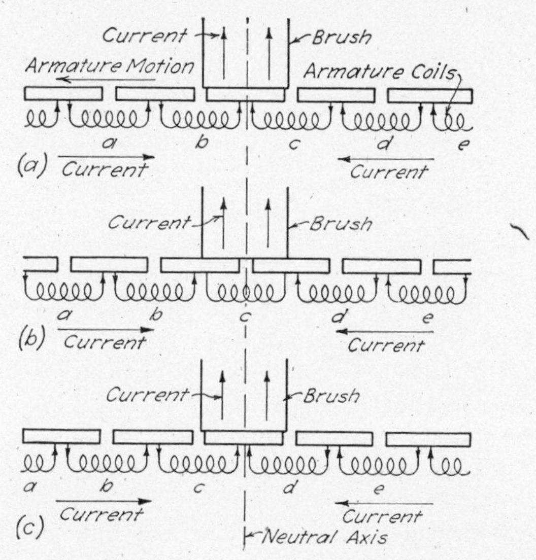

FIG. 1–6. Theory of commutation. The coil *c* passes through the period of commutation, and it will be observed that the current in the coil *c* has reversed in direction.

both tend to supply current in the same direction to the external circuit. In this position the current in coil *c* is in the same direction as the armature motion. When the coil has reached the position shown in Fig. 1–6*b*, coil *c* is being short-circuited by the brush and for ideal operation the current should be reversed without disturbance and the coil should not have an electromotive force induced in it. The current from each side of the brush reaches the external circuit by passing through the commutator bars into the brush without flowing through coil *c*. When coil *c* has passed under the brush, as shown in Fig. 1–6*c*, the current now flows in a direction opposite to the rotation and has been reversed. During this period of time to complete the reversal, the coil *c* has passed through commutation.

For this operation of current reversal to take place with the least disturbance to the physical and electrical operation of the machine, it is necessary that the current which is switched from full current to zero and back to full current in the opposite direction does not cause sparking. No electrical circuit can be short-circuited without a disturbance unless the voltage is zero, and this is one of the requirements for the coil in good commutation. To obtain zero induced voltage, it is necessary to eliminate any cutting of flux by the coil. Since the coil is moving, it must move in a region of zero flux or parallel to the flux which would be true only if the coil were coincident with the magnetic neutral plane. This latter condition can never be fulfilled with a physical machine. In addition to the main flux, there will be the influence of the current of the coil on the armature which causes a field of self-induction. As the coil approaches the period of commutation, there is present in the coil a load current which in a short period of time must be reduced to zero and reversed as the coil passes the brush. This change of current produces a field which links the coil during the commutation position, and this collapsing field creates an induced electromotive force of relatively high voltage in the coil during the short-circuit period. Immediately the coil leaves the commutation position under the brush, there is established a heavy field, produced by the increase of the current in the opposite direction. Commutation approaching the ideal is very hard to obtain and the design must be a compromise, attempting to reduce the undesirable effects to a minimum—a problem which, having been considered since the time of the very earliest machines, has as yet not been completely solved.

2. Practical Consideration of Factors that Influence Commutation. The kind of brush to use has been a problem in commutation since the beginning of dynamo design. The early brushes were made of copper which, being a good conductor to the external circuit, was likewise an excellent path for current which might be circulating in the short-circuited coil. The desire to increase the resistance of the local circuit and at the same time cause the minimum resistance in the external circuit led to the use of carbon brushes. Along with the desirable resistance and contact arc features of the carbon brush is its quality of being a lubricant for the commutator, if the proper grade of brush is selected. Where the machine voltage is very low and a low contact resistance is necessary, copper gauze brushes are still used. Since a copper brush can carry four times the current density of the carbon brush, the latter requires a relatively larger brush area and correspondingly larger commutator.

The position of the brush relative to the poles and the character of the brush resistance, as well as the width of the brush, will influence the commutation in a marked manner. The ideal commutation is the linear commutation shown in Fig. 2–6, where the current of the coil entering the commutation period is full armature current reduced to zero along a straight line as a function of time and then built up to full armature current in the opposite direction in a continued straight line, a uniform transition from initial to final current value. The period of commutation is very short, ranging from 2×10^{-3} to 5×10^{-4} seconds. The time factor depends upon the surface speed of the commutator, the thickness of the brush, and the thickness of the commutator segment and insulation.

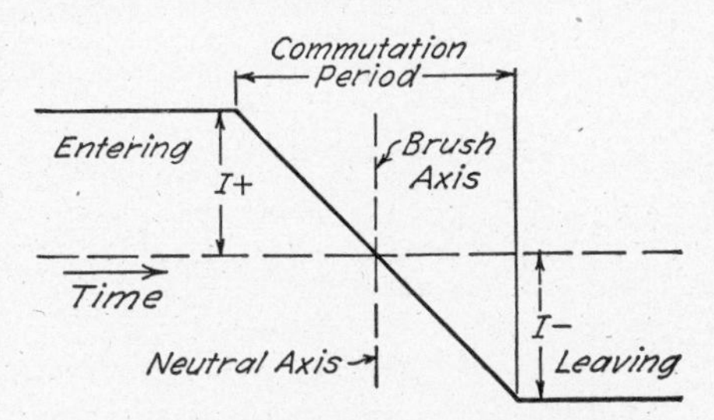

FIG. 2–6. Short-circuit curve for linear commutation would be the most satisfactory if it were possible to obtain it in practice.

Figure 3–6 shows three possible curves for current change during the short-circuit period. These curves are general types and show the deviations from the ideal, but one condition must be met in all of them: the initial and final currents must be equal if the armature windings are symmetrical. In curve *a* the resistance of the armature coil as well as the brush resistance is considered and the short-circuit curve will not follow a straight line but will produce what is designated as sinusoidal commutation. Sinusoidal commutation is satisfactory in operation if the armature coil resistance is not too large. The rate of change of current when the coil leaves the commutation period will determine the probable amount of sparking. In curve *b*, delayed current reversal, the rate of change is very high as the final stage of the short circuit is approached, and sparking will result if reversal is not complete when the brush leaves the bar; in curve *c* the current comes to the final value as in sinusoidal commutation—smoothly, with the rate of change at the end equal to zero. This should produce satisfactory commutation.

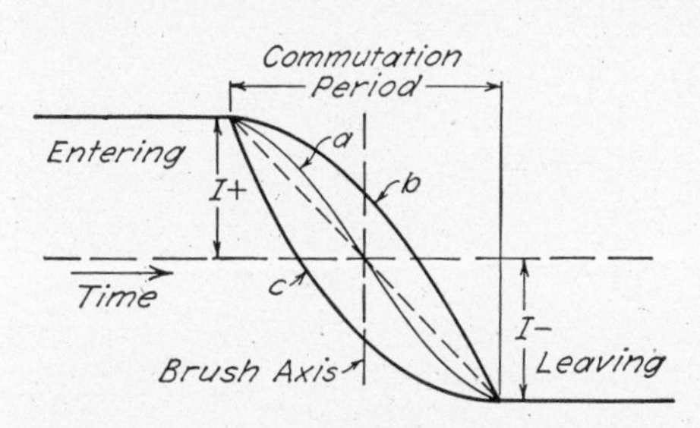

FIG. 3–6. (*a*) Short-circuit curve for sinusoidal commutation showing the influence of the coil resistance on the condition of commutation. (*b*) Undercommutation. (*c*) Overcommutation.

When the proper brush has been selected, there is still a mechanical feature that causes difficulty in commutation. The brush must be mechanically strong and must not have excessive current density. The proper current density can be obtained by increasing the brush contact area or adding brushes in parallel, but the mechanical strength must be obtained by increasing the thickness of the brush so that the brush arc in contact with the commutator will be increased to span, not one bar and insulation alone, but several bars. This increase in brush contact will decrease current density in the brush. If a brush is too wide, it causes the coil on either side of the one that lies in the neutral axis to be short-circuited. Since these coils contain generated electromotive forces, currents will flow in the short-circuited paths and the commutation will combine over and under commutation (current reversed too rapidly and not rapidly enough) with an increase of current at both the leading and the trailing edge of the brush, because the local circulating current is superimposed on the external current. Figure 4–6 shows the characteristic curve when the brush is too thick, a condition that may be encountered in making the brush sturdy enough to withstand heavy duty and of enough area to conduct away the current.

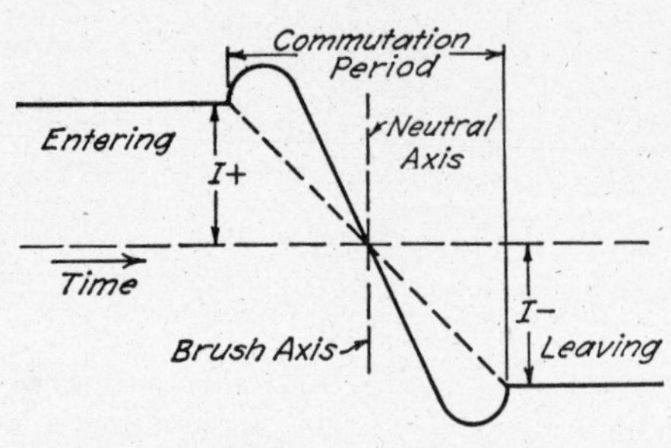

FIG. 4–6. The influence of too wide a brush on the conditions of commutation which cannot be avoided.

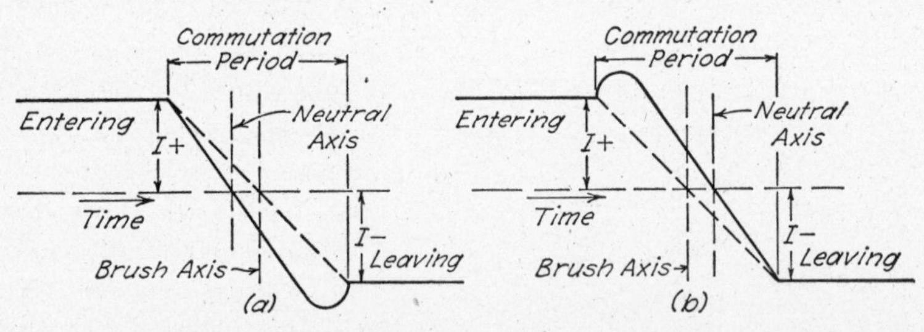

FIG. 5–6. The effect on the condition of commutation caused by (*a*) advancing and (*b*) retarding the brush with respect to the neutral axis.

If the brush is shifted from the neutral axis, there will be an accumulation of current at the leading or the trailing edge of the brush causing an excessive sparking or glow at the edge of the brush. Figure 5–6*a* shows the effect of the brush advanced in the direction of rotation, whereas Fig. 5–6*b* shows the brush retarded, or back of the neutral axis.

In addition those factors directly traceable to the physical construction of the machine and brush, there are others which are electrical in nature. Such phenomena as armature reaction and mutual and self-inductance of the coil increase the difficulty of predicting the commutation performance of the machine. Each of these electrical phenomena will be treated, and their effect on the performance of the machine will be shown.

3. Armature Reaction and Commutation. In the study of armature reaction, the effect of the armature magnetomotive force was to distort and change the value of the main magnetomotive force of the generator or the motor. The influence of the armature reaction on commutation does not depend upon the amount of distortion or weakening, but upon the shift of the magnetic neutral which takes place when the armature reaction combines with the main magnetomotive force to produce the resultant field. If this effect were a fixed condition, the neutral axis would be fixed and it would be necessary only to place the brush on the magnetic neutral to have the commutated coil in the neutral plane. However, since the armature reaction is a function of the load, there will be a resultant field and a position of this neutral axis for every load. To keep the brush in this neutral plane, it is necessary to shift it for each change of load. This would be impossible without very elaborate control equipment. In the earlier machines, it was accomplished by the attendant, who was operating the machine, or by an auxiliary solenoid arrangement in series with the line. The modern method of control uses a field which counteracts the armature reaction in the commutation region.

Figure 6–6 shows the flux distribution in the air gap of a four-pole generator of the d-c type. Figure 6–6*a* shows the distribution of the flux caused by the main field; Fig. 6–6*b* shows the field caused by the armature current, under load. In each instance, the distribution is drawn independent of any other magnetic influence. In Fig. 6–6*c*, the two fields have been combined and the resultant shows the new distribution of the flux under the field poles, and also the shift in the neutral axis. In the actual machine, these flux distributions must be determined by experimental means for prediction is unreliable, it being impossible to calculate magnetic fields accurately.

In the generator, the armature current produces an influence on the field of such nature that the electrical neutral is shifted in the direction of rotation. Therefore, the brush shift for a generator is in the direction of rotation. The normal neutral axis is described as the *geometrical neutral* and falls midway between the poles. When the operating neutral is shifted because of the load current, it is described as the *load neutral*

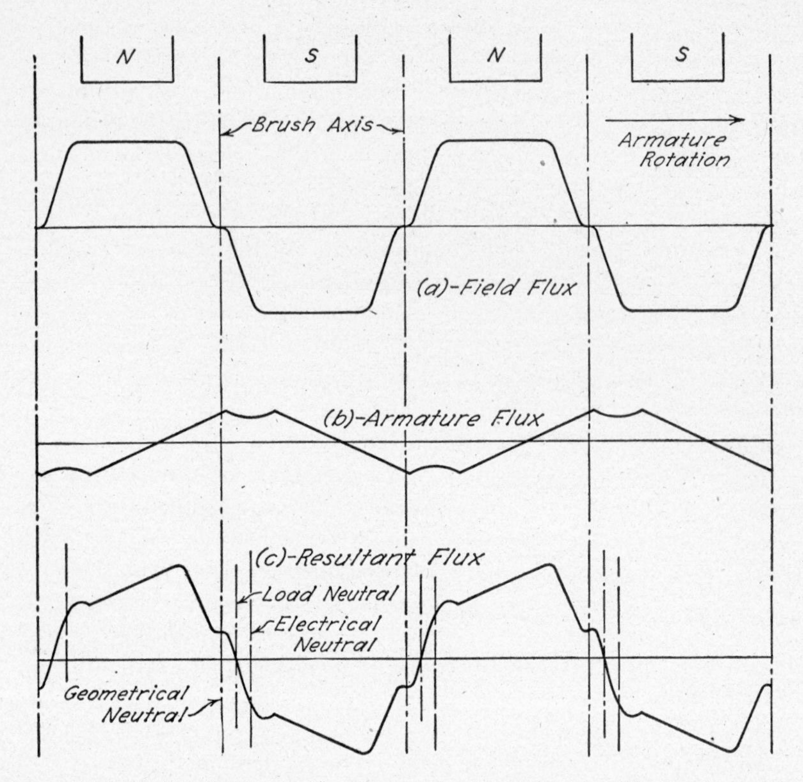

FIG. 6–6. Flux distribution in the air gap of a d-c generator. The brush must be shifted in the direction of rotation.

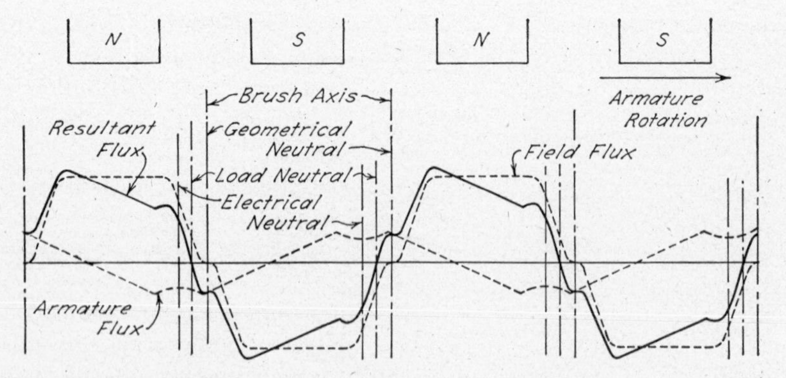

FIG. 7–6. Flux distribution in the air gap of a d-c motor. The brushes must be shifted opposite to the direction of rotation.

and would give the position of the brush if the load alone were influencing the main field; however, it is necessary to shift the brushes still more in the same direction, because of mutual and self-induction, to the *electrical neutral.* Figure 7–6 shows the flux distribution in a motor where the load neutral and the brush shift is in a direction opposite to the rotation. The brushes are shifted in this way to eliminate the sparking caused by loading the machine. In practice, where no other compensation is possible except that of brush shifting, it is customary to set the brushes so their position will satisfy the full-load condition and permit poor commutation at other loads but, since the current is less than at rated load, the resultant disturbance is usually not very serious. The armature reaction may be controlled in the commutating region by interpoles (also called commutating poles) and compensating windings.

4. Interpoles and Compensating Windings. The interpole is exactly what the name implies, a pole placed between the two main poles and located opposite the point on the armature at which the armature

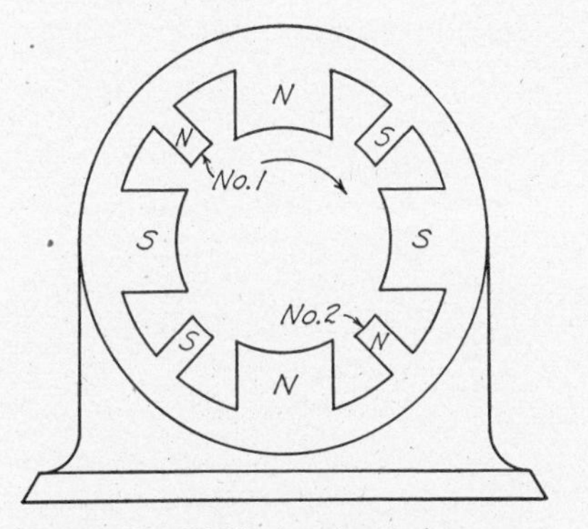

FIG. 8–6. Field structure of a generator showing the location of the commutating or interpoles. Poles 1 and 2 could be used alone.

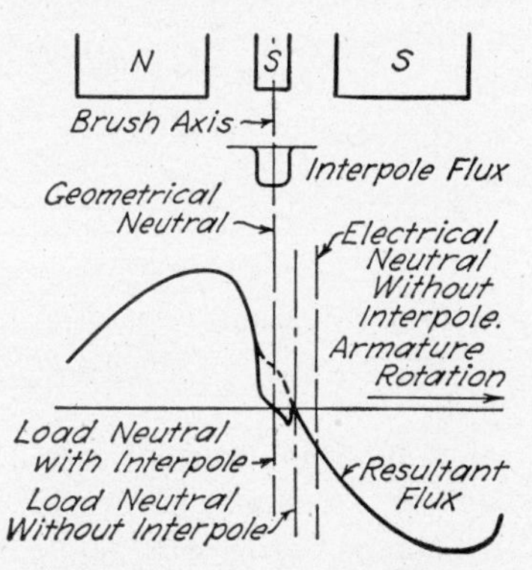

FIG. 9–6. The use of an interpole to correct the position of the electrical neutral axis so that the brush may remain on the geometrical neutral. The interpole flux corrects the armature reaction effect of the generator.

magnetomotive force is a maximum. Figure 8–6 shows the field structure of a four-pole generator with the interpoles of proper polarity in position. A study of Figure 6–6 will show that the armature reaction produces an air-gap flux which is north in polarity between the north and south pole in the direction of rotation. Along this axis, the interpole would have to be south in characteristic. The correct arrangement for this machine is shown in Fig. 8–6. Figure 9–6 shows the flux distribution in the air gap with an interpole field superimposed on the main and armature fields. It will be seen that the resultant field has the load neutral returned to the geometrical neutral. The machine may operate under load as if the only field present were the main field.

In the foregoing paragraph, it has been shown that the armature flux may be neutralized in the commutating zone. It is, however, also necessary to control the interpole flux so that it corresponds in magnitude with the influence of load on the armature flux. This is accomplished by connecting the interpole winding in series with the load; after which the flux of both the armature and the interpole will be a function of the change in load and proportional to this change.

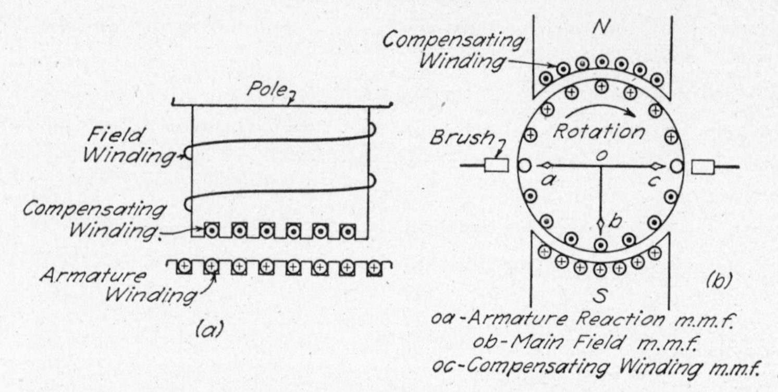

Fig. 10–6. Correction of the armature reaction effect by the use of a compensating winding on the face of the field pole.

The interpole concentrates a field to a closely confined region in the machine. A similar effect with regard to commutation may be obtained by a compensating winding, which helps correct field distortion. Figure 10–6 shows an auxiliary series winding wound on the pole face in such a manner that the ampere turns are opposite to those on the armature and therefore neutralize the magnetomotive force of the armature. This type of construction is very satisfactory for neutralizing armature effects and will give better results than the interpole; but because the additional expense of such a construction offsets the benefits the interpole is the more common method of compensating. Mutual and self-inductance effects on commutation may be controlled by a counteracting field with the result that the interpole may act to neutralize these effects as well as armature reaction.

5. Electromotive Forces Caused by Mutual and Self-Induction in the Short-Circuited Coil. The armature coil, partially buried in iron, is composed of one or several turns of wire; therefore, it has a relatively high inductance. At the same time, the coil is coupled with other coils that are in the same zone and these short-circuited coils affect the mutual inductance. These inductive effects tend to maintain the current in the coil as the coil enters the commutating period. Figure 11–6 shows the commutation curve when the inductance is considered. It will be seen that, instead of the current following a linear path, there is a delay in the change and the curve is arched as shown.

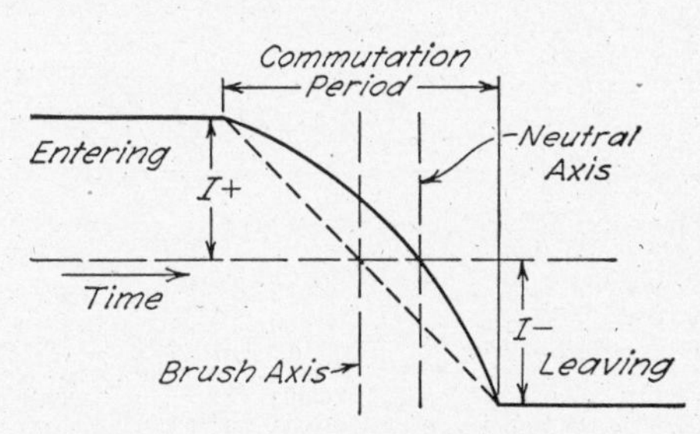

FIG. 11–6. The effect of voltages of self-induction upon the characteristics of the short-circuit curve during the commutation period.

Since there will be an induced voltage in the coil, even though it lies in the neutral plane, a current will circulate in the short-circuited coil undergoing commutation. The nature of this induced electromotive force is to oppose a change of condition in the generator. Consequently it will be of the same polarity as the field it is leaving and will be opposed by the field which it is entering; that is, it is necessary to introduce into the coil a flux of the same polarity as is found in the next field pole in the direction of rotation. If the coil in the generator is leaving a north pole and entering a south pole region, the induced electromotive force will be opposed by a voltage introduced by a south pole. To compensate for the self-inductance and mutual inductance effect it is necessary either to advance the brush into the region of the south pole or to introduce a south pole flux into the coil as it passes the neutral plane. This latter effect may be produced by the use of additional turns on the interpole, for it has been shown that the interpole will have the proper polarity. The composite effect of the interpole is shown in Fig. 12–6, where the pole has been designed to compensate for both the armature reaction and the induced voltage.

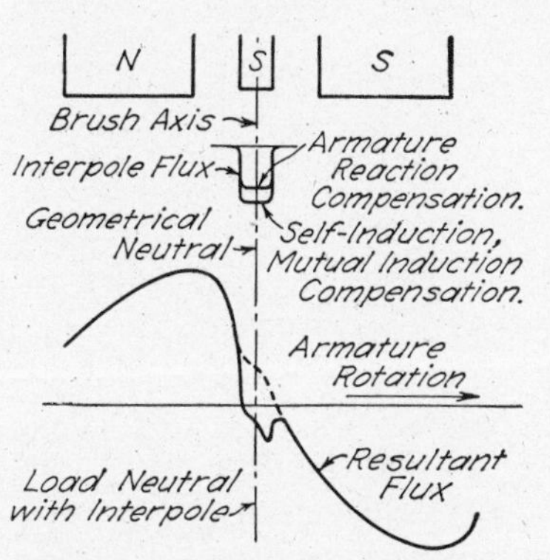

FIG. 12–6. The use of the interpole to correct both the armature reaction effect and the self-induced voltage for a generator.

6. Good Commutation. Commutation, the most difficult problem encountered in the design of d-c machines, cannot be predicted with certainty. The designer attempts to adjust proportionally the armature reaction, the voltages caused by the inductance, and also the grade, type, and dimensions of the brush for the best results. Good design eliminates the greater portion of the operating difficulties in the machine. The user, however, may defeat all the efforts of the designer by merely retarding or advancing the brushes too far. It is also possible to cause poor operation by changing the grade of brushes. Brushes of too soft a grade will cause a black commutator and dusty machine; those of too hard a grade may cause much heat as well as wearing away of the commutator.

The commutator itself may be a source of great annoyance because of high commutator bars and dirt in the slots between the bars where the mica has been undercut. After the copper of the commutator has worn away because of the arc action, the mica protrudes, causing the brush to jump. The jumping of the brush causes arcing which, in turn, roughens the commutator. The effects of poor commutation are indicated by excessive sparking, by the pitted condition of the commutator bars, or by the heat generated, which may even cause the leads to the commutator to become unsoldered.

A machine with the correct grade of brushes will require little attention if the brushes are kept at the position established by the manufacturer but, if the machine is repaired by a person not thoroughly informed, either the brush setting or the incorrect grade of brush may cause the machine to become a continuous source of trouble. The commutator should be kept clean and free from accumulated lint or carbon dust. It should *not* be polished with emery cloth but with a *good grade of sandpaper* and then wiped with clean cloth or some dusting paper. When a lubricant is needed, paraffin is a satisfactory material; oil should never be used. Poor commutation indicates that there is some defect, the cause of which should be removed by someone competent to judge the conditions.

7. Special Commutation Problems in A-C Machines. In d-c machines, it is possible to place the coil being commutated under approximately zero induced voltage conditions. This, however, is not the condition with the a-c machine of the commutating type, for the coil in the commutating position is the same as a short-circuited transformer secondary with respect to the main field. This coil, even when all other effects are removed, will act as a source of electromotive force caused by transformer action and cause current to flow in the winding.

The effect of this voltage may be minimized by the addition of resistance to the armature coil leads. This is equivalent to introducing resistance in series with the short-circuit current but in parallel with the external load current. It gives an effective resistance four times as large for the short-circuit current as for the external current.

The transformer effect may be decreased by reducing the number of turns in the armature coil, thereby reducing the induced voltage. This, in turn, will diminish the effective torque, which may be corrected by adding more coils and commutator segments, increasing the size of the commutator but decreasing the voltage between segments. This feature, though very desirable, will also increase the cost of the machine.

The interpole will not be so effective on the a-c machine as on the d-c machine, because the inductive reactance is not properly phased. If the interpole is shunted by a resistance to correct the phase relationship, however, the interpole magnetomotive force will counteract, to some extent, the resultant magnetomotive force and aid commutation. This effect will be satisfactory for one speed alone and, therefore, only partially effective at the greater portion of the operating cycle.

The compensating winding has been effectively used for the correction of the armature reaction and appears on many machines in a-c designs. It is fortunate that the problem of commutation in a-c machines is usually limited to single-phase and low power equipment. The exception to this is the single-phase railway motor and three-phase a-c motors with speed control, in which provisions are made for replacing and servicing commutators whenever it is necessary. Other types of commutating a-c machines fall into the class of speed control motors and, here again, the commutator and the commutation are handled with a recognition of the difficulties and the service involved.

The commutator and the recognition of principles of correct commutation, when applied to the so-called universal motor, produce a machine of such design that, when it is operated interchangeably on alternating current and direct current, it gives the best results when used on d-c circuits.

PROBLEMS

1–6. Assuming that a brush spans one bar, with the contact resistance uniform, determine the coil current, the lead currents, and the brush current when the brush is delivering 60 amp to the external circuit, under the following conditions: (*a*) with the brush covering one bar, (*b*) with the brush covering 25 per cent of one bar, (*c*) with the brush covering 50 per cent of one bar. Assume the spacing between the bars as negligible and the armature resistance zero. Plot a diagram showing the coil current versus commutation time.

2–6. A brush spans five coils and delivers 60 amp to the external circuit. The brush contact resistance is uniform and the space between the bars and the armature coil resistance are to be neglected. If the entering bar has a 25 per cent contact and the one leaving a 75 per cent contact area, determine the distribution of the current in the coils and leads. Plot a diagram showing the commutation (coil current versus commutation time).

3–6. A brush covers one and one-half bars with a uniform contact resistance, a zero resistance in the armature coil, and the slot exceedingly small. If the brush delivers 180 amp to the outer circuit, determine the current in the coils, in the leads, and in the brushes when the brush covers the following relative amounts of the bars.

		Bar 1	Bar 2	Bar 3
(*a*)	Brush coverage	0%	100%	50%
(*b*)	Brush coverage	33⅓%	100%	16⅔%
(*c*)	Brush coverage	75%	75%	0%

4–6. If five bars are covered by a brush and the neutral axis falls at the center of the brush determine (*a*) the coil currents and (*b*) the lead and bar currents under the following conditions: when there is a uniform contact resistance at the brushes, when the spacing between the bars is negligible, when the coil closest to the neutral axis has 5 amp of circulating current and the next coil has 15 amp. Consider an external load of 60 amp.

5–6. Determine the currents in (*a*) the coils and in (*b*) the leads and bars. The same type of five-bar span is considered as in Prob. 4 but with the brush too far back of the neutral plane (axis through fourth bar) so that the short-circuit currents are, counting from the neutral axis, 5, 15, and 45 amp respectively. The load current required is still 60 amp.

6–6. Determine the current (*a*) in the coils, (*b*) in the bars and leads. (*c*) Draw the characteristic coil current-commutation time curve. The same type of five-bar span is considered as in Prob. 4 but with the brushes too far forward. When counting from the neutral axis (axis through second bar) 5, 15, and 45 amp of short-circuit current will be found in the coils.

7–6. A brush, spanning five full bars in such a position that 25 per cent of the first bar is covered and 75 per cent of the last, is positioned with the neutral axis so that the center of the fifth bar under the brush is on the axis. The conditions are such that linear commutation would take place if it were not for the fact that the coil nearest the neutral axis has a short-circuit current of 5 amp and the other coils in sequence have 10, 15, and 20 amp of short-circuit current respectively. Sixty-eight amperes are delivered to the external circuit. Determine the currents in (*a*) the coils and in (*b*) the leads and bars. (*c*) Draw the coil current-time of commutation diagram.

8–6. Using the conditions of Prob. 7, except that the fourth bar is on the axis and 78 amp are delivered to the external circuit, determine (*a*) the coil current, (*b*) the current in the bars and leads. (*c*) Draw the current-time characteristics for a coil.

9–6. As in Prob. 7, except that the third bar is on the neutral axis and 120 amp are delivered to the external circuit. Determine (*a*) coil current and (*b*) the current in the bars and leads. (*c*) Draw the current-time characteristic for a coil during the commutation period.

10–6. As in Prob. 7, except that the second bar is on the neutral axis and 190 amp are delivered to the external circuit. Determine the (*a*) coil current and (*b*) the current in the bar and leads. (*c*) Draw the current-time characteristic for a coil during the commutation period.

CHAPTER 7

ALTERNATING-CURRENT GENERATORS

Generated electromotive force is produced by a change of linkages. In the transformer, this is produced in a static machine when the flux in the core changes. In the generator, the conductor has a relative motion with respect to the magnetic field, thereby cutting lines of force and, with the exception of the acyclic (homopolar) machine, the generated electromotive force is alternating. Since the greater portion of electrical energy is transmitted as alternating current, it is natural that the largest generating units are of this type.

The source of the direct current used to supply the excitation is electrically independent of the alternator itself and is not (for consideration in this book) influenced by the loading of the machine. The study of an alternator is a study of the performance of the armature under load conditions.

1. Generated Electromotive Force. The generated electromotive force is expressed by $e = -(Nd\phi/dt) \times 10^{-8}$, where N represents the active turns on the armature and is influenced by the number of coils per phase, ϕ is the flux in the air gap and is influenced by the ampere turns on the poles, and the time t is influenced by the angular velocity which is a function of the revolutions per minute. The voltage may be expressed as $E = 4.44N\phi_m f 10^{-8}$ volt where ϕ_m is the maximum flux, and f is the frequency. The air-gap flux must be such as to produce a sinusoidal voltage wave. The resultant voltage will be influenced by the breadth factor, the phase spread, and the pitch factor.

a. Breadth Factor. Since the coils of a distributed winding on the armature are not in exact space phase, the resultant electromotive force in the winding will depend upon the vector sum of the voltages in the coils. The resultant of these voltages is shown in Fig. 1–7.

b. Phase Spread. The phase spread of a winding is that percentage of the armature surface covered by one of the phases. Frequently the phase spread is expressed in electrical degrees. Sixty degrees per pole is the usual phase spread for a three-phase winding.

c. Pitch Factor. When the coil sides are placed 180 electrical degrees apart, the machine has a full pitch winding. When the coil sides are separated by less than 180 electrical degrees, the winding is spoken of as a fractional pitch winding and the electromotive forces generated in the two coil sides will be out of phase and must be added vectorially.

It is customary in studying the alternator to assume that the wave form is sinusoidal, though sinusoidal waves can be obtained only in specially designed machines. Normally the wave form approaches a

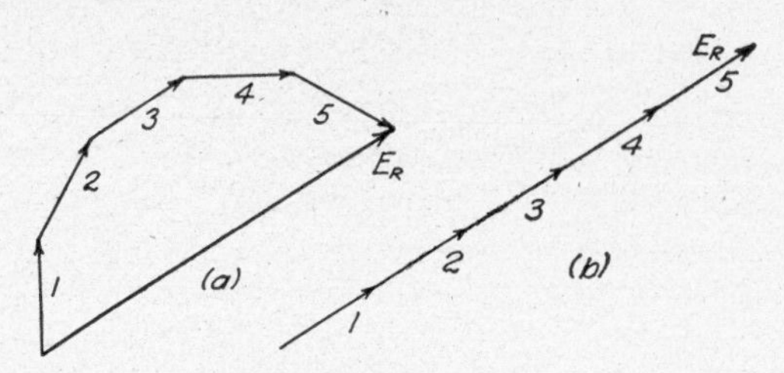

FIG. 1–7. (a) When the breadth factor is not unity the individual coil voltages are added by vector methods. (b) If the windings have a breadth factor of unity the total voltage is an algebraic summation.

sinusoidal wave but will have harmonics superimposed upon the fundamental sine wave. This produces periodic waves which are not waves of a simple nature, but may be analyzed by means of Fourier's Series. These harmonics are introduced into the wave form because of the teeth, the winding distribution, the coil pitch, and the shape of the slots. The analysis of alternators in this book will be confined to those producing sinusoidal waves.

2. Leakage Flux Reactance. Reactance is present in the armature of an alternator. When current flows through the armature, there is pro-

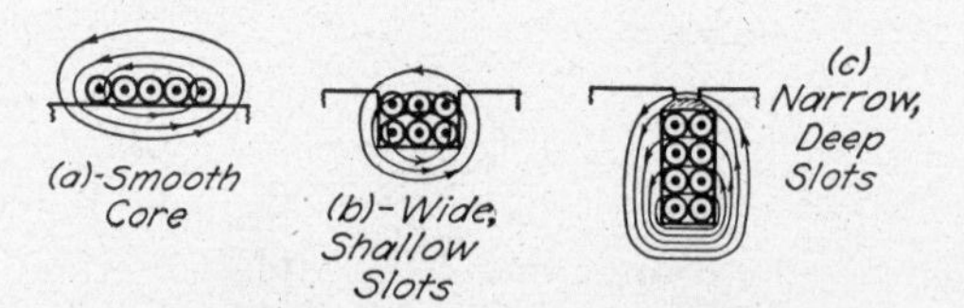

FIG. 2–7. The reactance of the armature winding depends upon the shape of the slot: (a) in a smooth core winding the reactance is small; (b) where the slot is wide and shallow the reactance increases; (c) narrow and deep slots give high reactance.

duced in the winding a voltage component which must be overcome by the generated voltage of the armature. This voltage component alters the terminal voltage of the machine under load conditions. The leakage flux of the armature will depend largely upon the shape of the slot, as shown in Fig. 2–7. When current flows in the armature of the alternator, magnetic lines are set up around these conductors. These magnetic lines link the current-carrying conductors and give an inductance. If a greater portion of the leakage flux is in the air, the reluctance of the air limits the flux; and, if the slot is wide and shallow, there will be less reactance than if it is narrow and deep.

It is customary to build the alternator with a high leakage reactance so that the machine is capable of a degree of self-protection in the event of short circuits. However, if this reactance is too high, the machine will have a very poor voltage regulation which may be overcome, in part, by ordinary regulating devices. Since the slot is of fixed size and shape, the reluctance $\mathcal{R}$ may be considered constant, the leakage flux is almost directly proportional to the armature current $\left(\phi = \frac{\mathcal{F}}{\mathcal{R}} = \frac{0.4\pi NI}{\mathcal{R}}\right)$; therefore, the reactance caused by this flux because of saturation effects is nearly constant.

The general expression for inductance is

$$\mathcal{L} = \frac{0.4\pi N^2 \mu A}{l \times 10^8} \quad \text{(see Chapter 4 of Volume I)}$$

One controlling factor in inductance is the number of turns; however, though this seems promising it cannot be satisfactorily used. For reactance control, through inductance, slot shape is the best. The other factors in the expression are not easily controlled but, when the coil side is so placed that the leakage flux must choose a path through air, the permeability is lowered and for that reason the inductance is lower, since inductance and permeability are directly proportional. The inductive reactance,

$$X_{\mathcal{L}} = 2\pi f \mathcal{L}$$

depends upon the frequency and the inductance. Since the normal frequencies in the United States are 25 and 60 cycles, the designer must control the variations in $X_{\mathcal{L}}$ through inductance rather than by frequency.

Figure 2–7 shows that leakage flux, the current in the conductors forming the linkages, and these linkages per unit current govern the inductance. This viewpoint aids in the analysis of slot effect upon leakage flux reactance.

3. Measurement of Armature Leakage Reactance. The measurement of the armature leakage reactance is similar to the measurement of reactance in an a-c system. A suitable voltage at rated frequency is applied to the armature, and current-limiting devices are connected in series with the armature to limit the current flow to the rated value for the armature. The voltage drop is taken across the armature winding at the rated current. The armature impedance Z_a is equal to V_a/I_a. If the effective resistance R_a of the armature is known, the reactance is

$$X_a = \sqrt{Z_a^2 - R_a^2}$$

The foregoing method is simplest but it is not satisfactory except in the crudest computations because of its inaccuracy for, in stability studies, it is necessary to make elaborate studies of the machine armature characteristics. In a good synchronous machine, the voltage component caused by reactance, when rated current flows, is of the magnitude of 13 to 25 per cent and it is added to the terminal voltage at such an angle that even a considerable error in the reactance component will have little effect on the resultant voltage. When the armature reactance must be known accurately, it is best to calculate the value from the physical dimensions.

4. Effective Resistance. The effective resistance, the resistance to a periodic current, is always greater than the ohmic resistance for, when direct current is flowing through a conductor, the opposition will be that of the ohmic resistance alone, since the magnetic field which surrounds the conductor does not change. However, when the magnetic flux surrounding a conductor does change and such a conductor is embedded in magnetic material (as in the case of the armature winding carrying alternating current) the change of the magnetic flux causes hysteresis and eddy current losses in the surrounding metal and skin effect. These losses are reflected in the operation of the electrical system by demanding additional power from the source. Since all losses are of the same nature, namely, heat losses, it is impossible to differentiate, at the supply, between the ohmic resistance demand and the additional demand caused by the iron losses. For this reason, it is practical to consider these magnetic losses as an increase in the resistance of the windings.

In addition to the effect produced by the magnetic material, there is a tendency for the magnetic field around the conductor to force the current toward the top of the slot. This tendency causes a concentration (or an increase) in current density which acts in the circuit as if the resistance were increased. This is known as skin effect.

In the study of the magnetic system, it has been shown that the hysteresis losses are proportional to $\phi_m^{1.6}$ and that the eddy current losses are a function of ϕ_m^2. Since the leakage flux is a function of the current, it is evident that these losses are practically proportional to the square of the current. The same is true for the skin-effect losses which are equivalent to an increased resistance.

It is necessary to consider the resistance at other than zero frequency as effective resistance, for it influences both the regulation and efficiency. The effective resistance will be 15 per cent or more greater than the ohmic resistance of the winding, and the effective resistance will depend upon the shape and size of the slot, the size of the conductors, and the frequency of the system.

5. The Measurement of Effective Resistance. It is questionable whether the effective resistance can be measured accurately. However, by examining the relative proportions of the reactance and the resistance in the armature of an alternator, it will be found that the armature resistance drop is relatively small as compared to the armature reactance

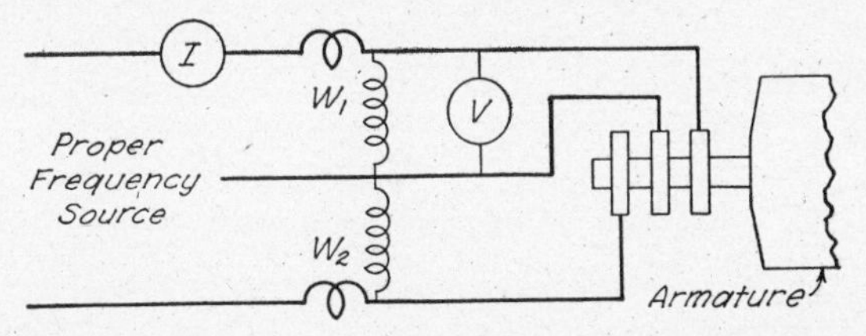

FIG. 3–7. Connection of meters to measure the approximate effective resistance and reactance of an a-c armature: I, ammeter; V, voltmeter; W, wattmeter.

drop; consequently even an appreciable error in the measurement of effective resistance will produce only a slight error in a study of the voltage loss in an armature.

To measure approximately the effective resistance it is necessary only to connect the armature to a voltage source of the proper frequency and adjust the current flow to the rated value for the armature. The power and the current can then be measured with wattmeters and ammeters, respectively. From these measurements it will be found that

$$R_a = \frac{W}{3I_a^2} \quad \text{(three-phase)}$$

where R_a and I_a are phase values. Figure 3–7 shows the proper arrangement of meters for the determination of armature reactance X_a and effective resistance R_a. During this test, the armature should be at operating temperature. No method determines R_a accurately.

Example a. If the windings of a 2500-kva, 3-phase, 60-cycle, 32-pole, 2300-volt alternator making 225 rpm are connected to a 3-phase supply, rated current will flow when 85 volts are applied and the power supplied will be 31 kw. Determine the effective resistance and armature leakage reactance for the machine if wye-connected; if delta-connected. Ohmic resistance between terminals is 0.03149 ohm. What is the ratio of effective to ohmic resistance? What is the per cent R_a, X_a, and Z_a?

$$I = \frac{2500 \times 1000}{\sqrt{3} \times 2300} = 627.57 \text{ line current}$$

$$I_p = 627.57/\sqrt{3} = 362.32 \text{ delta-connected}$$

$$V = 2300 \text{ line voltage} = V_\phi \text{ delta-connected}$$

$$V_p = 2300/\sqrt{3} = 1327.94 \text{ wye-connected}$$

$$\text{Power per phase} = \frac{31{,}000}{3} = 10{,}333 \text{ watts per phase}$$

$$R_a = \frac{W}{I_a^2} = \frac{10{,}333}{(627.57)^2} = 0.02624 \text{ ohm for wye}$$

$$R_a = \frac{W}{I_a^2} = \frac{10{,}333}{\left(\frac{627.57}{\sqrt{3}}\right)^2} = 0.07872 \text{ ohm for delta}$$

$$R_0 = \frac{R_t}{2} = \frac{0.03149}{2} = 0.01574 \text{ ohm for wye}$$

$$R_0 = \tfrac{3}{2} R_t = \tfrac{3}{2} \times 0.03149 = 0.04721 \text{ ohm for delta}$$

$$\%R_a = \frac{0.02624 \times 627.57 \times 100}{1327.94} = 1.24\%$$

$$\text{Ratio } \frac{R_a}{R_0} = \frac{0.02624}{0.01574} = \frac{0.07872}{0.04721} = 1.67$$

$$Z_a = \frac{\frac{85}{\sqrt{3}}}{627.57} = 0.07820 \text{ ohm for wye}$$

$$Z_a = \frac{85}{362.32} = 0.23460 \text{ ohm for delta}$$

$$\%Z_a = \frac{0.07820 \times 627.57}{1327.94} \times 100 = 3.70\%$$

$$X_a = \sqrt{(0.07820)^2 - (0.02624)^2} = 0.07367 \text{ ohm for wye}$$

$$X_a = \sqrt{(0.2346)^2 - (0.07872)^2} = 0.22100 \text{ ohm for delta}$$

$$\%X_a = \frac{0.07367 \times 627.57}{1327.94} \times 100 = 3.48$$

SUMMARY

Per Phase

	V	I	R_0	R_a	$\%R_a$	X_a	$\%X_a$	Z_a	$\%Z_a$
Wye	1328	628	0.0157	0.0262	1.24	0.0737	3.48	0.0782	3.7
Delta	2300	362	0.0472	0.0787	1.24	0.2210	3.48	0.2346	3.7

6. The Equivalent Circuit and Vector Diagram for the Alternator. Figure 4–7 shows the equivalent circuit and the vector diagram for an alternator supplying a lagging power-factor load. The armature resistance R_a and the armature reactance X_a determine the armature impedance Z_a since

$$Z_a = \sqrt{R_a^2 + X_a^2}$$

The generated electromotive force E_a is produced by the change of flux linkages which depend upon the resultant flux and the number of active conductors on the armature surface. As will be shown later, the value of generated electromotive force E_a depends upon the magnetic

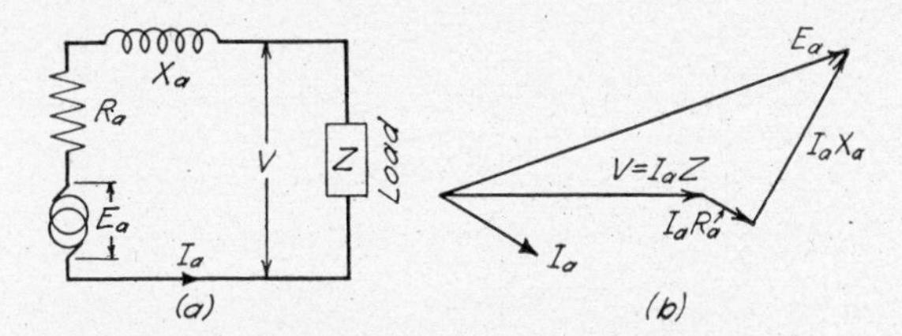

FIG. 4–7. (a) The equivalent circuit diagram of an alternator. (b) The vector diagram of an alternator with a lagging power-factor load. V, terminal voltage, R_a armature resistance, X_a armature reactance, E_a armature voltage caused by the resultant flux, I_a armature and load current.

characteristics of the machine for, after the generated electromotive force is established as a parameter, all the conditions of the system are such that E_a may be considered constant for any given armature current, and the alternator functions may be thought of as an electrical circuit in which the load impedance is considered a part of that circuit.

Only the load controls the demand upon the alternator, since the alternator does not establish either the magnitude of current flow or the power factor. However, when the load current flows through the armature, it encounters opposition in the form of an effective resistance and armature reactance, causing voltage components. These voltage components must be supplied from the generated voltage E_g.

An examination of Fig. 4–7 will show that

$$\bar{E}_a = \bar{I}_a\bar{R}_a + \bar{I}_a\bar{X}_a + \bar{I}_a\bar{Z}$$

or

$$\bar{E}_a = \bar{I}_a[(R + R_a) + j(X + X_a)]$$

where R and X are the load resistance and reactance, or the equivalent resistance and reactance for a group of loads in combination. From the above analysis, the generated electromotive force and the terminal voltage will differ from each other in proportion to the impedance component in the generator armature. This does not necessarily mean that the terminal voltage will be less than that generated, for power factor must be considered and leading power factor may require a generated voltage less than the terminal voltage.

Example b. What will be the internal voltage of the machine in Example *a*, if the machine carries full load at unity power factor? Give the results assuming both wye and delta connection.

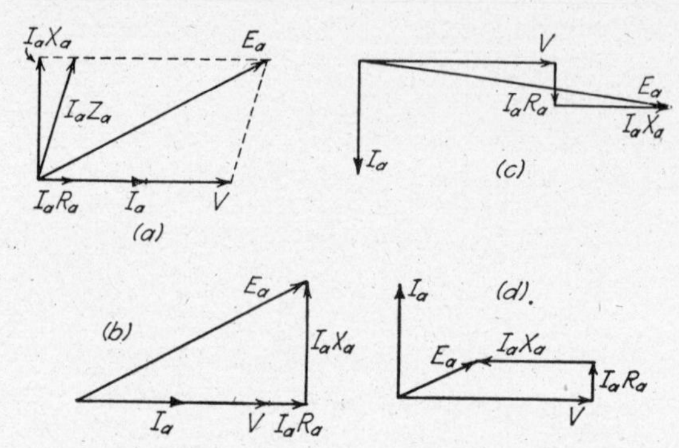

Fig. 5–7. (*a*) Vector diagram of an alternator at unity power factor. (*b*) Same as (*a*), but the construction is in the form of a voltage polygon. (*c*) Vector diagram of an alternator with 90° lagging current. (*d*) Vector diagram of an alternator with 90° leading current.

Refer to Fig. 5–7, reduced to one phase of a polyphase machine:

Wye-connected:

$$\bar{E}_a = \bar{V} + \bar{I}_a(R_a + jX_a)$$

$$\bar{E}_a = \frac{(2300 + j0)}{\sqrt{3}} + \left(\frac{2500 \times 1000}{\sqrt{3} \times 2300} + j0\right)(0.0262 + j0.0737)$$

$$\bar{E}_a = (1328 + j0) + (628 + j0)(0.0262 + j0.0737)$$

$$\bar{E}_a = 1328 + 16.45 + j46.28 = 1344.45 + j46.28$$

$$E_a = 1345.2 \text{ volts}$$

Delta-connected:

$$\bar{E}_a = (2300 + j0) + \left(\frac{2500 \times 1000}{\sqrt{3} \times \sqrt{3} \times 2300} + j0\right)(0.0787 + j0.221)$$

$$\bar{E}_a = (2300 + j0) + (362 + j0)(0.0787 + j0.221)$$

$$\bar{E}_a = 2300 + 28.48 + j80.00 = 2328.48 + j80$$

$$E_a = 2329.9 \text{ volts}$$

7. Effect of Power Factor on Generated Voltage. Figure 5–7 shows three vector diagrams for three types of loading on an alternator: (1) unity power-factor load, (2) 90° lagging power-factor load, (3) 90° leading current load. In Fig. 5–7*a* the load current and the terminal voltage, that is, V and I_a, are in phase with each other. The voltage component I_aR_a is in phase with the current, for a voltage component through a pure resistance is always in phase with the current, that is, flowing through the resistance. Since the armature is composed of a large number of turns on an iron core, the reactance is inductive. The voltage component of the inductive reactance leads the current that flows through the reactance by an angle of 90°. The I_aR_a and the I_aX_a components will add to the vector sum

$$\bar{I}_a\bar{Z}_a = \bar{I}_a(R_a + jX_a)$$

and, if the terminal voltage is V, the generated voltage is

$$\bar{E}_a = \bar{V} + \bar{I}_a\bar{Z}_a$$

Figure 5–7 shows the solution of the same type of problem by the use of a force polygon in place of a parallelogram construction. This is used because of the simplicity in the diagram obtained by the avoidance of a concentration of vectors at the origin. However, it must be clearly understood that, when these vectors represent sine waves, they must all radiate from the origin as the center. All studies in a-c machinery must recognize not a study of vectors and force polygons but a study of sine waves of uniform frequency.

Figures 5–7*b*, 5–7*c*, and 5–7*d* show the influence of the power factor upon the generated voltage. Figure 5–7*b* shows a vector diagram for a machine delivering unity power-factor current. In this case, the voltage will be

$$\bar{E}_a = \bar{V} + \bar{I}_a(R_a + jX_a)$$

$$E_a = \sqrt{(V + I_aR_a)^2 + (I_aX_a)^2}$$

In Fig. 5–7*c*, the alternator is carrying a load with a power-factor angle of 90° lagging; that is, the current lags the terminal voltage by 90°. In this case,

$$\bar{E}_a = \bar{V} + \bar{I}_a(R_a + jX_a)$$

$$E_a = \sqrt{(I_aR_a)^2 + (V + I_aX_a)^2}$$

and Fig. 5–7*d* shows a 90° leading power factor in which

$$\bar{E}_a = \bar{V} + \bar{I}_a(R_a + jX_a)$$

$$E_a = \sqrt{(I_aR_a)^2 + (V - I_aX_a)^2}$$

When the load consists of neither a pure resistance nor a pure reactance, the expression for the generated voltage will be

$$\bar{E}_a = \bar{V} + \bar{I}_a(R_a + jX_a)$$

$$E_a = \sqrt{(V \cos \theta + I_aR_a)^2 + (V \sin \theta \pm I_aX_a)^2}$$

where the plus (or minus) I_aX_a depends upon whether the load current is lagging or leading. Figure 6–7 shows the full-load locus diagram of an alternator from 90° lagging to 90° leading power-factor angle.

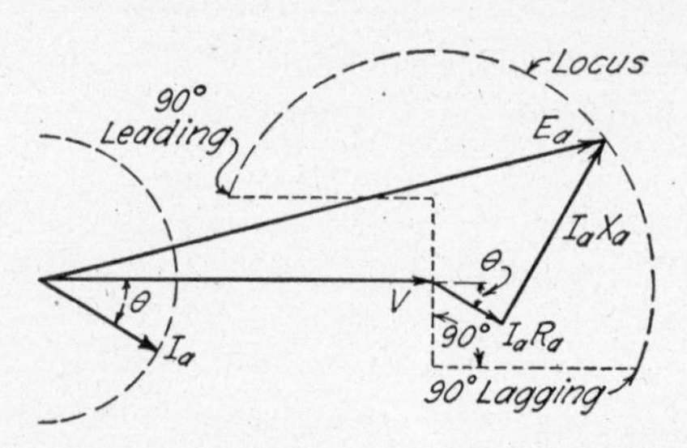

FIG. 6–7. Vector diagram of an alternator showing the locus of current and armature voltage as the power factor of the load changes.

Example c. What will be the internal voltage in Example *a*, if the machine carries full load at 0.8 lagging power factor? Give results assuming both wye- and delta-connection.

Referring to Fig. 4–7*b*, reduced to one phase of the polyphase machine:

Wye-connected:

$$\bar{E}_a = V(\cos \theta + j \sin \theta) + \bar{I}_a(R_a + jX_a)$$

$$\bar{E}_a = 1328(0.8 + j0.6) + (628 + j0)(0.0262 + j0.0737)$$

$$\bar{E}_a = (1062.4 + 16.45) + j(796.8 + 46.28)$$

$$\bar{E}_a = (1078.85 + j843.08)$$

$$E_a = 1369.2 \text{ volts}$$

Delta-connected:

$$\bar{E}_a = 2300(0.8 + j0.6) + (362 + j0)(0.0787 + j0.221)$$

$$\bar{E}_a = (1840 + 28.48) + j(1380 + 80.00)$$

$$\bar{E}_a = 1868.48 + j1460.00$$

$$E_a = 2371.2 \text{ volts}$$

Example d. What will be the internal voltage in Example *a*, if the machine carries full load at 0.8 leading power factor? Give results assuming both wye and delta connection.

Reduce to one phase.

Wye-connected:

$$\bar{E}_a = V(\cos\theta - j\sin\theta) + \bar{I}_a(R_a + jX_a)$$

$$\bar{E}_a = 1328(0.8 - j0.6) + (628 + j0)(0.0262 + j0.0737)$$

$$\bar{E}_a = (1062.4 + 16.45) + j(-796.2 + 46.28)$$

$$\bar{E}_a = 1078.85 - j749.92$$

$$E_a = 1313.8 \text{ volts}$$

Delta-connected:

$$\bar{E}_a = 2300(0.8 - j0.6) + (362 + j0)(0.0787 + j0.221)$$

$$\bar{E}_a = (1840 + 28.48) + j(-1380 + 80.00)$$

$$\bar{E}_a = 1868.48 - j1300$$

$$E_a = 2276.2 \text{ volts}$$

8. Armature Reaction. Armature reaction, which was discussed in Chapter 3, will influence the generated electromotive force of the generator. When there is a change in load, the generated electromotive force will not remain constant and the terminal voltage will be influenced by a change in both the generated voltage and the armature impedance.

In the previous discussion of armature reaction, it is demonstrated that the effect of unity power-factor load is to distort the magnetic field, whereas a lagging power-factor load will weaken the main field. However, the reverse is true for a leading power-factor load, as the effect is one of field strengthening. When the load is composed of either a combination of inductance and resistance or capacity and resistance, the effect is intermediate or a composite effect of field weakening or strengthening with distortion. The armature reaction is one of the factors which must be considered in determining the regulation of an alternator. Regulation of an alternator is a measure of the inability of the machine to maintain its terminal voltage constant under change of load. The armature reaction influences regulation through a change in flux, but the armature resistance and reactance influence regulation because of their voltage components in the electrical circuit.

9. Regulation. The regulation of an alternator is one of its most important characteristics of performance. Since all measurements must be made at the terminals of the machine, it is not possible to measure the induced electromotive force of an alternator. This makes it necessary to determine from the terminal voltage the actual influence exerted by the change of load on the generated voltage.

If a fully loaded alternator has the load removed, the voltage at the terminals will not represent the generated electromotive force that existed in the machine under load conditions, but the generated electromotive force that exists at no load.

If it were possible in testing alternators to apply full load to the machine with a voltmeter attached to its terminals and the load were removed, the difference in the two readings of the voltmeter at no load and full load would be a measure of the regulation. This type of test could be performed only when a satisfactory balanced load could be applied and the energy generated could be absorbed. In practice, regulation is important and it has been necessary to develop methods of predicting (or determining) the regulation of the alternator before it leaves the factory. These tests could not be delayed and performed during acceptance tests, for the cost of transportation and installation prohibits the manufacturer from taking a risk on the failure of the machine to perform properly.

There are several methods available for determining the regulation of an alternator by prediction. Two of these methods are of major importance in a study of electrical engineering: the first, the synchronous impedance method, because of the analysis involved, the second, the American Standards Association (A.S.A.) method, because of its acceptance in practice.

10. Synchronous Impedance. When the term synchronous impedance is used, the nomenclature becomes somewhat confusing, for the term means the accepted operating impedance of a synchronous machine. In Chapter 3 it has been shown that effects caused by a flux may be replaced by a reactance component of the proper value. Therefore, in the synchronous impedance method, the effects of armature reaction, which is a magnetomotive force, may be replaced by a reactance component and, in the final determination of the reactance of an alternator, the effect of the armature reaction is combined with armature leakage reactance into a single reactance called the synchronous reactance, and the synchronous impedance is a combination of the effective resistance of the armature and the synchronous reactance:

$$Z_s = \sqrt{R_a^2 + X_s^2}$$

In the following discussion, which justifies the use of a composite reactance in the determination of the regulation of the alternator, reference must be made to Fig. 7–7. In this study, as shown by the figure, it will be assumed that the load is of such a nature as to produce a lagging current. Then the I_aR_a component, which is in phase with the current, will be added vectorially to the terminal voltage and, if the armature reactance is known, the I_aX_a voltage component will be added vectorially to the terminal voltage and the I_aR_a component. The resultant vector will be E_a, which is the generated voltage of the armature as discussed in the previous paragraph. However, there will be an additional voltage gain if the load is completely removed for, with the removal of the load the armature reaction decreases to zero. Since, with a lagging load, the armature reaction weakens the main field, the resultant flux, by the elimination of the demagnetizing effect of armature reaction, will be strengthened and the generated voltage will increase beyond the voltage E_a to E_g.

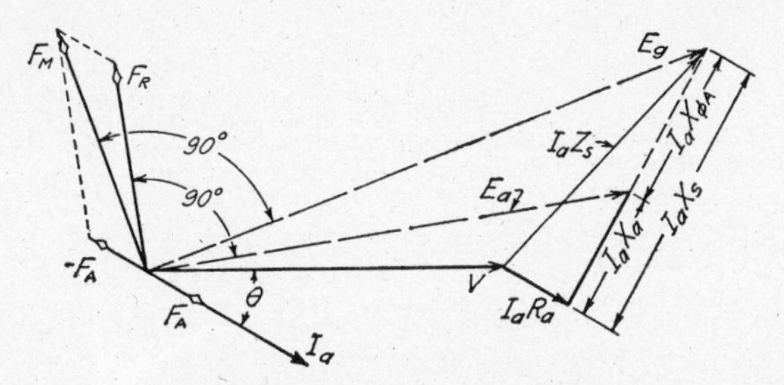

FIG. 7–7. Complete vector diagram of an alternator with load terminal voltage and no-load generated voltage.

The voltage E_a is produced by a resultant flux the magnetomotive force of which will lead E_a by 90°, which is marked on Fig. 7–7 as F_R. The armature current will produce a magnetomotive force F_A in phase with the armature current. The magnetomotive force diagram for the alternator, for a lagging power factor as given in Chapter 3 under the discussion of armature reaction, shows that

$$\bar{F}_R = \bar{F}_M + \bar{F}_A$$

and

$$\bar{F}_M = \bar{F}_R - \bar{F}_A$$

If this is applied to the diagram shown in Fig. 7–7, it will be seen that F_M is in a position which lies ahead of F_R.

The generated electromotive force produced by this main-field magnetomotive force F_M will be the generated electromotive force of the generator at no load and the no-load generated electromotive force E_g will be 90° behind the flux which produces it. This definitely establishes the direction of the generated electromotive force at no load, and it is only necessary to complete the voltage polygon for the alternator to determine the magnitude. When this polygon has been completed, as shown in Fig. 7–7, that portion of I_aX_a extended, which intercepts the

E_g vector, represents the portion of the voltage which compensates for armature reaction ($I_a X_{\phi A}$).

It is possible to show that the voltage lost by armature reaction is of the nature of a reactance voltage component with regard to generated voltage. The generated voltage must be of such a magnitude as to compensate for the armature reaction and the armature reactance and resistance voltage components in the armature. In Fig. 8–7, the load current of Fig. 7–7 is taken as a reference. The armature reaction F_A will be in phase with the current. The armature flux will be in phase with the magnetomotive force and will depend upon it. The voltage that would be produced by this magnetomotive force lags it by 90° and the voltage demanded from the generated electromotive force will be 180° out of phase with the 90° lagging voltage and equal in magnitude. The construction in Fig. 8–7 shows that this part of the generated voltage, which overcomes the effect of armature reaction, is 90° ahead of the current and is equivalent to a reactance component.

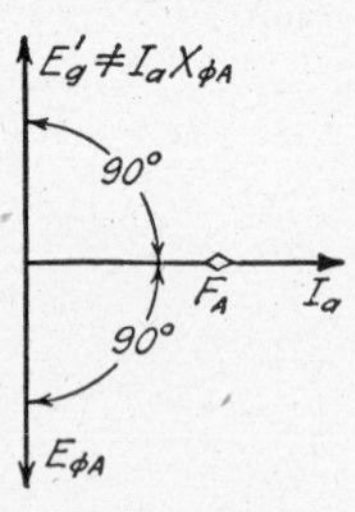

FIG. 8–7. Replacement of the armature reaction effect by an equivalent reactance drop.

When the information in Fig. 8–7 is used in Fig. 7–7, it will be noted that the voltage change caused by armature reaction is of the same nature as the voltage change caused by the armature reactance and, since these two reactance components are in phase (as shown by construction), the no-load generated electromotive force is equal to

$$\bar{E}_g = \bar{V} + \bar{I}_a R_a + j\bar{I}_a X_a + j\bar{I}_a X_{\phi A}$$

$$= \bar{V} + \bar{I}_a[(R_a + j(X_a + X_{\phi A})]$$

It is necessary to extend the reactance voltage component line until it intercepts the generated no-load voltage line. This completes the vector diagram with $I_a X_{\phi A}$ representing the hypothetical voltage component which replaces the change in flux caused by armature reaction.

As stated before, it is impossible by physical measurement to separate the effect of armature reaction and reactance. For this reason, it will be necessary to make measurements which will determine the two jointly. On the diagram, the sum of $I_a X_a$ and $I_a X_{\phi A}$ is designated as $I_a X_s$. The synchronous reactance and the resultant impedance of the alternator are designated as X_s and Z_s, respectively.

Since the foregoing method assumes the reluctance of the magnetic circuit to be constant, the results are approximately correct for the three-phase non-salient pole alternator. For the salient pole machine, the method must be modified since the reluctance varies and causes a definite amount of armature reaction to produce different results at different power factors. In the single-phase machine, even when the armature current is of constant value, the armature reaction is pulsating, giving an indefinite quantity for the synchronous impedance.

11. The Determination of Synchronous Impedance from Open-Circuit and Short-Circuit Tests. The method formerly used for determining the synchronous impedance from the open- and short-circuit tests did not give a constant value for synchronous impedance, because the synchronous impedance determined gave a value which was dependent upon the field current, chosen where the effects of saturation were included.

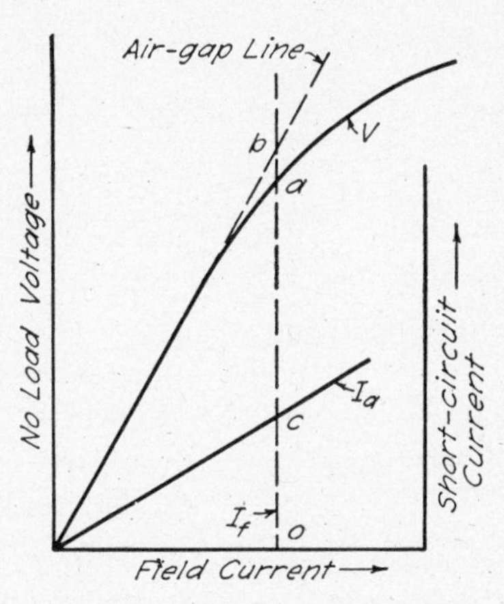

FIG. 9–7. Test data curves for determining the synchronous impedance from open-circuit and short-circuit tests.

Because the machine synchronous impedance was a variable, the determination of synchronous impedance was not satisfactory for mathematical analysis of the machine performance. To obtain a more satisfactory value of synchronous impedance, the engineers of the large machine manufacturing companies agreed to a definition for synchronous impedance. Instead of reading the open-circuit voltage from the saturation curve, the synchronous impedance is obtained by using the air-gap line, which is an extension of the straight portion of the saturation curve.

In Fig. 9–7 are shown, at the points a and b, the values considered by the old and new method of determining the machine synchronous impedance. This leads to the direct-axis synchronous reactance (short-circuit curve) given by the approved definition in "American Standard Definitions of Electrical Terms" of the A.S.A. This new definition eliminates the effects of saturation from the determination of a theoretical constant. The synchronous impedance may be defined as the ratio of the voltage on the straight line saturation curve to the corresponding short-circuit current for the same field current.

To determine the synchronous impedance of a three-phase alternator, the machine is connected as shown in Fig. 10–7. The open-circuit saturation curve, shown in Fig. 9–7, is plotted with field excitation as the abscissa and terminal voltage at no load as the ordinate. Figure 10–7 also shows the connection for determining the short-circuit values of current with various field excitations. This short-circuit curve is shown plotted in Fig. 9–7. The synchronous impedance of the machine will be determined from the open-circuit test and the short-circuit test for, at any field excitation (I_f), there will be generated in the armature

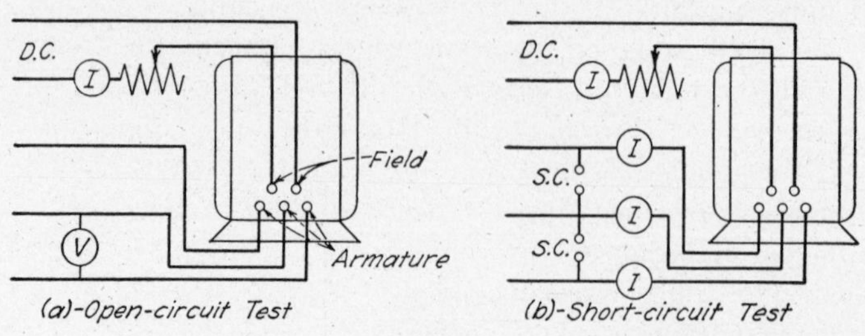

FIG. 10–7. Connections of meters and alternator for making open-circuit and short-circuit tests.

a voltage equivalent to *oa* on the open-circuit curve as shown in the figure but, by definition, the generated voltage will be considered as *ob*. It will be noted that the A.S.A. definition gives a value somewhat greater than that given by the old definition which is offset by the advantage of having a constant for the synchronous impedance Z_s in computation. When the machine is operated with the same excitation (I_f), the short-circuit current value is *oc*. Since the terminal voltage of the machine under short circuit is zero, all the generated voltage is absorbed in the windings of the machine and may be classified as an impedance component (I_aZ_a). Figure 11–7 considers the test data for the machine discussed in the computation (Example *e*).

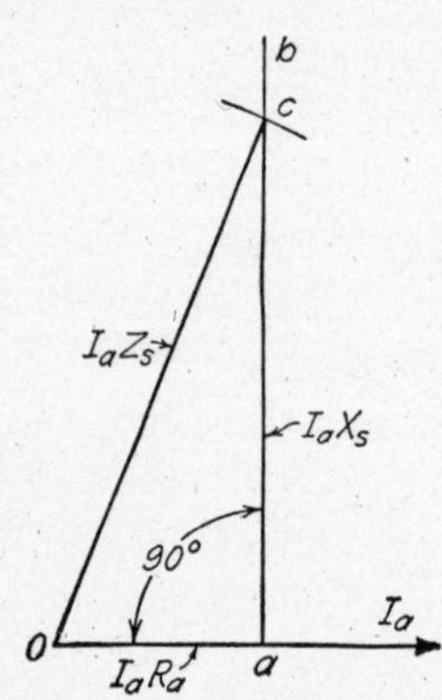

FIG. 11–7. Vector diagram showing the analysis of open-circuit and short-circuit tests for determining the synchronous impedance of the alternator.

To determine the synchronous reactance from the data given by the two laboratory tests, it is only necessary to reduce the synchronous impedance to its two components, the resistance component and the synchronous reactance component. Figure 11–7 shows the construction of an impedance triangle by placing on the current reference I_a a voltage equivalent to I_aR_a, where R_a is the effective resistance of the armature. From the end of I_aR_a is erected the perpendicular *ab* and, with *o* as a center and I_aZ_s as a radius, an arc is drawn which intercepts *ab* at *c*, where (by construction) the value of *ac* is I_aX_s.

This may be expressed by

$$I_a X_s = I_a \sqrt{Z_s^2 - R_a^2}$$

$$X_s = \sqrt{Z_s^2 - R_a^2}$$

In these tests the effect of the armature resistance is very small, and it is common practice to consider the synchronous impedance Z_s equal to the synchronous reactance X_s. This simplifies the determination for synchronous reactance which is now expressed by

$$Z_s = X_s = \frac{E_{sc}}{I_{sc}}$$

where E_{sc} is read from the straight line saturation curve and I_{sc} is determined from the short-circuit current curve at field excitation I_f.

The foregoing discussion has assumed that both the current and the voltage curves have been reduced to a single phase. However, since the test data are taken on a three-phase machine, it is necessary to consider the machine to be either delta- or wye-connected. It does not matter which type of connection is assumed in determining the synchronous impedance of the machine, but one definite type must be chosen and all currents and voltages reduced to that type or the results will be incorrect. It is not necessary that the machine be connected according to the type chosen, and it is frequently impossible to determine the connection of the machine being tested.

Example e. Figure 12–7 gives the open-circuit and short-circuit test data for the machine in Example *a*. Determine the synchronous impedance of the machine, assuming the machine connected either wye or delta.

At normal (rated) voltage excitation I_f on the air-gap saturation line, the short-circuit current is 2520 amp.

Wye-connected:

$$Z_s = \frac{2300/\sqrt{3}}{2520}$$

$$= \frac{1327.94}{2520} = 0.5269 \text{ ohm per phase}$$

Delta-connected:

$$Z_s = \frac{2300}{2520/\sqrt{3}}$$

$$= \frac{2300}{1454.97} = 1.5807 \text{ ohms per phase}$$

Percentage:

$$Z_s = \frac{627.57 \times 0.5269 \times 100}{1327.94} = 24.9 \text{ per cent}$$

The R_a may be neglected and $X_s = Z_s$.

It can be shown that the wye- or delta-connected machine will give results of the same order when measured from terminal conditions.

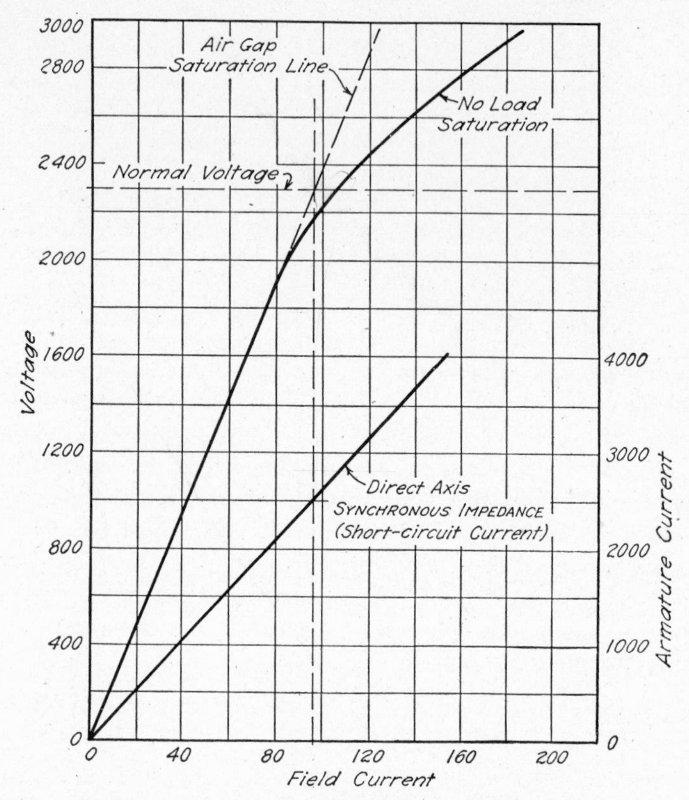

FIG. 12–7. Test data for an alternator giving the open-circuit and short-circuit characteristic curves.

Assume the two connections, as shown in Fig. 13–7; 13–7*a*, a delta, 13–7*b*, a wye connection when each impedance represents the winding of the machine. Since machines are built symmetrically, the impedances

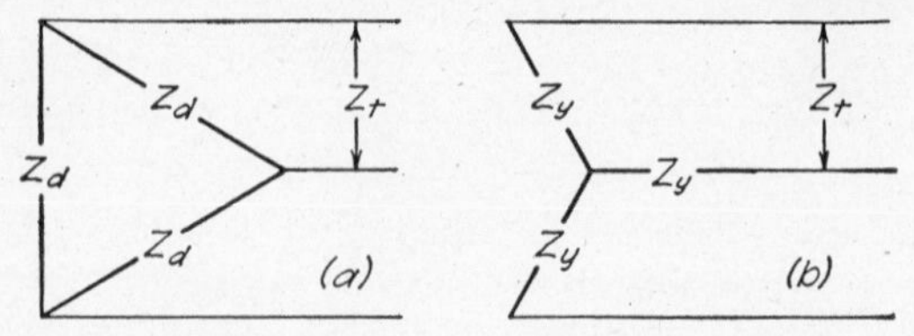

FIG. 13–7. Analysis of delta and wye connections from the terminal measurements.

will be equal and, if the impedance is measured between any two terminals, with single phase, the following development will show the relationships that the terminal impedance will bear to the actual winding measurements in the various machine phases.

Impedance between terminals measured with single-phase alternating current:

Delta (Figure 13–7*a*)	Wye (Figure 13–7*b*)
$\bar{Z}_t = \dfrac{\bar{Z}_d \times 2\bar{Z}_d}{\bar{Z}_d + 2\bar{Z}_d}$	$\bar{Z}_t = \bar{Z}_y + \bar{Z}_y$

Impedance:

Delta	Wye
$\bar{Z}_t = \dfrac{2\bar{Z}_d^2}{3\bar{Z}_d} = \dfrac{2}{3}\bar{Z}_d$	$\bar{Z}_t = 2\bar{Z}_y$
$\bar{Z}_d = \frac{3}{2}\bar{Z}_t$	$\bar{Z}_y = \frac{1}{2}\bar{Z}_t$

When the terminal resistance is determined by d-c measurements, the resistance of the winding is determined by the above expressions.

Having determined the effective terminal resistance, it is possible to show, by using these terminal measurements, that the copper losses in the delta and wye connection will be the same.

Power:

Delta	Wye
$R_\Delta = \frac{3}{2}R_t$	$R_y = \frac{1}{2}R_t$
$I_\Delta = \dfrac{I_L}{\sqrt{3}}$	$I_y = I_L$
$3P_\Delta = P_t = 3 \times \dfrac{3}{2} R_t \times \left(\dfrac{I_L}{\sqrt{3}}\right)^2$	$3P_y = P_t = 3 \times \frac{1}{2}R_t \times I_L^2$
$P_t = \frac{3}{2}I_L^2R_t$	$P_t = \frac{3}{2}I_L^2R_t$

From the foregoing development, it is evident that the relationship of the factors between the terminal and phase conditions of a delta as compared to a wye connection is three, and that it is only necessary to multiply the wye impedance by three to obtain the delta impedance in a phase. Regardless of how the machine is connected, measurements of impedance or resistance at the terminals of the machine may be interpreted correctly for either the wye or the delta connection.

12. The A.S.A. Method of Determining the Potier Reactance for an Alternator. The A.S.A. does not recognize a coefficient of synchronous impedance for alternator tests but many authors do and, in fundamental instruction, this factor is considered. The standards * proceed directly

* American Standards for "Rotating Electrical Machinery" approved January 6, 1936. The method for deducing the excitation under load at any assigned power factor from no-load saturation, the short-circuit characteristic, and the zero power factor excitation must be regarded as empirical. Its value depends on the fact that experience has demonstrated the reasonable correctness of the results obtained.

from the test data (Fig. 14–7) to determine the regulation and this will be studied under the heading of regulation.

This digression will be made for its instruction value and for the purpose of comparison of the analytical and empirical results. It is to be understood that neither of the methods herein outlined gives the final

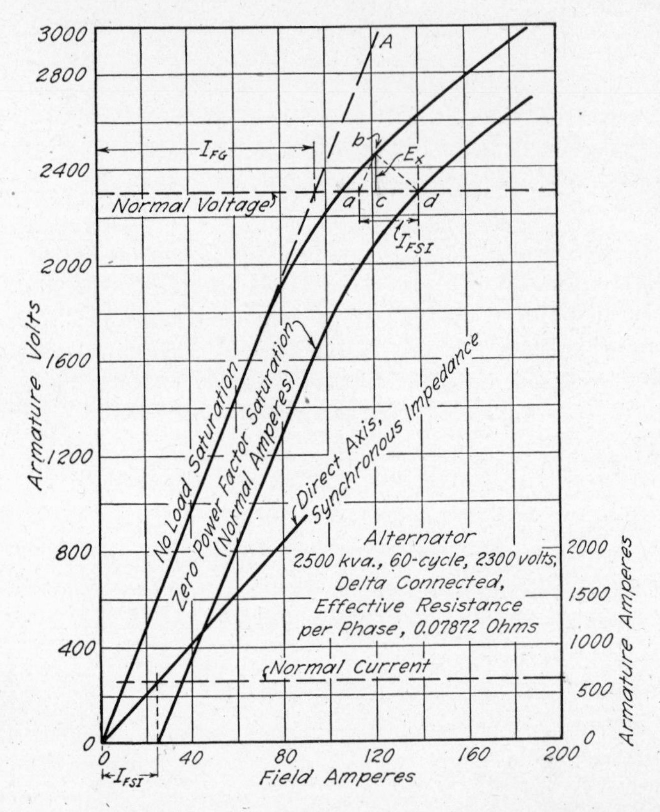

FIG. 14–7. Test date for determining the Potier reactance for an alternator.

result that will be obtained by test. The synchronous impedance ("pessimistic") method fails because the machine is operating under a low power factor and a low saturation for the magnetic field, whereas, for the A.S.A. method, there is a gain in accuracy as the machine is carrying full current. For that reason the saturation is correct but the power factor is low.

In determining the Potier coefficient of reactance, it is necessary to obtain an open-circuit saturation curve and a zero-power-factor saturation curve. The first is obtained by the method used under synchronous impedance determinations and is the open-circuit characteristic curve of the machine.

Figure 14–7 shows the zero-power-factor saturation curve obtained by loading the overexcited generator with a load of idle-running underexcited synchronous motors. The method requires the determination of the Potier reactance from the test curves in the figure.

The procedure is as follows: Take the value of the field current, I_{FSI}, corresponding to normal (rated) armature load current from the direct-axis synchronous impedance curve, Fig. 14–7. Lay off this value on *da* the normal voltage line, with the right end *d* at the amperes field for zero power factor, normal voltage, and normal current. The other end of I_{FSI} is *a*. Draw *ab* parallel to the straight line part of the open-circuit saturation curve *OA*, *b* being the point of intersection with the open-circuit saturation curve. The reactance X_p at rated kilovolt-amperes is then equal to E_x (*bc*) divided by normal current and is called the Potier reactance.

Example f. Figure 14–7 gives the open-circuit and zero power-factor characteristic data for the machine in Example *a*. Determine the Potier reactance X_p of the machine assuming connections either wye or delta.

At normal voltage, excitation I_{FSI}, the Potier reactance drop is 160 volts for rated current (Fig. 14–7).

Wye-connected:

$$X_p = \frac{160/\sqrt{3}}{627.57} = 0.1472 \text{ ohm per phase}$$

Delta-connected:

$$X_p = \frac{160}{627.57/\sqrt{3}} = 0.4415 \text{ ohm per phase}$$

Percentage:

$$X_p = \frac{627.57 \times 0.1472}{2300/\sqrt{3}} \times 100 = 6.96 \text{ per cent}$$

13. Calculation of Alternator Regulation. When the effective resistance and the equivalent reactance, X_s or X_p, are determined by either of the foregoing methods, the calculation of regulation depends upon the determination of the no-load voltage at some assumed power factor and loading. The characteristics of the machine are normally calculated at rated load. In every instance the power factor for the load should be specified, since this influences the regulation as much as the magnitude of the load.

Percentage regulation of an alternator is defined as the ratio of the voltage change from full load to no load, to the full-load voltage or

$$\text{Percentage regulation} = \frac{\text{no-load voltage} - \text{rated voltage}}{\text{rated voltage}} \times 100$$

The determination of regulation from test data, which merely evaluates the machine constants, is a determination by prediction, and such tests must be accepted as merely indicative and not conclusive.

The vector diagrams to be used in calculating the no-load voltage are shown in Fig. 5–7, where X_a is replaced by X_s, and the voltage calculated will be the no-load generated voltage E_g. The following examples will demonstrate the use of the constants in the calculation of regulation.

Example g. Calculate the regulation for the generator in Example *a* if the $R_a = 0.0262$ ohm and the $Z_s = X_s = 0.5269$ ohm per phase, considering the machine to be wye-connected. Determine the regulation if the machine is considered delta-connected. In both considerations the power factor is 80 per cent lagging.

Wye-connected:

$$\bar{E}_g = \bar{V}_t(\cos\theta + j\sin\theta) + \bar{I}_a(R_a + jX_s)$$

$$\bar{I}_a = \frac{2500 \times 1000}{\sqrt{3} \times 2300} + j0$$

$$\bar{E}_g = \frac{2300}{\sqrt{3}}(0.8 + j0.6) + \left(\frac{2500 \times 1000}{\sqrt{3} \times 2300} + j0\right)(0.0262 + j0.5269)$$

$$\bar{E}_g = 1327.94(0.8 + j0.6) + (627.57 + j0)(0.0262 + j0.5269)$$

$$\bar{E}_g = 1062.352 + j796.764 + 16.442 + j330.667$$

$$\bar{E}_g = 1078.794 + j1127.431$$

$$E_g = 1560.416 \text{ volts}$$

$$\text{Percentage regulation} = \frac{1560.42 - 1327.94}{1327.94} \times 100 = 17.5 \text{ per cent}$$

Delta-connected:

$$\bar{E}_g = 2300(0.8 + j0.6) + \left(\frac{627.57}{\sqrt{3}} + j0\right)(0.0262 \times 3 + j0.5269 \times 3)$$

$$\bar{E}_g = 1840 + j1380 + 28.480 + j572.171$$

$$\bar{E}_g = 1868.48 + j1952.17$$

$$E_g = 2702.255 \text{ volts}$$

$$\text{Percentage regulation} = \frac{2702.26 - 2300}{2300} \times 100 = 17.5 \text{ per cent}$$

If the resistance and reactance are expressed in percentage, the regulation may be calculated directly by considering the rated full-load current and voltage as 100 per cent. In calculations of this nature it is not necessary to assume either a wye or a delta connection, for this decision, when made in determining the constants, gives a value which is applicable to the connection assumed.

Example h. Solve Example *g* by the percentage method.

From Example *a* $R_a = 1.24$ per cent

From Example *e* $Z_s = X_s = 24.9$ per cent

Rated voltage and current 100 per cent

Since the percentage method need not consider the machine either wye- or delta-connected, the solution satisfies either condition.

$$\bar{E}_g = V_t(\cos\theta + j\sin\theta) + \bar{I}(R_a + jX_s)$$

$$\bar{E}_g = 100(0.8 + j0.6) + (100 + j0)(0.0124 + j0.249)$$

$$\bar{E}_g = 80 + j60 + 1.24 + j24.9$$

$$\bar{E}_g = 81.24 + j84.9$$

$$E_g = 117.5 \text{ per cent}$$

$$\text{Percentage regulation} = 117.5 - 100 = 17.5 \text{ per cent}$$

or

$$(E_g \text{ in percentage} - 100) = \text{percentage regulation}$$

The determination of regulation, from the characteristic curves shown in Fig. 14–7, will follow the specification set forth by the A.S.A. Refer-

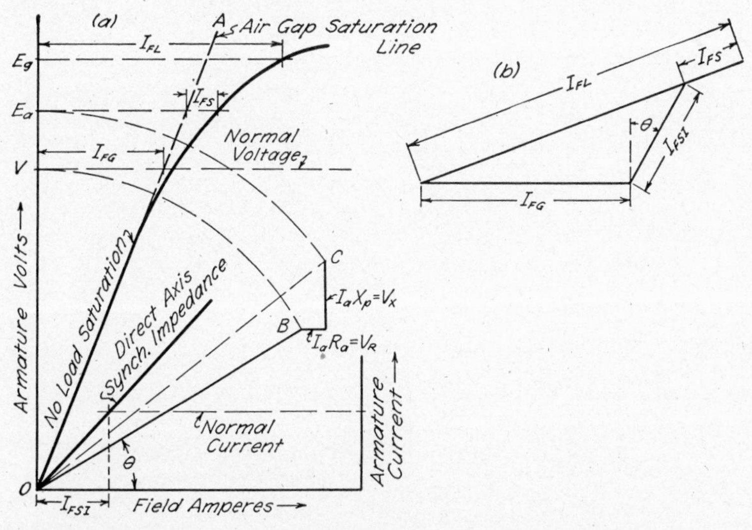

FIG. 15–7. (*a*) Diagram of induced voltage and regulation. (*b*) Determination of load field current.

ring to Fig. 15–7*a* draw the no-load saturation curve and direct-axis synchronous impedance curve of the machine from test data. Draw the line *OA* tangent to the no-load saturation curve and through the origin.

This line is called the air-gap line. Draw OB equal to V in length and at the power-factor angle from the horizontal. To the line OB add the resistance drop (I_aR_a) for I_a amperes horizontally, the Potier reactance drop for I_a amperes vertically, and to the same voltage scale as OB. Line OC, the vector sum for OB, I_aX_p, and I_aR_a, is the internal voltage (E_a) for I_a amperes load. I_{FS} is the difference in field amperes between the air-gap line and the saturation curve at the internal voltage E_a.

The load field current I_{FL} for I_a amperes load at normal voltage is determined as in Fig. 15–7*b*. Let I_{FG} be the value of field current corresponding to the air-gap line at normal voltage and I_{FSI} the value of field current corresponding to I_a armature amperes taken from the direct-axis synchronous impedance curve. Draw I_{FG} horizontally and add I_{FSI} vectorially at the angle θ degrees (θ is the load power factor angle) to the right of the vertical. Add I_{FS} directly to the resultant to obtain I_{FL}.

The voltage E_g from the open-circuit saturation corresponding to the field amperes I_{FL} is the voltage at the terminals of the machine when the total load is removed and the excitation and speed are not changed. The percentage regulation is

$$\frac{E_g - V}{V} \times 100$$

Example i. For the data given on Fig. 14–7 calculate the regulation of the alternator by the A.S.A. method for an 80 per cent power-factor lagging load.

From the data the machine is delta-connected.

$$R_a = 0.07872 \text{ ohm per phase}$$

$$I_p = \frac{627.57}{\sqrt{3}}$$

$$I_aR_a = \frac{627.57}{\sqrt{3}} \times 0.07872 = 28.48 \text{ volts}$$

$E_x = 160$ volts by construction, Fig. 14–21. By construction shown graphically in Fig. 15–7*a*,

$$I_{FG} = 95.5 \text{ amp}$$

$$I_{FS} = 18.0 \text{ amp}$$

$$I_{FSI} = 25 \text{ amp}$$

To determine the value of I_{FL} it is necessary to add the vector quantities as shown in Fig. 15–7*b*.

$$\bar{I}_{FL} = \bar{I}_{FG} + \bar{I}_{FSI} + \bar{I}_{FS}$$

$$\theta = \cos^{-1} 0.8$$

From Fig. 15–7*b*,

$$I_{FL} = \sqrt{(95.5 + 25 \times 0.6)^2 + (25 \times 0.8)^2} + 18$$
$$= 130.3 \text{ amp}$$

From Fig. 14–7,

$$\text{for } I_{FL} = 130.3 \qquad E_g = 2540 \text{ volts}$$

$$\text{Percentage regulation} = \frac{2540 - 2300}{2300} \times 100 = 10.4 \text{ per cent}$$

14. Alternator Regulation by Test. The alternator is connected to the load with voltmeters, ammeters, and wattmeters in the lines. In making a test of this kind, it is necessary to have control of the load and the power factor; also, the excitation shall remain constant at a value which gives rated load at normal voltage. Usually it is impossible to make this test at the manufacturing plant, as neither the driving power nor the power sink is available for the larger machines. The load test is made when the machine is actually installed and in operation. Such tests are considered acceptance tests.

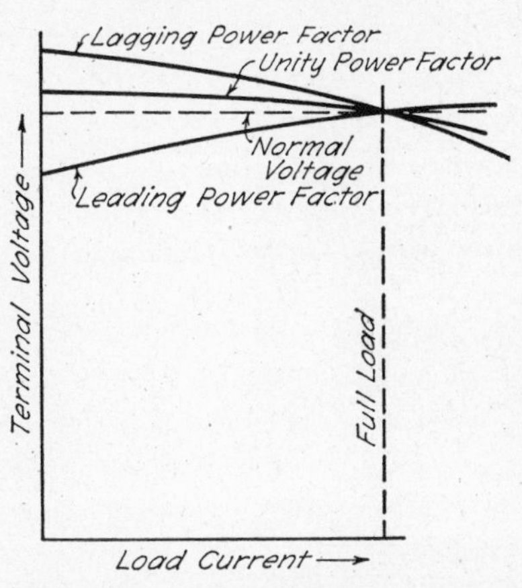

FIG. 16–7. Characteristic regulation curves for an alternator.

The machine is loaded to full load with the desired power factor and normal voltage. The load is removed and the speed and excitation are adjusted for determining the no-load voltage. The regulation is determined according to the definition previously given.

Example j. The alternator in Example *a* during an acceptance run when operating at 80 per cent power-factor (lagging current) rated current has the rated terminal voltage of 2300 volts. When the load is removed, the no-load voltage is 2510 volts. What is the regulation?

$$\text{Percentage regulation} = \frac{2510 - 2300}{2300} \times 100 = 9.1 \text{ per cent}$$

15. Alternator Characteristics. Since the regulation of the alternator depends upon both the load and power factor, it is necessary to have several characteristic curves of the machine to determine its performance. Figure 16–7 gives the characteristic curves for an alternator with a change in load for power factors of unity, lagging, and leading loads. With a leading power factor, the regulation may be negative, giving a rise in voltage with the application of load.

The normal condition is for the generator to deliver a load with a lagging power factor and a lagging power factor of 80 per cent is the one considered in power plant design. With such a power factor on the machine, it will not be necessary for the prime mover to have full generator rating. The characteristic curves in the figure and the efficiency curves of the machine, which will be discussed under efficiency and losses, embody a complete description of the performance of the machine under operating conditions when the system is free from marked disturbances.

16. Induction Generators. In Chapter 5 the fundamentals of the induction motor were discussed. The rotor of the induction motor operates at a speed less than the synchronous speed of the machine. If the speed of the rotor is increased by driving with an outside prime mover until it is more than synchronous speed, the machine becomes a generator. This type of machine does not have a wide application (some railway regenerative breaking) but may be located at an isolated station and will operate by means of alternating current. There is no need for an attendant and the unit requires little maintenance. If a central station has access to a power source located at such a point that it is not economical to develop the resources by a major development, it is possible to locate an induction generator at this point which will operate on the transmission system and will deliver power as the demand is applied.

Like the synchronous generator, the induction generator requires excitation, but, in this instance, the excitation comes from the transmission line. If a three-phase winding, wound on a stator, is attached to an alternating system, a rotating field of constant magnitude, revolving at synchronous speed as shown in the discussion in Chapter 3, will be developed in the winding.

If the rotor of the induction generator is driven at a greater speed (negative slip) than that of the synchronous rotating field, energy will be supplied to the rotating element which has no other outlet except the exciting system. The cutting of the field by the rotor winding generates the potential difference for delivering this electrical energy to the system. Since the exciting system controls the frequency, an increase in speed of the rotating element merely increases the power delivered. The amount of power delivered is directly proportional (approximately) to the difference in speed between the rotating field and the rotating element. This is called the slip and is negative. The induction generator cannot operate without being connected to a system that will supply a suitable amount of reactive volt-amperes to produce the flux that generates the electromotive force.

The excitation supply may come from any machine, a synchronous motor, or a converter, or even condensers. It is possible to deliver power to one phase of such a generator and to use the generated three-phase power for operating motor installations, for any motor winding has generated voltage in it. This latter system has been extensively used in Australia, where economy could not justify the delivery of limited power over long distances on three-phase systems, but where it was desirable to have three-phase power for motor operation.

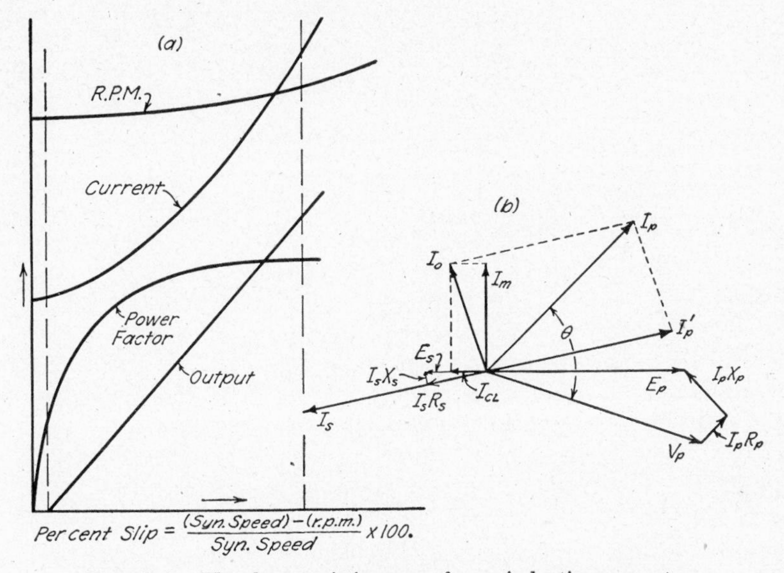

Fig. 17–7. The characteristic curves for an induction generator.

Figure 17–7 gives the characteristic curves for an induction generator. As the applied power is increased the delivered load (or current) is likewise increased. One of the principal objections to this type of generation is that it will not supply the lagging component of current demanded for its own excitation, but only a leading component. Therefore, the lagging component must be supplied by the line, because the power factor of the induction generator is fixed by its slip and machine constants and not by the load, whereas its voltage and frequency are determined by the synchronous machines connected to the system. Contrasted to this disadvantage is the fact that the machine is rugged and does not require constant attention. Also, the induction generator will not hunt (oscillate about synchronous speed) and when a short circuit occurs the excitation of the machine, because of voltage failure, falls to zero with a corresponding decrease in the delivery of power.

17. Voltage Regulators. The earlier types of voltage regulators depended upon relays and contacts for automatically adjusting the generator field resistance and thereby controlling the excitation. These regulators were of the magnetic type, of which the most common is the Tirrill regulator (Art. 12, Chapter 9). In addition to being very expensive, these regulators require attention.

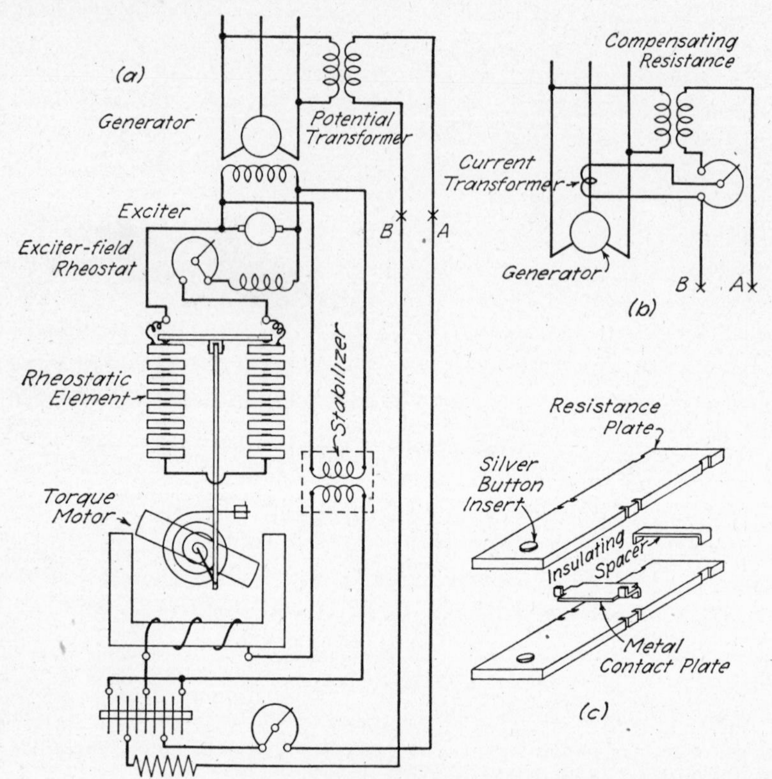

FIG. 18–7. Schematic diagram and connection of the General Electric Company torque-element generator-voltage regulator.

Two types of voltage regulators have been developed which require less attention and, because of the simplicity of construction, are less expensive. One type uses a torque motor instead of relays; the other type depends upon electron tube controls.

Figure 18–7*a* shows the schematic diagram of the torque-motor type of regulator. Under normal operating conditions, the torque motor is at rest and the parts are in equilibrium. If the voltage changes, the balancing spring and the torque-motor armature adjust themselves to a position of equilibrium and change the resistance in the rheostat element by means of the rod. A change in this element changes the resistance in the field excitation circuit of the exciter which, in turn, changes the a-c voltage and restores the regulator to a balanced condition. The stabilizer is a transformer on a d-c voltage which functions only when there is a change of current in the exciter voltage. The voltage of the stabilizer combines with that of the rectifier to halt the original movement of the torque motor. This combined action tends to prevent hunting.

The rheostat element is formed of resistance plates, metal contact plates, and insulating spacers, and it is so designed that it may be varied over its full range with very little motion of the rod. The resistance plates are equipped with silver buttons at the front, and the metal contact plates are located at the center of the bar and act as fulcrums. The highest resistance is obtained when the silver contacts are up and the current flow is through the fulcrums and resistance plates; the lowest resistance is obtained when the silver contacts form a path for the current. At intermediate points as the resistance plates tilt forward, there is a decrease in resistance between part of the resistance plates and the metal fulcrum at the center of the stack, since the silver contacts short-circuit the plates as they come together. The unit is fast operating, for these resistance changes take place with very little movement and pressure.

The torque-motor regulator has a flat voltage characteristic which tends to maintain a constant voltage regardless of the load or power factor on the machine. When a cross-current compensator (shown in Fig. 18–7*b*) is used, the excitation tends to divide the reactive volt-amperes between parallel generators automatically. The phase relationships between the current and potential transformers are such that the voltage component across the compensating rheostat tends to add to the a-c potential on the regulator for lagging reactive output and to subtract for leading reactive output.

Figure 19–7 shows one type of electronic regulator. The field of the exciter is supplied by a full-wave rectifier (1) using one tube (*A*) with a grid control, which, in turn, is controlled by a phase-shifting circuit (2) containing a manually operated controlling rheostat (*B*). The a-c supply for the excitation is taken from the source to be regulated. The triode (*C*) acts as an adjustable resistor and is controlled by the grid bias voltage, which is supplied by the triode (*D*), because it controls the current flow through the resistor. The triode (*D*) is operated with the plate saturated so that the maximum possible current will flow in the anode circuit and will vary only with a temperature change in the cathode. A change in voltage in the alternator circuit will be reflected in the phase-shifting circuit (2) through the control transformer (3). This changes the cathode temperature of the triode (D) and the anode current, and thereby changes the output of rectifier system (1). The regulation is exceedingly rapid because it is accomplished by electrical changes instead of mechanical changes. Though it is not shown, the system can be equipped with anti-hunting features and, by means of cross-current compensation, may be used in the regulation of alternators in parallel.

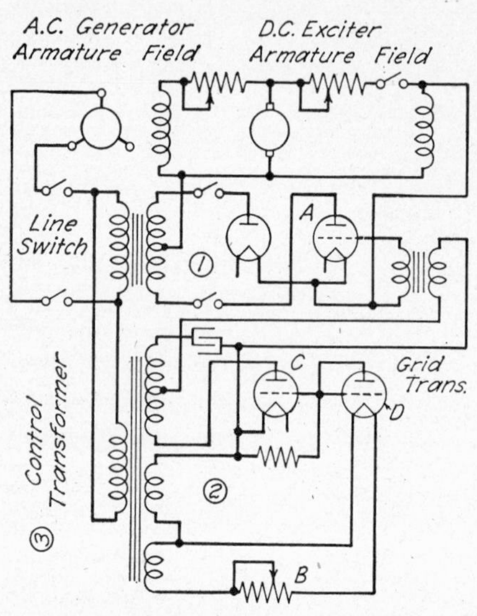

Fig. 19–7. Ward-Leonard Electric Company electronic voltage regulator.

Figure 20–7 shows another type of electronic regulator which uses three grid glow tubes (A) and two amplifier tubes (B). The grid glow tubes supply current to the field, whereas the amplifier tubes control the grid glow tubes. A decrease of the generator voltages in conjunction with the 45-volt battery causes a bias on the grids of the amplifier tubes. The resistor (a) and the capacitor (b) are anti-hunting devices, for, with the exciter tied to 7 and 8, a change in exciter voltage resulting from regulation will cause a voltage component in the resistor (a) which will vary the amplifier (B) grid voltage in such a way as to oppose the regulating action, thereby stabilizing it.

A change in alternator voltage will cause the grid voltage of the amplifier (B) to change and this also changes the voltage across the resistor (C). With this variation of voltage across the resistor (C), the grid glow tubes (A) supply a different current to the exciter field. Because the grid glow tubes (A) are connected to the star windings of the transformer, and the neutral is connected to 5, with the exciter between 4 and 5, the grid glow tubes (A) supply rectified current to the exciter field. The grid control of the tubes (A) is obtained by a combination of d-c and a-c voltage control. The alternating current is obtained from transformer (D) which is displaced 90° with the anode voltage from transformer (E), while the d-c grid voltage component is obtained from two resistors (C and d) in series. By varying this d-c voltage, it is possible to shift the point on the a-c anode voltage wave at which the grid glow tubes will

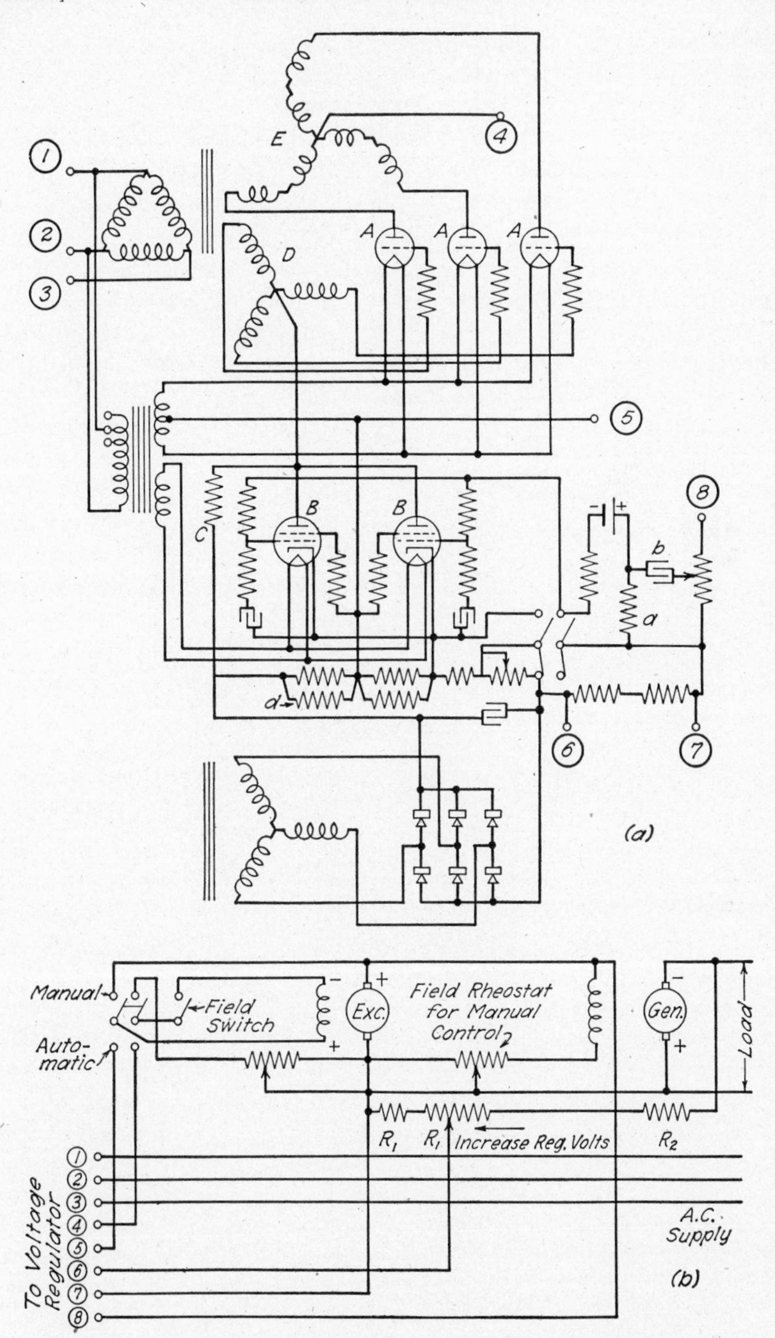

FIG. 20–7. Westinghouse Electric Corporation electronic voltage regulator.

break down. The multiplicity of tubes insures continued operation while defective tubes are replaced.

When operated under constant temperature conditions and with not more than a 5 per cent change on the a-c supply, the sensitivity of this regulator is 0.25 per cent. When no exciter is used, the response is from 3 to 8 cycles whereas, with a compound-wound exciter, the response is from 15 to 40 cycles.

Electronic regulators with proper maintenance and frequent tests and inspections may be depended upon to give satisfactory service. The chief advantages lie in the relatively low cost and the absence of inertia time lag, moving parts, and insensitive zones, all three of which are found in the mechanical type of regulator.

PROBLEMS

1–7. The generated voltage per coil, in an alternator, is 20 volts and the coils are displaced 10 electrical degrees with 6 coils per phase. (*a*) What will be the voltage generated per phase? (*b*) If the coils could be placed in space phase what would be the voltage per phase?

2–7. A 2000-kva, 2000-volt, 3-phase, 60-cycle alternator has a measured resistance between terminals of 0.04 ohm. What is the per cent resistance (*a*) if wye-connected, (*b*) if delta-connected?

3–7. A 50-kva, 220-volt, 1-phase, 25-cycle alternator has a reactance of 0.07 ohm. What is the per cent reactance?

4–7. A 2000-kva, 440-volt, 3-phase, 60-cycle, wye-connected alternator has a resistance of 1 per cent and a reactance of 20 per cent. Determine (*a*) the armature voltage at 85 per cent leading power factor and (*b*) 85 per cent lagging power factor, using the per cent method.

5–7. A 10,000-kva, 13,500-volt, 3-phase, 25-cycle alternator has a resistance of 1 per cent and a reactance of 22 per cent. Determine the resistance per phase (*a*) if wye-connected, (*b*) if delta-connected; (*c*) the armature voltage at full load 80 per cent lagging power factor if wye-connected, (*d*) the armature voltage at full load 80 per cent leading power factor if delta-connected.

6–7. A 1000-kva, 1100-volt, 3-phase, 60-cycle, delta-connected alternator with a 1 per cent resistance and a 4 per cent reactance is operating with an 85 per cent lagging power factor. (*a*) Draw the vector diagram; determine (*b*) the armature voltage by using complex quantities with voltage as a reference, (*c*) the values of the resistance and reactance in ohms.

7–7. A 2000-kva, 4000-volt, 3-phase, 60-cycle, delta-connected, a-c generator has an ohmic resistance between terminals of 0.05 ohm and a reactance of 4 per cent per phase. The effective resistance is 30 per cent more than the ohmic and the effects of armature reaction are to be neglected. Determine (*a*) the line voltage at no load with rated voltage excitation after a 90 per cent leading power factor load is removed, (*b*) the reactance in ohms and the reactance voltage drop, (*c*) the resistance in ohms and the resistance voltage drop.

8–7. A 2500-kva, 2300-volt, 3-phase, 25-cycle, delta-connected alternator has a phase resistance of 0.0787 ohm and a phase reactance of 0.2210 ohm. Determine (*a*) the per cent resistance, (*b*) the per cent reactance, (*c*) the ratio of the effective to the ohmic resistance, if the ohmic resistance between terminals is 0.0314 ohm.

9–7. A 4000-kva, 4000-volt, 3-phase, 60-cycle, wye-connected, a-c generator has a 1 per cent resistance and a 10 per cent synchronous reactance. If the machine is tested at short circuit with rated current and the effective resistance is 120 per cent of the ohmic resistance, what will be the short circuit test data?

10–7. A 10-kva, 2000-volt, 1-phase, 25-cycle alternator has a resistance of 2 per cent and a synchronous reactance of 3.64 per cent. What will be the regulation at 85 per cent lagging power factor?

11–7. A 2000-kva, 1000-volt, 1-phase, 60-cycle alternator has a 1 per cent resistance and a 10 per cent synchronous reactance. (*a*) What will be the resistance and synchronous reactance, and (*b*) the regulation when the machine supplies an 80 per cent leading power-factor load?

12–7. A 1000-kva, 1100-volt, 3-phase, 60-cycle alternator on test has a field current of 100 amp, a straight line saturation voltage of 1200 volts, and a short-circuit current of 2600 amp. If the effective resistance between terminals is 0.0242 ohm determine the regulation at unity power factor by the per cent method.

13–7. A 1350-kva, 2600-volt, 3-phase, 60-cycle alternator has a 2 per cent resistance and a synchronous reactance of 20 per cent. Calculate (*a*) the regulation at 60 per cent lagging power factor, (*b*) the regulation at 60 per cent leading power factor, (*c*) the resistance and synchronous reactance if delta-connected, (*d*) if wye-connected.

14–7. A 5000-kva, 6600-volt, 3-phase, 25-cycle alternator, with the field current held constant, has a line current of 440 amp on short circuit and a corresponding open circuit line voltage of 3050 volts. The ohmic resistance between terminals is 0.18 ohm and the effective resistance is 111 per cent of the ohmic resistance. Determine (*a*) the synchronous impedance per phase if wye-connected, (*b*) the synchronous impedance per phase if delta-connected, (*c*) the per cent resistance, (*d*) the per cent synchronous reactance.

15–7. An alternator was tested by the A.S.A. method and it was found, from the direct-axis synchronous impedance curve, that the field current at rated armature load was 20 amp. The field current determined at rated voltage, from the straight line no-load saturation curve (air-gap line) was 70 amp. The difference in field amperes between the air-gap line and the no-load saturation curve at the internal voltage of the machine was 16 amp. What will be the field current required to give the rated terminal voltage, for normal lead, at 80 per cent lagging power factor?

CHAPTER 8

ALTERNATING-CURRENT MOTORS

A-c motors are the most widely used motors in electrical applications. These motors are classified into two groups according to their speed characteristics (synchronous and asynchronous): the first will operate at a speed definitely determined by the number of poles on the motor and the frequency of the system; the latter will vary from the frequency-pole or synchronous speed by some percentage, depending upon the size of the motor and the load. This variation from synchronous speed in the asynchronous motor may be caused by some method of speed control. The disadvantage of all a-c motors lies in the difficulty of obtaining speed control at a reasonable cost.

The fundamentals of a-c motors have been treated in Chapters 1, 3, and 5 where construction, rotating magnetic fields, and motor theory have been discussed. The a-c motors are more conveniently studied when divided into three classes: the polyphase induction motors, the synchronous motors, and single-phase motors.

POLYPHASE INDUCTION MOTOR

By far the greater part of the energy used for a-c drives is supplied to the polyphase induction motors. This motor is self-starting, has practically a constant speed from no load to full load, is relatively inexpensive, and has few sliding contacts or electrical connections which cannot be soldered, thereby making it easy to maintain. This motor has expanded the use of electrical energy because of its ruggedness, low cost, and starting torque, and probably has been the determining factor in the development of the large power networks.

The study of induction motor operation may be grouped under three divisions: starting characteristics, running characteristics, and the tests for predicting the performance of the machine under operating conditions.

1. Starting Characteristics. Figure 1–8 shows the relationship of the various quantities which determine the starting characteristics of the polyphase induction motor to the slip, from standstill to no-load running. The characteristics of the induction motor depend in part upon the rotor resistance and reactance; the last is a function of the rotor frequency. In the study of the motor characteristics, it is assumed that the inductance and the resistance of the machine (when referred to the stator) remain constant, the fact that inductance is a function of the current because of the variation of the permeability of the magnetic circuit being neglected.

2. Slip. In Chapter 3, it was shown that a flow of polyphase current in a polyphase winding caused a rotating magnetic field which rotates at the synchronous speed of the machine with respect to the winding.

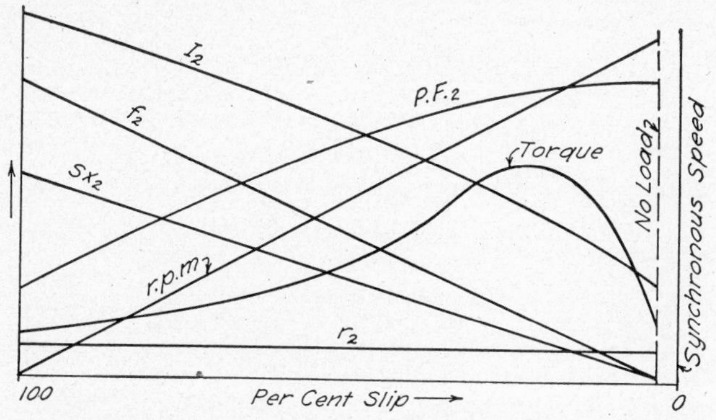

FIG. 1–8. Qualitative characteristic curves plotted against the percentage slip. Curves for the starting characteristics of an induction motor rotor.

It was also shown that this field is constant in magnitude. The speed (in revolutions per minute) of the rotating magnetic field is expressed by the following:

$$\text{Synchronous speed} = \frac{120f}{p}$$

where f (cycles per second) is the frequency of the system and p is the number of poles produced by the winding on the motor.

If the rotor of an induction motor is blocked and a potential applied to the stator, the rotor will be cut by the revolving field at a speed equivalent to the synchronous speed of that field, and the frequency of the induced electromotive force in the rotor will be the same as the system frequency. If the rotor is released, it begins to revolve in the direction of field rotation (as shown in Chapter 5). As both the field and the rotor revolve in the same direction, the relative motion between the rotor and the synchronous field is decreased, and this is accompanied by a decrease in the rotor frequency. If the rotor attained synchronous speed (which is impossible, as demonstrated in Chapter 5), the rotor frequency and generated voltage would be reduced to zero.

By definition, the slip is the difference between the synchronous speed and the operating speed of an induction motor. Though this is normally expressed as percentage of the synchronous speed, it may also be expressed in revolutions per minute, or as a decimal fraction of the synchronous speed. Therefore, slip may be expressed by

$$s = \frac{N_s - N}{N_s} \times 100 \quad \text{(per cent)} \tag{A}$$

$$s = \frac{N_s - N}{N_s} \quad \text{(a decimal)} \tag{B}$$

$$s = N_s - N \quad \text{(rpm)} \tag{C}$$

where s is the slip, N_s is the synchronous speed, and N is the actual speed of the rotor. The running speed of the rotor may be expressed as $N = (1 - s)N_s$, where s is the decimal fraction of the synchronous speed of the motor. Figure 1–8 shows the relationship of the speed of the rotor to the slip during the starting period of the machine.

Example a. Determine the slip in revolutions per minute, the percentage slip, and the synchronous speed of an 8-pole polyphase induction motor operating at 882 rpm on a 60-cycle system.

$$N_s = \frac{120 \times 60}{8} = 900 \text{ rpm}$$

$$s = 900 - 882 = 18 \text{ rpm}$$

$$s = \frac{900 - 882}{900} \times 100 = 2 \text{ per cent}$$

3. Rotor Frequency. It is possible to determine the rotor frequency from the slip for, when the rotor is blocked, the rotor frequency is line frequency; but, if the rotor could attain synchronous speed, the frequency would be zero. The relationship between the rotor frequency and the system frequency (which is the stator frequency) may be expressed by

$$f_2 = sf_1$$

where f_2 is the rotor frequency, s is the slip as a decimal fraction, and f_1 is the system (or stator) frequency. Figure 1–8 shows the relationship between the slip and the rotor frequency.

Example b. In Example *a*, what would be the rotor frequency of the induction motor described?

$$f_2 = 0.02 \times 60 = 1.2 \text{ cycles}$$

4. Rotor Resistance and Reactance. When the motor is loaded, the load on the shaft is reflected back into the electrical circuit as a decrease of resistance and must be considered as such when the rotor power factor is discussed.

The reactance of the rotor is inductive because the structure is composed of copper conductors buried in iron. The inductive reactance is expressed by

$$X_{\mathcal{L}} = 2\pi f \mathcal{L}$$

If it is assumed that the permeability of the iron does not change with a change in current, the inductance may be considered constant and the rotor reactance is proportional to the rotor frequency, which, in turn, is proportional to the slip of the induction motor.

Figure 1–8 shows curves for the resistance and reactance of the rotor as the motor starts from zero speed and attains no-load speed.

5. Rotor Generated Electromotive Force and Rotor Current. The generated electromotive force, which must be considered per phase, will be a function of the slip (which determines the time element), the turns, and the flux cut by the rotor. This flux cut does not remain constant because of the component of rotor current in the stator during the starting period but does remain practically constant from no load to the rated load of the machine. The rotor generated electromotive force may be expressed as

$$E = -N\frac{d\phi}{dt} \times 10^{-8}$$

or

$$sE_2 = K\phi N$$

where s is the slip and E_2 is the voltage in the rotor, if the rotor is blocked; the foregoing limits are placed upon ϕ during the period.

The current flowing in the rotor depends upon the impedance of the rotor. The impedance will be a variable, since the inductive reactance depends upon the slip and this slip determines the rotor frequency. The rotor current is expressed by

$$sE_2 = I_2Z_2 \quad \text{or} \quad \bar{I}_2 = \frac{s\bar{E}_2}{\bar{Z}_2} = \frac{s\bar{E}_2}{r_2 + jsx_2} = \frac{\bar{E}_2}{\frac{r_2}{s} + jx_2} \qquad (a\text{–}8)$$

where the value of

$$Z_2 = \sqrt{r_2^2 + s^2x_2^2}$$

$$E_2(1 - s) = \text{rotational or counter voltage}$$

r_2/s represents the apparent resistance of the rotor (winding and load) referred to the stator. The power factor of the rotor current may be determined from the impedance expression and is

$$\cos \alpha_2 = \frac{r_2}{\sqrt{r_2^2 + s^2 x_2^2}}$$

Both the rotor generated voltage and the reactance are a function of slip which plays an important part in the characteristics of the induction motor. The rigorous treatment of the induction motor, from a mathematical analysis, is beyond the scope of this book and only those relationships that are qualitative are discussed. The various curves in Fig. 1–8 show the characteristics of the rotor as plotted against the slip from standstill to no-load running speed.

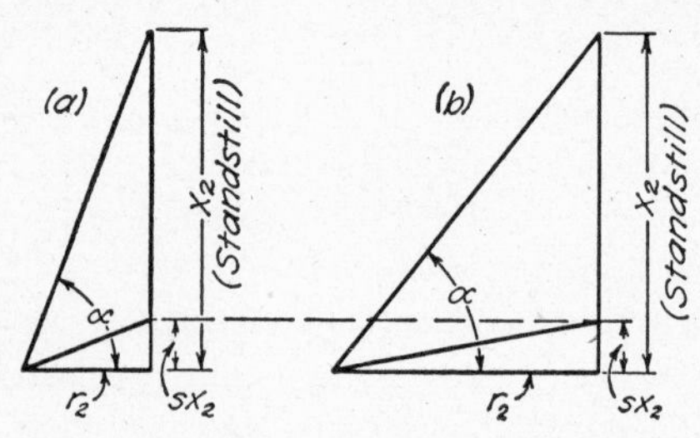

Fig. 2–8. The effect of rotor resistance on the power-factor angle of the rotor.

6. Starting Torque. The foregoing establishes the basis for the consideration of the most important characteristic of the induction motor, that is, the torque. It can be established that the maximum starting torque occurs when $r_2^2 = r_1^2 + (x_1 + x_2)^2$ but, for the best running torque value, r_2 should be as low as possible. The best starting combination will be obtained by so adjusting the values of r_2 and sx_2 that the current is limited to that amount necessary to overcome the resisting torque of the load with sufficient additional torque to accelerate the motor. The value of sx_2 in the motor cannot be made adjustable, but there may be some control of the value of r_2 as in the wound-rotor induction motor. In the squirrel cage motor, the nature of the service of the motor determines the proportion of r_2 and sx_2 best adapted for any application.

Figure 2–8 shows the effect produced on rotor power factor by the change of reactance as the slip changes. The power factor improves as the rotor gains in speed, reducing the slip and decreasing sx_2 proportionally. The addition of resistance in the rotor with the same reactance improves the power factor, as shown in Fig. 2–8*b*. This fundamental principle is utilized by applying resistance in the wound-rotor motor for additional torque at starting, the resistance being removed after the motor is running. If the value of r_2 in the squirrel cage motor is increased to gain starting torque, the efficiency will decrease because of the increased rotor copper loss of the motor when it is under normal load conditions. In special designs of squirrel cage rotors, provision is made to give a higher value of r_2 for starting and lower value of r_2 for running. The inclusion or omission of resistance control in the rotor depends upon the nature of the load which the machine must start.

In Fig. 3–8, the effect of the rotor power factor on the torque of the motor is shown. If the rotor consists of pure resistance, the maximum current and the maximum generated voltage occur at the same instant and in phase with each other. Under these conditions, the space quadrature and time-phase relationships of the fields are a maximum and

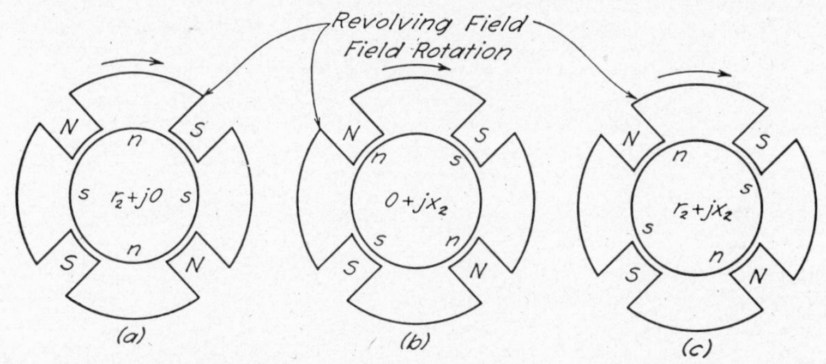

FIG. 3–8. Effect of the impedance of the rotor on the torque of the induction motor.

produce maximum torque. Since the rotor cannot be built without reactance, this relationship cannot be realized in practice. The other extreme (Fig. 3–8*b*) with the rotor having reactance only, produces fields in space phase and time quadrature (90° out of phase). If such a condition were possible, no torque would be produced, but, as above, the assumption cannot be reproduced in the physical machine.

Figure 3–8*c* shows a machine with parameters which may occur in the rotor of the induction motor. Here, both resistance and reactance occur, and the torque values depend upon the proportion in which each of these is present. The stator and rotor poles shown in the figures move in synchronism and, therefore, the instantaneous conditions shown in the figure are representative of every instant in the operation of the motor. In Chapter 5 and Fig. 6–5 are given the details of the torque analysis.

The above explanation and figures show why the torque of an induction motor may be very low at starting and improve as the rotor gains speed because of the improvement of the power factor of the rotor as the slip and the rotor reactance decrease. The actual torque may be expressed by

$$T = T_m \cos \alpha$$

where T is the torque, T_m is the maximum torque which can occur with optimum current and flux relationships, and α is the angle between the primary flux (assumed constant) and the rotor current. This is also the rotor power factor.

Before making a further study of the starting torque, it is necessary to understand the influence of the addition of resistance in the rotor circuit, either as permanent resistance or as temporary resistance for starting.

7. Influence of Rotor Resistance on Torque. Figure 4–8, showing the torque and slip relationship of an induction motor with various rotor

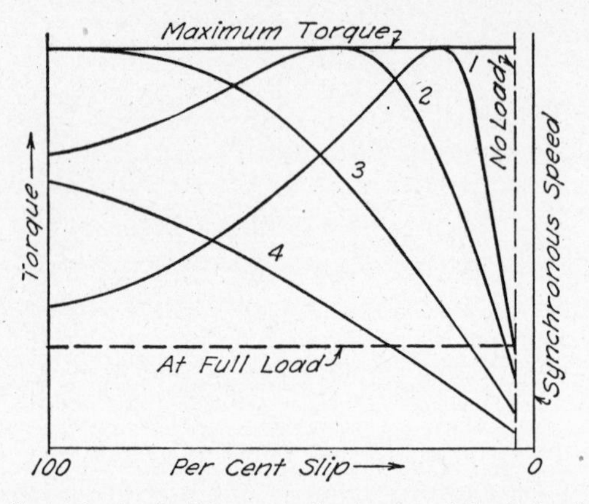

FIG. 4–8. The effect of rotor resistance on the torque of the induction motor: (1) is a low resistance rotor and (4) is a high resistance rotor, whereas (2) and (3) are for intermediate values of resistance.

resistances, is a clear picture of the influence of the rotor resistance on the starting torque. The part of the torque curve which represents the low percentage slip is the operating region under normal load.

When resistance is introduced into the rotor circuit, the starting torque increases and the maximum torque will occur at a greater slip. There is a rotor resistance that will cause the maximum torque at starting, which occurs when $s = 1$. Increase of the rotor resistance by design increases the starting torque but will also affect the operating characteristics of the motor, making the efficiency and speed regulation of the machine very poor. The introduction of temporary resistance in the rotor for starting requires an expensive wound rotor; also, the addition of resistance in the winding of the squirrel cage rotor gives poor operation. The designer must accept some compromise, influenced by the type of the load that must be started and the economics of the operation.

A compromise is possible by the use of double winding rotors of the squirrel cage type, which give a simple rotor construction and, at the same time, fair starting conditions with acceptable operating characteristics. The construction consists of two windings in the same slot. The deeper winding is essentially a high reactance winding in which the effect of the reactance is increased by reducing the resistance to a minimum and introducing a low reluctance path. On the other hand, the surface winding has a greater part of its magnetic path through air and is, therefore, low in inductive reactance and, if small wire or higher resistance material is used, has high resistance.

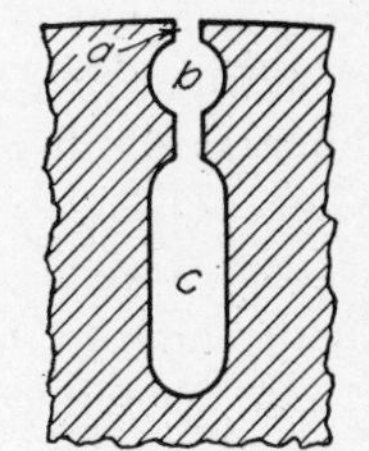

FIG. 5–8. The arrangement of the high and low resistance windings in a double-winding induction motor rotor. See Fig. 14–1.

The synchronous frequencies in the rotor at starting cause the deeper windings to have a very high impedance. This limits the current and causes the greater portion of the rotor current to flow in the outer winding which has a high resistance but a relatively low reactance. In this manner, the desired starting torque is obtained by effectively increasing the rotor resistance at starting.

When the machine has reached normal operating speed, the reactance of the deeper (or low resistance) winding has been reduced, for the slip has decreased and the major portion of the current now flows in the deeper winding. This adjustment of current flow in the two windings may be controlled by the designer so that the torque may be a maximum under any one operating condition for a specific machine. Figure 5–8 shows the slot arrangement for the windings used in this type of machine.

8. Summary of Starting Torque. The foregoing articles have discussed the factors that influence the starting torque of the induction motor and the control that may be exercised over these torque conditions. The influences have been traced through the rotor resistance and reactance, which lead to the rotor impedance and power factor, and these control the current flow in the rotor. The starting torque of the induction motor may be expressed by the general form

$$T_s = \frac{KnV_1{}^2a^2r_2}{(r_1 + a^2r_2)^2 + (x_1 + a^2x_2)^2} \; *$$

and the maximum torque by

$$T_m = \frac{KnV_1{}^2}{2[r_1 + \sqrt{r_1{}^2 + (x_1 + a^2x_2)^2}]} \; *$$

* Complete development in Christie's *Electrical Engineering*, Lawrence's *Principles of Alternating Current Machinery*, and Langsdorf's *Theory of Alternating Machinery*.

where T_s is the starting torque, T_m is the maximum torque, n, r, x, and V are the number of phases, the resistance, the reactance, and the voltage, respectively, and the subscripts 1 and 2 represent the stator and rotor, respectively, with all values referred to the stator.

These two expressions are not to be considered the final answer to the design of a polyphase induction motor but merely a concise method of expressing the influence of quantitative coefficients on the torque of the machine at two of the most important points of operation for the machine. On Fig. 1–8 is plotted a torque curve with the other curves previously discussed. Note that the torque, power factor, and current curves bear a relationship such that, as torque is increased with higher rotor power factor caused by reactance decrease resulting from lower slip, the rotor current falls off correspondingly.

9. Operating Characteristics of the Polyphase Induction Motor. The mechanical load applied to the shaft of the induction motor is reflected in the electrical circuit as additional copper losses and, therefore, is equivalent to the decrease of resistance and increase of current in the rotor. The addition of the load to the shaft not only introduces less (apparent) resistance into the rotor but it also influences the rotor frequency. The application of load causes the rotor to slow down (as explained in Chapter 5) and, as a result, the slip increases and there is a corresponding rise in rotor frequency. Upon this slip and apparent resistance change, the characteristic performance of the motor under operating conditions may be established.

As previously explained, the rotor of the induction motor cannot reach synchronous speed but, likewise, it usually does not operate at speeds far below the synchronous speed and may be considered, for commercial application, a constant speed motor. As the load is applied, the rotor speed decreases to a value which establishes equilibrium, where the added torque required is developed by the increased rotor current, which increases more rapidly than the rotor impedance for low values of slip, and is caused by a greater rotor-induced electromotive force. The full-load slip varies from approximately 10 per cent in the smaller motors to 1 per cent in the larger. Since the speed of the rotor depends upon the slip, the speed regulation of the machine may be determined if the slip and synchronous speed are known. The speed regulation at full load (in percentage) is expressed by

$$\text{Percentage regulation} = \frac{\text{no-load speed} - \text{full-load speed}}{\text{full-load speed}} \times 100$$

The no-load speed for purposes of computation may be considered the synchronous speed.

In Fig. 6–8 are shown the various characteristic curves of the polyphase induction motor.

The power factor of the motor is controlled by its exciting current and the increment of energy component of load current. The exciting current I_0 (larger than in the transformer because of the air gap), which is very nearly a pure magnetizing current, is practically constant at all loads, whereas the load adds a current which is in phase with the voltage. The resultant of the exciting current (I_0) and the energy component of load current determines the total current. Figure 7–8 shows the change in current and power factor as equal increments of load current are added vectorially to the exciting current of the induction motor.

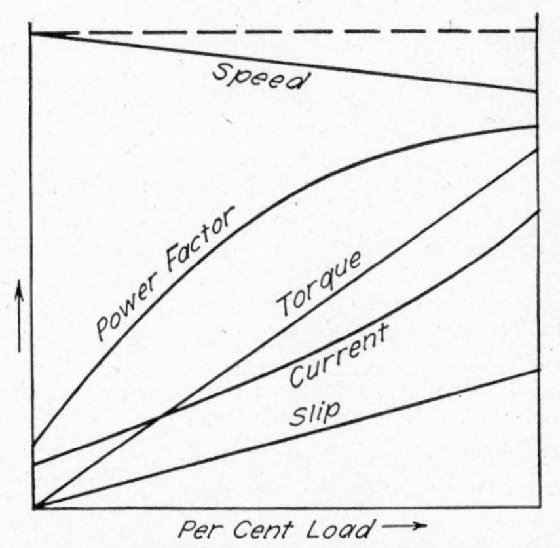

FIG. 6–8. External characteristics of the induction motor.

The power factor at first increases very rapidly, its rate of change decreasing as the load increases. The initial gain of torque results from the rapid improvement of power factor. In a study of the current change, the opposite effect will be observed. The initial rate of change in stator current is small with the light loads but, under the heavier loads, the current increases more rapidly. Both the power factor and current characteristics are shown on Fig. 6–8.

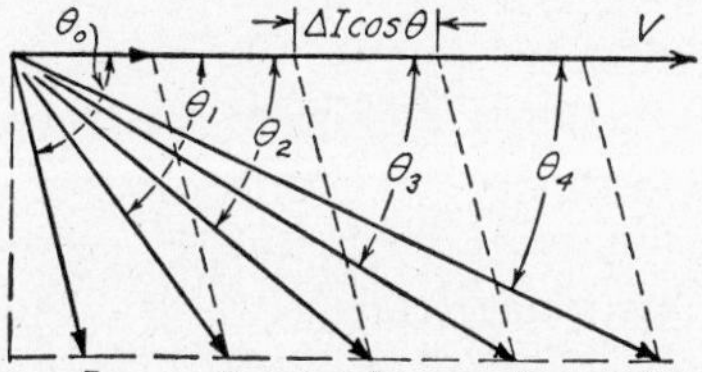

FIG. 7–8. Change in current and power factor as load is applied to the shaft of a polyphase induction motor.

In the consideration of starting torque, the machine resistance and reactance are the controlling factors as an indication of the final effect, and the same is true under operating conditions. The change of stator current and power factor controls the demand placed on the electrical system so that the necessary torque may be supplied to the shaft.

Figure 4–8 shows that the torque curves as they approach the value of no slip (synchronous speed) are practically straight lines. Since even the smallest motors do not have slips in excess of 10 per cent, the characteristic torque curve for the polyphase induction motor will be practically a straight line within the operating range.

10. The Equivalent Circuit of the Polyphase Induction Motor. Like all other electrical equipment, the induction motor may be reduced to an equivalent electrical circuit. In its functional characteristics the induction motor is essentially a transformer with a non-inductive load. Under locked-rotor operating conditions, the rotor being stationary, the induction motor is a transformer in its true sense and the currents in the rotor are those of the secondary of a short-circuited transformer. Since the

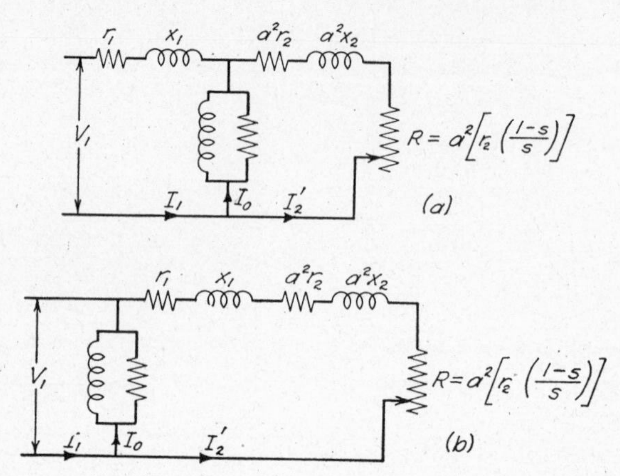

FIG. 8–8. The equivalent circuit of the polyphase induction motor, showing one line to neutral: (*a*) accurate equivalent circuit; (*b*) approximate equivalent circuit.

rotor when operating is free to rotate, the relationship still remains true except that the load on the shaft affects the secondary (which is the rotor circuit) in the same manner as the decrease of a resistance load affects a transformer. At the same time the slip of the rotor establishes a frequency in the rotor circuit which influences the rotor reactance.

The parameters for the equivalent circuit of the induction motor (Fig. 8–8*b*) may be developed by expanding the equation $(a - 8)$. The rotor current may be expressed as

$$\bar{I}_2 = \frac{\bar{E}_2}{\dfrac{r_2}{s} + jx_2}$$

When this rotor current is referred to the stator,

$$aE_2 = V_1$$

$$I_2 = aI_2'$$

$$a\bar{I}_2' = \frac{\bar{V}_1}{a\left(\dfrac{r_2}{s} + jx_2\right)}$$

$$\bar{I}_2' = \frac{\bar{V}_1}{a^2\left(\dfrac{r_2}{s} + jx_2\right)} = \frac{\bar{V}_1}{a^2\dfrac{r_2}{s} + ja^2x_2}$$

$$a^2\frac{r_2}{s} = a^2r_2 + R$$

Therefore,

$$R = a^2r_2\left(\frac{1-s}{s}\right)$$

where $r_2[(1 - s)/s]$ is a fictitious resistance depending upon the load. The equivalent resistance and reactance of the secondary (rotor) are added to the resistance and reactance of the primary (stator) just as the equivalent parameters of the transformer are added (Chapter 4). The expressions for the voltage, current, and equivalent parameters are

$$R_{01} = r_1 + a^2r_2 + R \qquad X_{01} = x_1 + a^2x_2$$

$$= r_1 + a^2r_2\left(1 + \frac{1-s}{s}\right) \qquad \bar{I}_1 = \bar{I}_0 + \bar{I}_2'$$

$$= r_1 + \frac{a^2r_2}{s} \qquad \bar{V}_1 = \bar{I}_2'(R_{01} + jX_{01})$$

When the induction motor is represented by an equivalent electrical circuit or the associated vector diagram, it is understood that none of the requirements of circuits and vector diagrams are to be violated. The laws of circuits (and the assumption of one frequency throughout) are still true, and no deviations from these assumptions are made when the induction motor is converted into a circuit, always (in practice) in terms of the stator. The error caused by assumptions that are made in the circuit may be neglected on the premise that, for practical purposes, these circuits and diagrams have proved successful in dealing with induction motors.

Figure 8–8 and Fig. 9–8 show the circuits and vector diagrams for the equivalent circuits of the induction motor. The induction motor is reduced to an equivalent transformer (ratio 1 to 1) and the load is represented as a pure resistance, the value of which depends upon the magnitude of the load. If values are assigned (or determined by experiment) to the various parts of the circuit, the determination of the values for the rotor current and the line current for a predetermined load is the solution of an electrical circuit.

The exciting current (I_0) may be determined by measurement. This current is very much larger in the motor than in the transformer and it is, therefore, necessary to consider the exciting current. There is an error introduced (not over 10 per cent) if the voltage drop caused by the exciting current through the stator impedance is neglected, and the circuit is drawn with the machine constants combined; and the branch, representing the no-load losses, is in parallel with this equivalent series

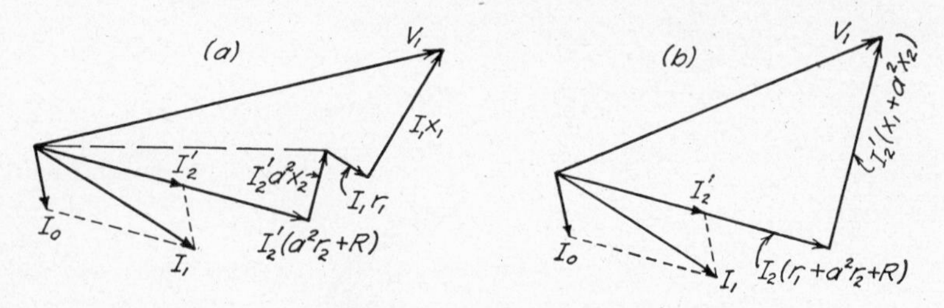

FIG. 9–8. The vector diagram for the equivalent circuit of an induction motor circuit for one phase from line to neutral: (*a*) accurate equivalent circuit; (*b*) approximate equivalent circuit.

branch, as shown in Fig. 8–8*b*. The rotor resistance is equivalent to the ohmic resistance because of the low frequencies involved but, in the stator, the effective resistance should be used. The resistance measurements for the primary and secondary can be made if the machine has a wound rotor but, if the machine is a squirrel cage induction motor, the total equivalent resistance may be measured from the stator side.

Example c. For a 25-hp, 440-volt, 60-cycle, 1200-rpm, wye-connected induction motor, determine the no-load current and power factor; also, the power factor, current, and speed at 5 per cent slip. The stator resistance per phase is 0.25 ohm and the reactance 0.7 ohm; the rotor resistance and reactance referred to the stator are 0.5 ohm and 0.7 ohm, respectively. The exciting conductance is 0.008 mho and the exciting susceptance is 0.055 mho.

$$V_1 = \frac{440}{\sqrt{3}} = 254 \text{ volts}$$

$$\bar{Y}_0 = 0.008 - j0.055 = |\, 0.0555 \,|$$

$$\bar{I}_0 = (254 + j0)(0.008 - j0.055)$$

$$= 2.03 - j13.97 = |\, 14.12 \,| \text{ amp}$$

$$\cos \theta_0 = \frac{0.008}{0.0555} = 0.144 \qquad \text{power factor} = 14.4 \text{ per cent}$$

$$\bar{Z}_{01} = 0.25 + 0.5 + 0.5\left(\frac{1 - 0.05}{0.05}\right) + j(0.7 + 0.7)$$

$$= 10.25 + j1.4$$

$$\bar{Y}_{01} = 0.0958 - j0.0131$$

$$\bar{Y}_1 = \bar{Y}_{01} + \bar{Y}_0 = 0.1038 - j0.0681 = |\,0.1241\,| \text{ mho}$$

$$\cos\theta_1 = \frac{0.1038}{0.1241} = 0.836 \qquad \text{power factor} = 83.6 \text{ per cent}$$

$$\bar{I}_1 = (254 + j0)(0.1038 - j0.0681)$$

$$= 26.37 - j17.30 = |\,31.5\,| \text{ amp}$$

$$\text{Speed} = 1200(1 - 0.05)$$

$$= 1140 \text{ rpm}$$

11. Circle Diagram of the Induction Motor. The circle diagram of the induction motor is useful in predicting the motor characteristics from test data. This diagram is, essentially, a stator-current diagram and, when it is used for the determination of motor characteristics, the intercepts may be used without reference to current values except when considering torque, line current, and power output. For these a scale unit will be necessary to convert the intercepts to proper values.

With few exceptions, the intercepts used are the "in-phase" (or power) components of currents. This is true for determining all characteristics except the line current and power factor which depend upon the actual current in the diagram.

In the preceding article, the induction motor has been studied from its equivalent circuit; Fig. 8–8*b* shows the modified equivalent circuit and Fig. 9–8*b* the vector diagram of such a machine. An analysis of the circuit shows that the constants (when referred to the stator) form an impedance which is placed across a constant voltage source. When the load is varied, both the resistance drop and reactance drop change in value; the first changes because of the addition of power requirements to the electrical system and the second changes because of the slip. Under every condition of load the value of IZ will be equal to the terminal voltage. As shown by Fig. 10–8, the vector sum of IR and IX will be equal to IZ, the terminal voltage. With IR and IX at right angles the intersection of IR and IX will always fall on the arc of a semicircle, because they form a right angle where they meet. The value of the current is inversely proportional to the impedance Z and is in phase with IR. For this reason it will, likewise, trace a semicircle and, when the exciting current (a constant) is added to the equivalent rotor current value, the resultant follows a circular path. Because the current locus is a circle, the prediction of the motor operating performance depends upon the determination of the no-load current and its power factor establishing one point on the circumference of the semicircle and also upon the determination of an additional point on the arc for the construction of the circle.

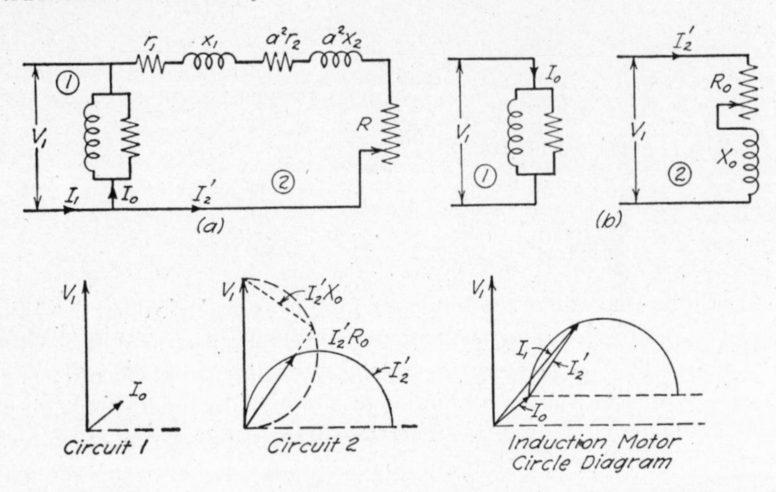

Fig. 10–8. The locus of currents for an induction motor is a circle; (*b*) shows the two parallel branches of (*a*).

12. Test Data Necessary for Constructing the Motor Circle Diagram. It is necessary first to determine two points on the arc of the motor current locus to construct the semicircle. These data are obtained from the two characteristic tests of electrical equipment used for predictions: namely, the open-circuit and short-circuit test. The latter test for the induction motor is made with the rotor of the machine locked in position and using only a fraction of the rated voltage.

The no-load test of the induction motor is made by operating the machine at no load, with the rotor shorted (if a wound rotor), and measuring the input into the stator. The values of power, current, and voltage will locate and establish the magnitude of the no-load current, I_0.

In the blocked rotor test, the rotor is held so that it cannot turn, and readings similar to those taken in the no-load test are obtained. The impressed voltage must be reduced to a value that will limit the current to a safe value for the machine and, also, the current must be extrapolated for rated voltage. Readings are taken for voltage, current, and power.

It is necessary to obtain additional data for the determination of the division of the copper losses between the rotor and the stator. This additional information is the resistance between the stator terminals. If it is desirable to correct the ohmic resistance to effective resistance, the factor for the characteristic type machine should be known, but the error involved in using the ohmic resistance will not seriously influence the results in calculating the output or the torque. This will be evident when the intercepts involved on the completed diagram are considered. All data must be reduced to values per phase and the machine may be considered either delta- or wye-connected when reduced to a single phase.

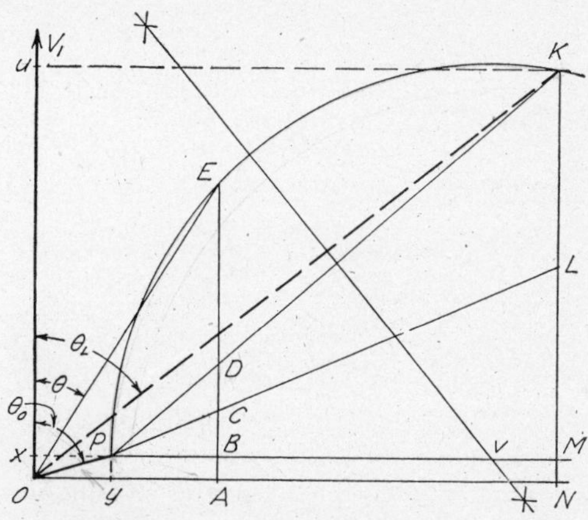

FIG. 11–8. The circle diagram for a polyphase induction motor.

13. Construction of the Circle Diagram. The circle diagram is constructed with reference to the phase voltage and, since the reference is of minor importance in this diagram, the normal procedure of diagram construction is to draw V_1, the reference, vertically. This reference voltage is shown on Fig. 11–8 as OV_1.

If a wye connection is assumed, from the no-load data, which will be the power W_0, the current I_0, and the terminal voltage V, the following information may be obtained:

$$\cos \theta_0 = \frac{W_0}{\sqrt{3}VI_0} \quad \text{(line values)}$$

and, after the value for $\cos \theta_0$ is determined, the $\sin \theta_0$ may be ascer tained. By construction, the value of

$I_0 \cos \theta_0$ is drawn parallel to OV_1 (yP)

$I_0 \sin \theta_0$ is drawn at 90° to OV_1 (xP)

The vector OP is the no-load stator current per phase in proper phase relationship with the terminal voltage.

From the short-circuit test, by a similar process, may be constructed the current vector OK, which is the phase current that would be taken by the stator if rated voltage were applied to the stator terminals, with the rotor locked. Since direct measurement is impossible, the value must be obtained from a reduced voltage test by increasing the values in the proper proportion (in ratio of voltages). Only the current (not the power factor) would be changed by reducing voltage if the motor is not operating at high flux density. As in the determination of the no-load power factor, the locked rotor power factor will be

$$\cos \theta_L = \frac{W_L}{\sqrt{3} V_L I_L} \quad \text{(line values)}$$

When the value of $\sin \theta_L$ has been determined, the current is calculated by increasing the test current in proportion to the voltage

$$I_{OK} = I_L \times \frac{V}{V_L}$$

and correctly plotting the values I_{UK}, which is $I_{OK} \sin \theta_L$, and I_{NK}, which is $I_{OK} \cos \theta_L$. The values of current are located by the coordinates, rather than by value and angle, because of the difficulty of laying out angles accurately. The current I_{OP}, the exciting current I_0, with the terminal voltage V_1 or reference vector, are the only permanent vectors on the diagram when determining the motor characteristics. All other values of current will change with a change of load.

The points K and P represent two points on the arc of the current semicircle. The perpendicular bisector of a line drawn from K to P will lie on a diameter of the semicircle. The other diameter for determining the center is a line through P perpendicular to the reference V_1. The smallest possible power component of current will be that at no load. With point v as a center, the arc PEK is drawn.

The resistance between line terminals is used in determining the proportions of the intercepts KL and LM. The intercept KN is the power component of current when the rotor is locked and is, therefore, a measure of all the power lost in the motor, since no power leaves by the shaft when the rotor is locked. The power is consumed by the fixed losses (a combination of core and no-load copper, windage, and friction losses) and the locked-current copper losses in the windings of the stator and rotor. Frequently, the point L is located midway between K and M and, as previously stated, a division of this type does not greatly influence the important characteristics but simplifies the solution. If it is desirable to locate the point L by the division of the copper losses (I^2R losses), these losses in the stator may be interpreted as a power component and measured as the intercept LM, because (regardless of whether the machine is considered delta- or wye-wound) the total stator loss will be equal to

$$\text{Watts stator copper} = \tfrac{3}{2} I^2 R_t \quad \text{(line current)}\dagger$$

where the current in the stator will be the value of current determined for I_{OK}. This value for power consumed must now be converted to an energy intercept ($I \cos \theta$), which will be

$$I_{LM} = \frac{\text{Watts stator copper loss}}{\sqrt{3}V} \quad (V \text{ rated voltage})$$

The drawing of the line LP completes the construction of the circle diagram from the test data taken for the induction motor and proportions the copper loss between the stator and rotor.

14. Induction Motor Characteristics Predicted from the Circle Diagram. Although results for other than full-load rating for the machine may be obtained, they are not used, since the intercepts will be very small unless the diagram is constructed unusually large. The usual procedure is to determine the characteristic values at rated load.

If a line AE is drawn parallel to OV_1, it will intercept the diagram construction at points so located that

DE represents the power component of current of the output
CD the power component of current of rotor copper losses
BC the power component of current of stator copper losses
AB the power component of current of the fixed losses, and
AE the power component of current of the input

The line DE may be constructed at any load and the length of DE is determined from the power component of output by

$$I_{DE} = \frac{\text{horsepower} \times 746}{\sqrt{3}V} \quad \text{(total horsepower)}$$

when the motor is assumed to be wye-connected, as previously discussed. This intercept, I_{DE}, may be located at two points between arc PEK and the line PK for some horsepower output, but one intercept would be beyond the operating range and is of no interest except in special machines.

† This was explained on page 153.

Once the intercepts have been evaluated (in inches, where ratios are taken, would be satisfactory), the characteristics may be determined as follows.

$$I_{OE} \times \text{scale} = \text{the line current (wye-connected)}$$

$$\frac{I_{AE}}{I_{OE}} \times 100 = \text{the power factor}$$

$$\frac{I_{CD}}{I_{CE}} \times 100 = \text{the slip in percentage}$$

$$\frac{I_{DE}}{I_{AE}} \times 100 = \text{efficiency in percentage}$$

$$\text{Rotor speed} = \frac{120f}{P}(1 - s)$$

where f is the frequency and s is the slip expressed as a decimal.

$$\text{Torque} = \frac{7.04nI_{CE}V_1}{\text{synchronous speed}}$$

which is not per phase but for the machine, with n the number of phases and V_1 the phase voltage.

The circle diagram has been discussed for the three-phase machine only, but the same relationships could be applied to any polyphase machine and the only changes would be in the coefficients.

By the proper choice of tangents to the arc of the semicircle, it is possible to find the maximum power factor, the torque, and the maximum power input and output (see advanced electrical engineering text and handbooks).

Example d. By means of a circle diagram, determine the characteristics at full load for a 50-hp, 3-phase, 440-volt, 60-cycle, 8-pole, 875-rpm, squirrel cage induction motor if the following test data are taken.

	W	I	V
No-load test	1140	16	440
Locked rotor test	6920	87.2	88
Terminal resistance		0.314 ohm	

(*Note.* In general, this type of motor has an efficiency of 88 per cent, a power factor of 90 per cent, and a line current of 63 amp. The results may be checked against these values.)

Assume the motor to be wye-connected and all notation referred to Fig. 11–8.

$$(Ox)\ I_0 \cos \theta_0 = \frac{1140}{\sqrt{3} \times 440} = 1.496 \text{ amp in-phase current at no load}$$

$$(Oy)\ I_0 \sin \theta_0 = \sqrt{16^2 - 1.5^2} = 15.88 \text{ amp magnetizing current}$$

$$W_L = 6920 \times [\tfrac{440}{88}]^2 = 173{,}200 \text{ watts}$$

$$I_L = 87.2 \times \tfrac{440}{88} = 436 \text{ amp}$$

$$(KN)\ I_L \cos \theta_L = \frac{173{,}200}{\sqrt{3} \times 440} = 227 \text{ amp in-phase current at locked rotor}$$

$$(ON)\ I_L \sin \theta_L = \sqrt{436^2 - 227^2} = 372.2 \text{ amp quadrature current at locked rotor}$$

In-phase current of stator copper losses:

$$\tfrac{3}{2}(436)^2 \times 0.314 = \sqrt{3} \times 440 \times I \cos \theta$$

$$(ML)\ I \cos \theta = \frac{3(436)^2 \times 0.314}{2 \times \sqrt{3} \times 440} = 117.48 \text{ amp}$$

Full-load output:

$$(DE)\ I \cos \theta = \frac{50 \times 746}{\sqrt{3} \times 440} = 48.9 \text{ amp}$$

From the foregoing evaluations, the circle diagram was constructed, and the following measurements were obtained for a scale of 20 amp per in.

$AB = 0.07$ in.
$BC = 0.12$ in.
$CD = 0.16$ in.
$DE = 2.45$ in. 48.9 amp
$OE = 3.02$ in. 60.4 amp
$AE = 2.80$ in.
$CE = 2.61$ in. 52.4 amp

Machine characteristics:

$$I_L = 3.02 \times 20 = 60.4 \text{ amp}$$

$$\text{Power factor} = \frac{2.80}{3.02} \times 100 = 92 \text{ per cent}$$

$$\text{Slip} = \frac{0.16}{2.61} \times 100 = 6.1 \text{ per cent}$$

$$\text{Efficiency} = \frac{2.45}{2.80} \times 100 = 88 \text{ per cent}$$

$$\text{Rotor speed} = \frac{120 \times 60}{8} \times (1 - 0.06) = 845 \text{ rpm}$$

$$\text{Output} = P = \frac{\sqrt{3} \times 440 \times (2.45 \times 20)}{746} = 50 \text{ hp}$$

$$\text{Torque} = \frac{7.04 \times \sqrt{3}(2.62 \times 20)440}{900} = 312 \text{ lb-ft}$$

THE SYNCHRONOUS MOTOR

The application of synchronous motors differs from that of induction motors because of their characteristics. The induction motor is for general application whereas the synchronous motor is for very specific application. The speed of the induction motor is asynchronous with respect to the generating source whereas the synchronous motor will have an average constant speed; but in both instances the speed is a function of the system frequency and the number of poles on the machine.

The major field of application for the synchronous motor is one of either power-factor correction or voltage regulation. A mechanical load, if present on the shaft, must be fairly constant and not varying. When equipped with large flywheels, a synchronous motor is satisfactory for driving air compressors and rock crushers. The slow speed machines are used for driving conveyors. The synchronous motor is uneconomical except in the larger sizes and it lacks both the ruggedness and simplicity of the induction motor. The recent application of the single-phase synchronous motor as a clock motor has extended the use of synchronous motors considerably.

The fundamental principles of synchronous motor operation and loading have been discussed in Chapter 5 and, here, the machine characteristics while functioning under operating conditions and its specific characteristics will be considered.

15. The Equivalent Circuit and Vector Diagram of the Synchronous Motor. Figure 12–8 shows the equivalent circuit and vector diagram of the synchronous motor. Since the counterelectromotive force of the

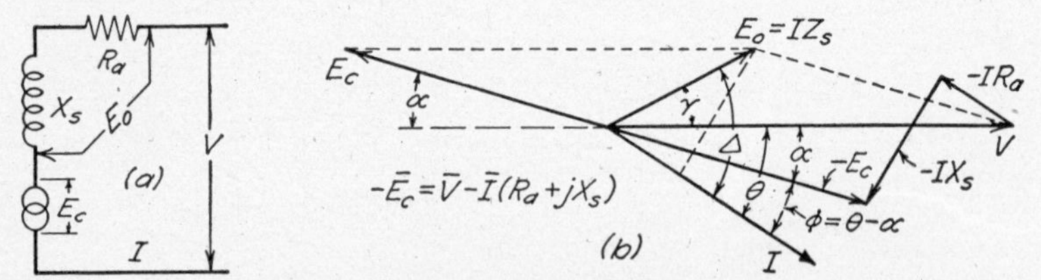

FIG. 12–8. The equivalent circuit and vector diagram for a synchronous motor; line to neutral for a polyphase motor.

armature is a generated electromotive force, the circuit is similar to that of the alternator. The impedance of the machine is the synchronous impedance, as it is in the alternator, wherein the effect of armature reaction is replaced by an equivalent reactance component added to the leakage reactance voltage in the construction of the vector diagram.

This vector diagram differs from the generator diagram in that there are two opposite voltages present, the applied voltage and the generated voltage, which in the ideal machine would be equal and 180° out of time phase at no load. The voltages will be displaced in the actual machine by a small angle α from 180°, a normal excitation being assumed. This displacement results in a voltage, $\bar{E}_0 = \bar{E}_c + \bar{V}$, and a current, I, which is the demand upon the source for no-load operation. As shown in Chapter 5, the angle α increases with loading, causing the resultant voltage, E_0, to increase and, thereby, allowing more current to flow through the impedance of the machine. This results in additional current for producing torque for the shaft load. This process may be continued until the additional current ceases to increase the energy component of current. When this occurs, the machine falls out of step and stops.

A study of the vector diagram of the synchronous motor will show the following relationships to be true: the component of the applied voltage per phase, which counteracts the counterelectromotive force, is equal to

$$-\bar{E}_c = \bar{V} - \bar{I}(R_a + jX_s)$$

and the power demand from the system per phase is

$$P = VI \cos \theta$$

where V and I are the phase voltage and current, respectively. Other relationships are

$$\bar{E}_0 = \bar{I}\bar{Z}_s$$

the internal power developed per phase

$$P_1 = -E_cI \cos (\theta \pm \alpha)$$

and the power input is less by the amount of friction and windage and the copper losses per phase

$$E_0I \cos \Delta = E_0I \cos (\gamma \pm \theta) = I^2R_a$$

Example e. Determine the resultant current when a three-phase, 2500-kva, 2300-volt synchronous motor with $R_a = 1.24$ per cent and $X_s = 24.9$ per cent is operating idle at 20 per cent overexcitation. The no-load losses are to be neglected. Assume wye connection and E_c out of phase with V by 180°.

$$I_L = \frac{2500 \times 1000}{\sqrt{3} \times 2300} = 627.57 \text{ amp}$$

$$V_p = 2300 \div \sqrt{3} = 1327.94 \text{ volts}$$

$$X_s = \frac{0.249 \times 1327.94}{627.57} = 0.5269 \text{ ohm}$$

$$\bar{E}_0 = (\bar{V} + \bar{E}_c) = (1327.94 + j0) + (-1327.94 + j0) \times 1.2$$

$$= -265.58 + j0$$

$$\bar{I} = \frac{\bar{E}_0}{X_s} = -\frac{265.58 + j0}{0 + j0.5269} \quad (R \text{ neglected})$$

$$\bar{I} = 0 + j504$$

$$I = 504 \text{ amp}$$

Example f. The machine in Example *e* has normal excitation, and the shaft load causes the induced electromotive force to fall back 8°. Determine the angles α, Δ, γ, and θ, and also the power delivered (including the friction and windage), the power required, and the copper losses, not neglecting the no-load losses.

$$\cos 8^\circ = 0.9903 \qquad \sin 8^\circ = 0.1392$$

$$\bar{E}_c = -(0.9903 \times 1327.94) + j(0.1392 \times 1327.94)$$

$$= -1315.06 + j184.85$$

$$\bar{V} = 1327.94 + j0$$

$$\bar{E}_0 = \bar{E}_c + \bar{V} = 12.88 + j184.85$$

$$\bar{I} = \frac{12.88 + j184.85}{0.02624 + j0.5269} = 351.18 - j6.96$$

Angle (Fig. 12–8*b*)		Sin	Cos	
α	8°	0.1392	0.9903	$V = 1327.94$ volts
γ	86.1°	0.9976	0.0695	$E_0 = 185.30$ volts
Δ	87.2°	0.9988	0.0488	$E_c = 1327.94$ volts
θ	1.1°	0.0198	0.9998	$I = 351.25$ amp

$$P_{cu} = \frac{3 \times 185.3 \times 351.25 \times 0.0488}{1000} = 9.5 \text{ kw} \quad \text{(copper losses)}$$

$$P = \frac{\sqrt{3} \times 2300 \times 351.25 \times 0.9998}{1000} = 1399 \text{ kw} \quad \text{(input)}$$

$$P_{del} = \frac{3 \times 1327.94 \times 351.25 \times \cos(\theta \pm \alpha)}{1000} = 1389 \text{ kw} \quad \text{(delivered)}$$

16. The Synchronous Motor under Constant Load with Changing Excitation. If a specific load is applied to the shaft of the synchronous motor, the power input to the motor remains constant, neglecting the small change in the copper losses regardless of the change in field excitation. There will be no change in the speed of the machine since this is only possible by a change of poles or system frequency. The resultant effect of field change upon E_c with constant input is shown in Fig. 13–8, where the resultant current locus is a straight line for constant power input.

If the excitation is changed as shown in Fig. 13–8, the power factor of the current supplied will change in value, while the power input remains constant. With the armature current change, there will be a change in the I^2R losses but, if this small change is neglected, the input current will follow a straight line as shown in the figure.

This property of the machine, requiring a power-factor change with change in excitation, is one of the useful features of the synchronous motor. By utilizing this feature, it is possible to make the machine function in the system as if it were an inductive or capacitive reactance. If it is desired, the machine may be overexcited to produce a leading power factor and, when the motor is placed in parallel with an inductive load, it will correct the system power factor by neutralizing all or part of the reactive component of the current taken by the inductive load. The reverse is true when the machine is underexcited, for then the synchronous motor has a lagging power factor and is capable of correcting for a capacitive current.

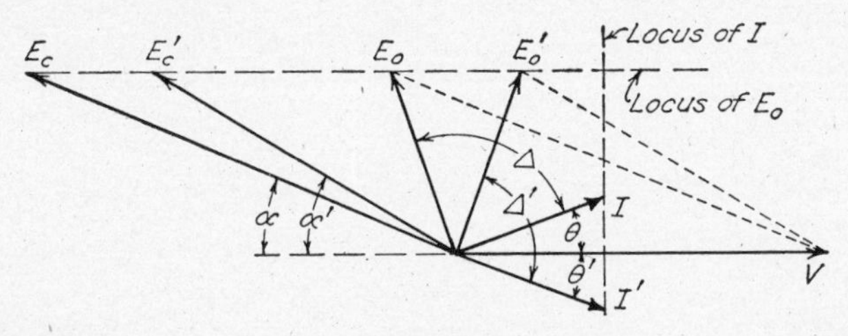

FIG. 13–8. The locus diagram for a synchronous motor with constant load and variable excitation.

Where a manufacturing establishment depends upon induction motors for power drives, because they are more adaptable, light load conditions will result in very poor power factors. By proper selection of a synchronous motor and utilization of its capacity effect, when overexcited, it is possible to make a saving on the power bill through power-factor correction. Frequently it is possible to drive some types of plant loads with this same motor with even a greater increase of economy.

The introduction (by use of a synchronous motor) of an inductive reactance load upon the transmission line is used in the power-generating plants and distribution networks to counteract the line capacity for voltage regulation.

17. The Synchronous Motor as a "Synchronous Condenser." If the synchronous motor is operated without load on its shaft and is overexcited, the machine will act as a condenser on the system. A machine for this type of application may be large because of the large conductors needed to handle the current necessary to correct the power factor, but it need not be designed for large mechanical stresses. The shaft, since it does not deliver power, need act only as a support for the rotating member. Figure 14–8 shows a circuit diagram for the connection of a synchronous machine to a system and the resultant vector diagram of the system when the synchronous machine has been excited to change the power factor.

In the vector diagram, Fig. 14–8*b*, it is assumed that the synchronous machine is ideal (losses neglected) and the current taken under these conditions leads the applied voltage by an angle of 90°. This assumption is erroneous, because the machine has an internal resistance and there are friction, windage, and iron losses which must be counteracted. However, for practical purposes, the error is not appreciable (less than 5 per cent in large machines).

The reactive load has a lagging reactive component of current (see Fig. 14–8) equivalent to *oc* and, at the same time, the synchronous motor

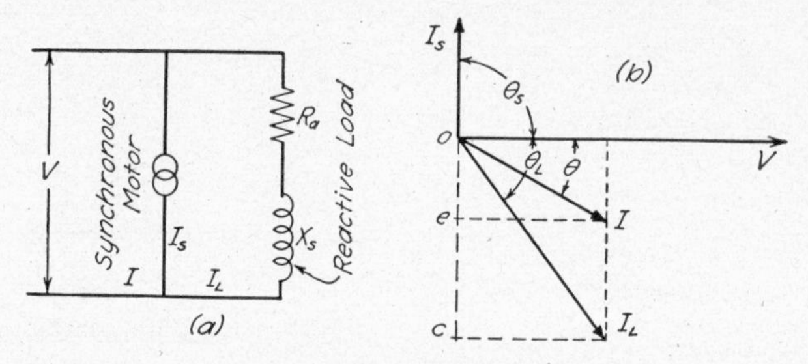

FIG. 14–8. The use of a synchronous machine as a "synchronous condenser" for power-factor correction.

supplies, as the result of overexcitation, a leading reactive component I_s opposite to that of the load. The resultant will be *oe*, which is the reactive component of the line current. It is seldom economical to invest capital for an industrial plant correction to unity power factor.

Example g. A 2000-kva, 2300-volt load has a 0.6 power factor lagging. A synchronous condenser of what size will correct the power factor to 0.8 lagging? Refer to Fig. 14–8*b*.

$$(oc) \quad 2000 \times \sin \theta_L = 1600 \text{ kvars}$$

$$2000 \times \cos \theta_L = 1200 \text{ kw}$$

$$(oe) \quad 1200 \times \tan \theta = 900 \text{ kvars}$$

$$(oc - oe = od) \quad 1600 - 900 = 700 \text{ kva motor rating}$$

POWER-FACTOR CORRECTION BY A LOADED SYNCHRONOUS MOTOR

The correction of power factor alone would not be the usual condition encountered in the smaller industrial establishments. Here the problem is one of deciding between the application of a synchronous motor with its power-factor correction features and the purchase of an additional induction motor. In problems of this type, it is necessary to select a synchronous motor to supply the desired shaft load and, at the same time, have enough electrical rating available in the windings to operate successfully for power-factor correction. Under these conditions, the synchronous motor demands not only a leading component of current but also a power component of current as well. Figure 15–8 shows the schematic circuit and vector diagram of a synchronous motor having a shaft load and correcting the power factor of an inductive system.

In Fig. 15–8, the final current is composed of two energy components, the load *oe* and the synchronous motor load *od*, whose sum makes the

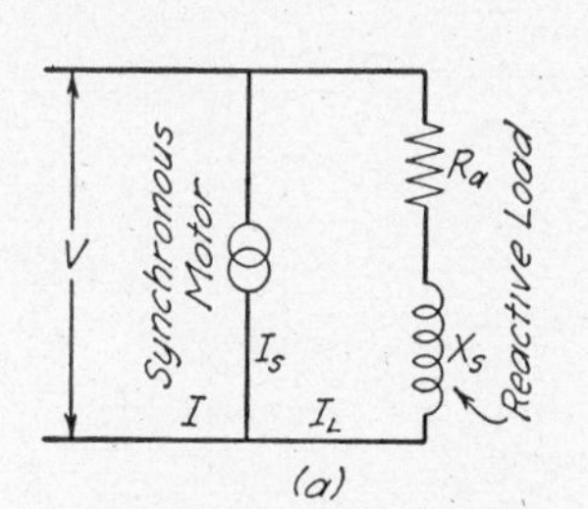

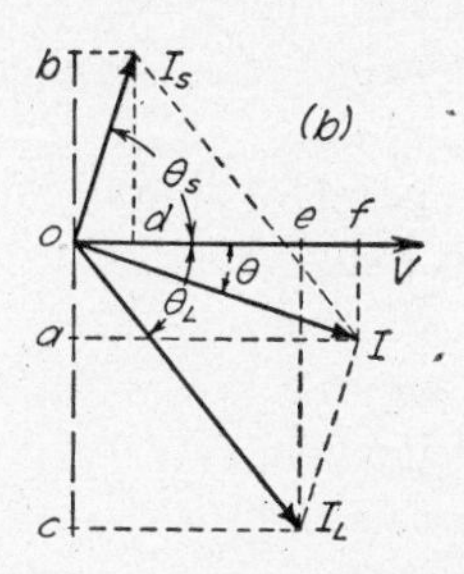

Fig. 15–8. Power-factor correction by the use of a synchronous motor carrying a shaft load.

system energy component *of*. For the reactive components, the load *oc* is inductive and the synchronous motor *ob* is capacitive; the difference between *oc* and *ob* is *oa*, the reactive component of the system. The power factor of the synchronous motor is $\cos \theta_s$, the power factor of the load is $\cos \theta_L$, and the system power factor is $\cos \theta$. The determination of the rating of a synchronous motor for a specific application is shown by a demonstration problem (see Example *h*).

These diagrams in the examples are not considered from the viewpoint of current diagrams, which are the true diagrams, but the vectors are considered in kilowatts and kilovolt-amperes. Neither of these is a vector quantity, but they are symbolic and will be proportional to the currents when the voltage is constant, and calculations using the active, reactive, and apparent power values for the vectors tend to simplify the work. These calculations are based on the electrical input, not the shaft output.

Example h. A 2000-kva, 2300-volt load has a 0.6 lagging power factor. A synchronous motor is to be installed which corrects the power factor to 0.8 lagging and delivers the electrical equivalent of 100 kw load to the shaft. Neglecting the motor losses, determine the rating of the synchronous motor.

Refer to Fig. 15–8*b*.

$$\begin{aligned}
&(oe) \quad 2000 \times \cos \theta_L = 1200 \text{ kw} \\
&(od) \quad \text{given as} \quad 100 \text{ kw} \\
&(of) \quad 1200 + 100 = 1300 \text{ kw} \\
&(oc) \quad 2000 \times \sin \theta_L = 1600 \text{ kvars} \\
&(oa) \quad 1300 \times \tan \theta = 975 \text{ kvars} \\
&(ob) \quad 1600 - 975 = 625 \text{ kvars}
\end{aligned}$$

$$\text{Motor} = \sqrt{625^2 + 100^2} = 633 \text{ kva}$$

18. Capacitors. In recent years condensers have been developed that are small in size, relative to kilovolt-ampere capacity, and have losses equal to about one-fifth those of a transformer having the same rating. The capacitors are used in distribution systems to reduce the current between the point of supply and the capacitor, to reduce the voltage drop, and to reduce the losses in the circuit and equipment which are caused through lowering the current. Using capacitors on a distribution system increases its power capacity, thereby releasing line and transformer capacity of greater value than the cost of additional or larger circuits. In this respect the capacitor acts in the same manner as the synchronous motor used as a "synchronous reactor."

Since these capacities are manufactured in small units, they can be adapted to low power-factor equipment and can be used to correct the power factor of manufacturing plants. The determination of the capacitor kilovolt-ampere capacity for power-factor correction is similar to the "synchronous condenser" problem (Example *g*). The vector diagram is shown in Fig. 14–8.

19. The Synchronous Motor as a "Synchronous Reactor." By adjusting the excitation of a synchronous motor, it is possible to regulate the voltage on a transmission line at any point between the synchronous motor and the source. When the line power factor is low and lagging and the load is heavy, the synchronous motor is overexcited to increase the voltage at the load and, when the load is light and the power factor leading, the motor is underexcited to prevent the voltage from increasing to abnormal values.

Figure 16–8 shows the effect the addition of synchronous motor current of the proper power factor has on the requirements of sending end voltage. It is usual to hold the sending end voltage constant and regulate the receiving end voltage. The solution and vector diagram for this arrangement is much more complicated. If the load is essentially capacitive as, for instance, in a lightly loaded transmission line, the correction must be for the removal of the leading reactive component. The reverse is true when the line is heavily loaded and the effect is that produced by inductance. This control of voltage permits the line to be used at its maximum power capacity and reduces the fluctuation of voltage at the load.

The use of synchronous reactors permits steady voltages at intermediate points on the line and, with steady line voltages, lightning protection can be adjusted closely. The full power capacity of the lines may be utilized, thereby giving better system control and operation.

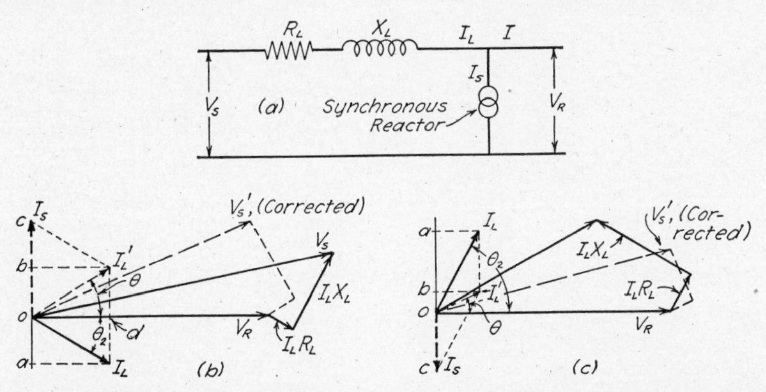

FIG. 16–8. The use of a synchronous motor as a "synchronous reactor" for line voltage regulation: (*a*) a circuit diagram; (*b* and *c*) vector diagrams of the circuit.

Example i. A generating station supplies 5000-kva, 33,000-volt, 0.6 power factor lagging load through a line with an inductive reactance of 37 ohms and a resistance of 14 ohms per conductor. What would be the capacity of the synchronous motor installed to keep the voltage the same value at both ends as the load varies from no load to full load?

Refer to Fig. 16–8*b*.

$$I_L = \frac{5000 \times 1000}{\sqrt{3} \times 33{,}000} = 87.5 \text{ amp}$$

$$V_s' = V_R = \frac{33{,}000}{\sqrt{3}} = 19{,}053 \text{ volts}$$

$$I_L \cos \theta_2 = 87.5 \times 0.6 = 52.5 \text{ amp}$$

$$I_L' \cos \theta = 52.49 \text{ amp}$$

$$V_s' = \sqrt{(V_R + I_L' R_L \cos \theta - I_L' X_L \sin \theta)^2 + (I_L' X_L \cos \theta + I_L' R_L \sin \theta)^2}$$

$$V_s' = \sqrt{(19{,}053 + 734.86 - 37 I_L' \sin \theta)^2 + (1942.13 + 14 I_L' \sin \theta)^2}$$

$$(ob) \quad I_L' \sin \theta = 23.53 \text{ amp}$$

$$(oa) \quad I_L \sin \theta_2 = 87.5 \times 0.8 = 70.0 \text{ amp}$$

$$(oc = ob + oa) \quad I_s = 23.53 + 69.98 = 93.51 \text{ amp}$$

Rating of the synchronous reactor:

$$\frac{3 \times 93.51 \times 19{,}053}{1000} = 5345 \text{ kva}$$

20. The Synchronous Motor under Constant Excitation and Changing Load. It is possible to set the synchronous motor at one excitation and, as the load changes, there will be a change in both the power factor and the current demand on the system. This would be the normal condition when the load on the shaft of the synchronous motor fluctuated and there was no provision made for the adjustment of the excitation by either automatic devices or an attendant. For the synchronous motor this type of load is not recommended, for it is better to have the machine operate under fixed shaft loads.

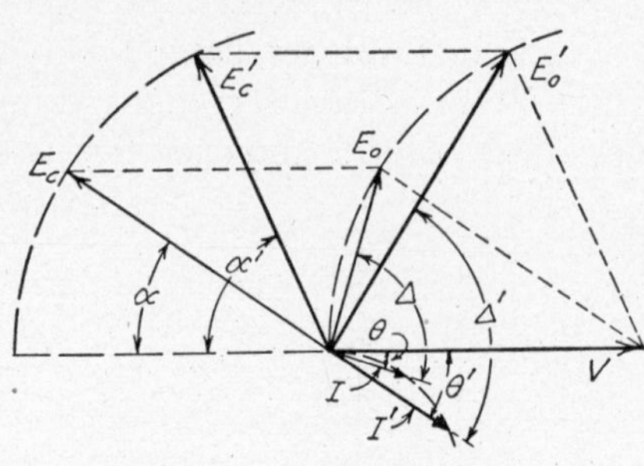

FIG. 17–8. Current and resultant voltage loci for a synchronous motor with variable load and constant excitation.

Figure 17–8 shows loci of changes that take place in the synchronous motor as the input load changes, the excitation being constant.

21. The Circle Diagram of the Synchronous Motor. As stated before, the synchronous motor circle diagram is not of the same value as the induction motor circle diagram, but it does permit quick qualitative analysis of the relationships between power factor, field excitation, and the power output. The limiting values for the foregoing quantities are easily determined from a complete diagram. Figure 18–8 shows the Blondel diagram (circle diagram) of the synchronous motor. The radii of the power circles are obtained from the expression

$$\text{Radius of output power circle} = \frac{Z_s}{R_a}\sqrt{\frac{V^2}{4} - PR_a}\ \ddagger$$

where P is the power output (per phase) in watts, Z_s is the synchronous impedance per phase in ohms, R_a is the effective armature resistance per phase in ohms, and V is the applied voltage per phase in volts.

In drawing the diagram with the phase voltage PR, construct the zero output power circle by locating the center of the circle at O, with the radius given above; with this as a center, all other power curves may be drawn. The sum of the voltage vectors constructed on the phase voltage line PR and intersecting on a constant power line (as at S) will be the vector sum of the impedance drop of the armature and the counterelectromotive force, which are PS and SR, respectively. The angle Δ depends upon the ratio of R_a to Z_s and represents the angular displacement between the phase current and the resultant voltage across

‡ Developed *loc. cit.*, page 175.

the armature impedance equal to E_o (PS). The angular displacement between the current and the resultant voltage in any machine will be the angle Δ.

With R as a center, a series of concentric circles may be drawn, each of which will represent constant excitation. This composite diagram represents the power-factor and load changes with the additional information for determining the limiting conditions. In the diagram given, the values for actual machines have been drawn out of proportion to

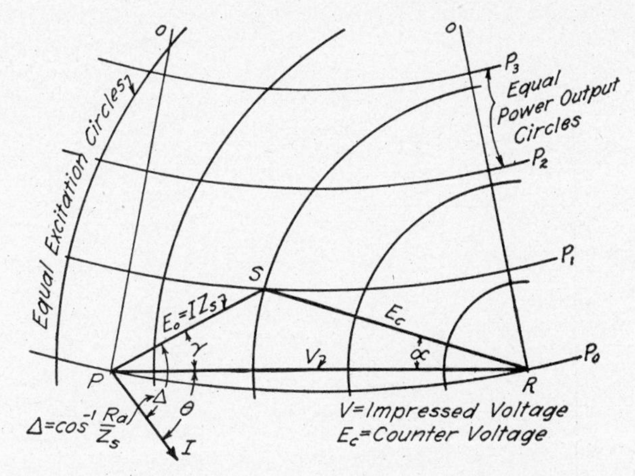

FIG. 18–8. Circle diagram (per phase) of a synchronous motor.

demonstrate the method. In fact, the value for the angle Δ is so near 90° that, in the actual diagram, OP and OR approach parallel lines, each of which is at 90° to the voltage line PR.

As previously stated, the circle diagram of the synchronous motor has qualitative rather than quantitative value. The diagram summarizes the material given in the foregoing articles. A study of the circle diagram of the synchronous motor will show

1. That when S falls to the left of OP the power factor is leading.
2. That when S falls to the right of OP the power factor is lagging.
3. That when S falls on OP the power factor is unity.
4. That the maximum power which can be delivered at constant excitation will occur when E_c lies along OR.
5. That, for a given excitation, the power factor depends upon the load.
6. That the greatest power output occurs when PS equals PO, which in the normal machine is beyond the capacity of the windings.
7. That the value PS decreases for smaller output.
8. That when PS is zero there is no demand on the system.
9. That power circles with radii greater than OP are for generation, because PS would be negative and the output would be negative.

10. That for unity or leading power factor there are definite excitation limits.
11. That with current vectors proportional to the resultant voltage E_o the current vectors may be made proportional to PS and will make an angle with PS whose cosine is R_a/Z_s for the machine.

22. V-Curves. In actual operation of the synchronous motor for power-factor correction, the V-curves are the most useful data available. These curves are taken by determining the line current required with power-factor change under constant load condition by varying excitation. Constant load can be measured by reading the power input to

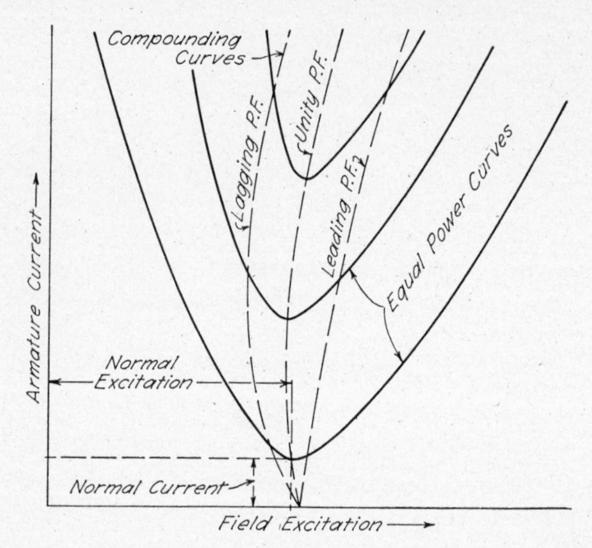

FIG. 19–8. V-curves and compounding curves for the synchronous motor.

the motor, which is easier than regulating the shaft output, by prony brake, or dynamometer measurements. If curves are taken at several loads with the corresponding power factors, and the information is plotted as shown on Fig. 19–8 (that is, line current plotted against the field current), the curves are called the V-curves of the synchronous motor.

If the observed power factor is plotted on this same curve sheet, the resultant curves of equal power factor are called the *compounding curves*. The power-factor curves to the left of unity power factor are for lagging conditions and those to the right are for leading conditions.

The excitation which gives unity power factor likewise gives the lowest required current. This excitation is called the normal excitation and the load current at unity power factor is called the normal current of the machine.

These curves, for armature current, as in all other three-phase machines, must be discussions on values per phase, assuming the machine to be either wye- or delta-connected.

23. Operation of Synchronous Motors. One of the early objections to the synchronous motor was the difficulty in starting it under load. As explained under motor theory, it is necessary to bring this type of motor to approximately synchronous speed so that the direct current will lock it into step before it will operate as a synchronous motor. When this had to be accomplished by an outside prime mover, either by the use of the exciter as a motor or by mechanical means, the application of the motor was quite limited.

Later, by the addition of a short-circuited winding on the field poles similar to a squirrel cage rotor, the machine could be started as a polyphase induction motor and, if operated with little or no load under starting conditions, the machine could be pulled into step by exciting the d-c field by means of an outside source of direct current or an exciter mounted on the machine shaft. In the first instance it was necessary to have the machine operated by an experienced individual familiar with the process of synchronizing, which will be discussed under parallel operation, whereas, by the introduction of the induction motor starting principle (Amortisseur winding), the machine was placed on the same basis as the ordinary induction motor, which could be operated by the most inexperienced person.

The difficulty of the first self-starting synchronous motor was the lack of starting torque. The latest designs, by proper control of the induction-motor starting torque characteristics, and even by the use of external resistance in the starting winding, allow starting torques equivalent to 125 to 150 per cent of full-load torque, with reasonable starting current. Special provisions are made to isolate the field coils from each other while the high voltages caused by the slip at starting are present. These would cause high induced voltages in the field windings. The induced voltages are reduced as the slip decreases and near synchronous speed the field coils may be reconnected for application of the direct current prior to the synchronizing of the machine.

24. The Brush-Shifting Motor. The brush-shifting motor is a three-phase motor, with speed control possibilities, which operates upon a counterelectromotive force type of control. The primary winding is located on the wound rotor whereas the secondary winding is on the stator. Figure 20–8 shows the arrangement of the windings, the commutator, the brushes, and also the auxiliary winding, which is in the top of the slots on the rotor. The auxiliary winding is connected to the commutator which has two sets of brushes making contact with it, each set of which is rigidly fastened to a rocker arm. These two rocker arms may be moved in relationship to each other. When the two sets of brushes are on the same commutator bars, the machine has the characteristics of an induction motor but, when the brushes are so placed that they are separated relative to each other, addition or subtraction of voltage takes place. The portion of the revolving auxiliary winding which lies between two brushes of a pair is cut by the air-gap flux at slip speed, and an induced electromotive force is produced in the winding which adds or subtracts with respect to the voltage in the secondary winding, increasing or decreasing the speed, respectively.

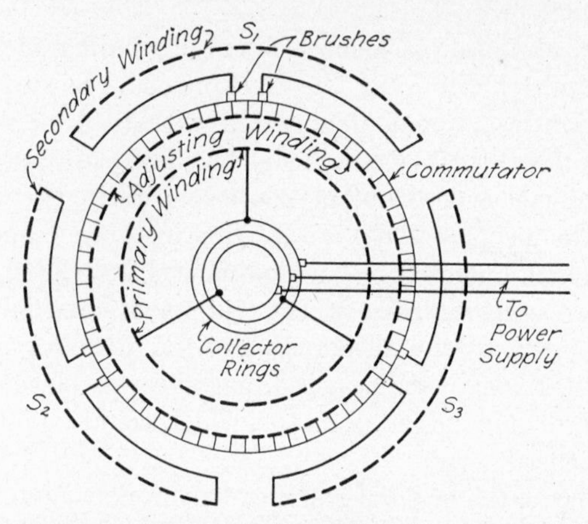

FIG. 20–8. Schematic diagram of the windings for a brush-shifting motor.

This type of machine may have a wide range of speed (generally 3 to 1 or 4 to 1) and, within this range, it may be adjusted for any speed. At its different speeds, it will deliver torque from no load to full load with characteristics similar to those of the d-c shunt motor. This motor is started at full rated voltage with the brushes in low speed position and, in this position, the starting current is from 125 to 175 per cent of load current. The maximum running torque will vary from 140 to 200 per cent, depending upon the size of the machine. The average efficiency is high and the power factor is high at high speeds. Manual or remote control may be used to adjust the motor speed.

SINGLE-PHASE MOTORS

The single-phase motor is universally applied and will be found as a part of, and for the control of, all types and sizes of electrically driven equipment. This type of motor seldom exceeds 10 hp in rating, the greater number of them being less than 1 hp. More of these motors are found in the fractional horsepower groups, some being of such small rating that they are known by their type of service rather than by horsepower rating. In this last group are the clock and timing motors found in the home and on metering devices.

25. Single-Phase Induction Motors. The polyphase induction motor is self-starting, but the single-phase motor does not have the rotating field necessary for the production of starting torque. Figure 21–8*a* shows the condition of the magnetic fields when the rotor is stationary and the voltage is applied to the stator. The rotor, being short-circuited,

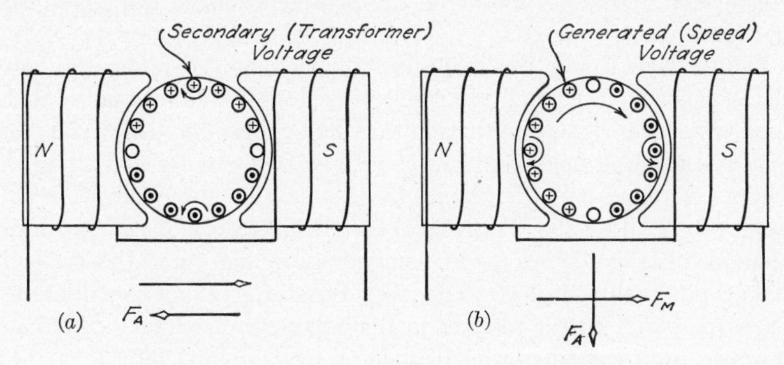

FIG. 21–8. Starting and operating conditions in the single-phase induction motor: (*a*) the rotor at standstill (transformer action); (*b*) the rotor speed voltage after starting.

acts as the secondary of a transformer with a magnetomotive force opposite to the applied magnetomotive force; this is also true at starting. Under these conditions, the rotor will remain stationary and there will be a hum. The same results occur when a polyphase motor has a single-phase voltage applied to it because of the failure of one of the three line fuses.

If the single-phase motor rotor is turned rapidly enough in either direction, the motor will continue to rotate in the direction and will develop torque for both acceleration and shaft load. The development of this torque is explained by two theories: one which deals with the single-phase magnetomotive force as composed of two equal and opposite rotating components and another which explains the rotating field by the 90° time and space-phase relationships between the rotor and the main-field magnetomotive forces.

As explained in Chapter 3, the resultant field of two opposite rotating equal magnetomotive forces is a field that is stationary in space and pulsating. These two components, which cause equal torques of like characteristics at standstill, would each tend to rotate the rotor in opposite directions and, therefore, the effects would be neutralized and the rotor would have no starting torque. When the rotor is started in one direction, this equilibrium is disturbed and the torque is strengthened in the direction of rotation. There is always an opposing torque, for the opposite rotating magnetomotive force is present but, as the rotor reaches operating speed, this countertorque is reduced to a very low value (zero at synchronous speed). This theory has considerable application in the treatment of a-c machinery but is not as rigorous for the single-phase induction motor as the consideration of the time-phase and space-phase analysis.

Figure 21–8 shows the main-field magnetomotive force, the rotor magnetomotive force, and the result of generator action because of the application or torque conditions in the running machine. It would seem that this rotating field would react in the same manner as that in the polyphase motor, but this cannot be true because the quadrature field is not produced by the stator winding. Also, because of its quadrature position, it cannot react (as in a polyphase motor) upon the stator to make a power current flow. Therefore, the stator cannot contribute the necessary power to the rotor as in the polyphase machine. There are, however, rotor currents present produced by combined rotor and stator flux which cause a resultant torque acting on the rotor in the direction of the initial rotation.

At standstill, the rotor flux and the stator flux are in space phase and the torque is zero. When running, the field caused by the rotor speed current is in space quadrature with the stator field. This rotor flux would develop torque with the stator current, if not in time quadrature. As stated above, neither of these conditions, with the motor running, will explain an operating torque; in fact, these arguments can be used to prove the reverse to be true.

The following summarizes the actual established condition when the rotor is rotating:

1. The component of current produced by the speed voltage in the rotor establishes a flux with an axis at right angles to the stator field.
2. This component current, if not at time quadrature, could develop torque with the stator flux.
3. This component current cannot react on the stator to cause any change in the stator current, for its flux axis is at right angles to the stator axis.
4. The stator cannot supply power to this component of current in the rotor and, for that reason, power consumed in the rotor must be power developed by generator action.

5. An analysis of this component current divides it into an exciting current and a core loss current, which produce the rotor field and supply the losses of this field.
6. Since power is developed for core losses, there must be generator action.
7. Since this power does not come from an interaction between the stator and the speed voltage current in the rotor, it must originate from some other current in the rotor producing an equivalent motor action.
8. This equivalent current must produce a field in space phase with the stator field, where it will have the ability to demand a component of current in the stator winding.
9. By this indirect method, the rotor has torque by transformer action because a rotor current producing the quadrature field and supplying core loss does demand current in the stator.
10. Under normal load the generator action supplying the losses is relatively small as compared to the motor action.

It is not necessary to have complete 90° space relationship (Fig. 22–8) to produce a torque for induction motor operation. Some of the starting methods produce fields that are of a small angular displacement in space,

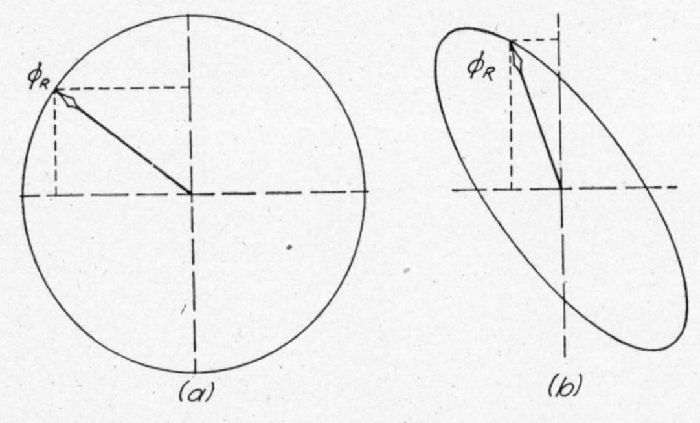

FIG. 22–8. The resultant fields for a single-phase induction motor after starting: (*a*) when the rotor and stator fields are equal and at 90° time phase; (*b*) when the rotor and stator fields are not equal and the time phase angle is less than 90°.

with the result that the rotor starts from standstill and gains torque as its speed increases. When operating at full speed, the starting device may continue to give its increment of torque or be disconnected, depending upon the design of the motor.

26. Methods of Starting Single-Phase Induction Motors. Usual ways of providing starting torque to the single-phase motor are by means of the shading pole, by the split-phase method, and by the use of the repulsion motor principle. This last will be treated in Art. 30, on repulsion-starting and induction-running single-phase motors.

The shaded pole is produced by isolating a portion of the main-field pole by means of a slot and placing a low resistance short-circuited winding upon this isolated portion. The fields of the main and the shading poles are space-phased an angle α and displaced in time phase because of the opposition to flux change produced by the current in the short-circuited ring. The result of this effect is a rotating field similar to that shown in Fig. 23–8*b* which produces an initial torque for starting. It is to be understood that many of the rotating fields produced are not smooth curves, as shown, but have irregularities forming a locus that has no simple geometric form. This type of starting device is used only for low torque requirements, and in the single-phase watt-hour

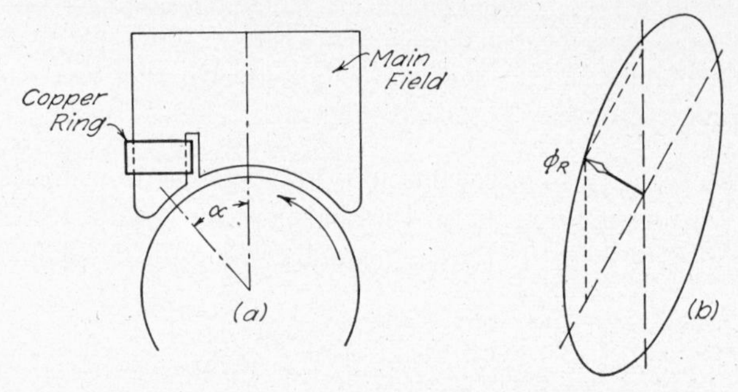

FIG. 23–8. Shading pole starting of single-phase induction motor: (*a*) the shading pole and short-circuited winding; (*b*) the resultant field produced by the main and shading poles.

meter, clock motors, timing motors, and small fan motors this device is used to give the initial starting torque and may continue while the motor is operating.

For the fractional horsepower motors in general domestic and industrial service, the split-phase method of starting is used, the capacitor motor being one of the most recent types perfected and, probably, the most satisfactory motor with this starting device. The capacitor motor will be treated separately in Art. 27.

In split-phase starting, the term is descriptive of the method employed. The single-phase winding is split into two phases producing a two-phase motor for starting. Another (or second) set of coils is wound on the machine displaced 90 space degrees with respect to the main-field coils. This displacement is supplemented by a time-phase displacement in the starting winding with respect to the main field caused by the introduction of a high resistance in the auxiliary winding. This resistance is usually a part of the winding, fine wire being used. These windings are usually built only for starting and not for continuous operation. After the motor has attained a predetermined speed, a centrifugal switch disconnects the starting winding. Figure 24–8 shows a split-phase arrangement of field poles and the resultant component magnetomotive forces. This time-phase displacement may be accomplished also by the use of a high inductance or capacity in the starting winding. Since the main field is of high inductance and poor power factor, the addition of another field of even higher inductance will result in a much lower power factor and usually with less torque than if resistance is used. The addition of a capacity in series with starting winding will improve the power factor and a time phasing approaching 90° displacement may be obtained.

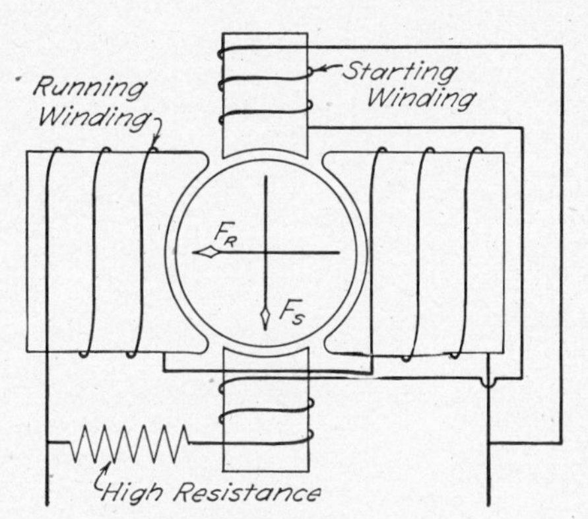

FIG. 24–8. Split-phase method of starting a single-phase induction motor.

27. Capacitor Motors. With the advent of household electrical refrigeration and automatic home heating, the single-phase induction motor became an appreciable load in residential districts. Heretofore the residential load was of excellent power factor because it was composed mostly of lighting load. The addition of the low power factor and intermittent load of the refrigerator motor caused very poor operating characteristics for this residential load. The merits of the capacitor motor have long been recognized but the size and life of the capacity needed made the designs economically impractical. With the development of radio and its accompanying condensers, the cost of condensers has been materially reduced. The addition of autotransformers to step up the voltage at the machine has also reduced the size and cost of the condenser.

It is necessary only to replace the resistance by a condenser, in Fig. 24–8, to obtain a split-phase capacitor motor. The phase differences may be made approximately 90° in time and 90° in space and, in that way, produce a true two-phase condition. With this latter arrangement a larger starting torque results than with resistance split phase; this is needed on the compressor. If the capacity is left in the circuit, the power factor will approach unity.

28. Series Motors. The single-phase series motor has the same operating characteristics as the d-c series motor; that is, high speed at light torque and low speed at heavy torque. The characteristic curves are referred to in Chapter 10, dealing with the d-c series motor.

The principal source of difficulty of the series a-c motors lies in the poor commutation, as discussed under this subject in Chapter 6. For its operation, it functions as will any d-c series motor, the frequency of the alternating current merely limiting the maximum torque. When any d-c motor is placed on a d-c system, the torque developed, as explained in Chapter 5, will be in the same direction, regardless of the change of polarity at the terminals. The change of polarity at the terminals, when alternating current is applied, is very rapid but this would not affect the torque produced if it were not for the high inductance introduced by the windings. The normal shunt motor will not function on alternating current because of the large number of turns on the field winding, but the series motor might function, though very poorly. To build a motor for a-c operation, the relative number of turns on the field are reduced and the armature conductors increased to develop the required torque; also, the necessary changes to control commutation are made as explained in Chapter 6.

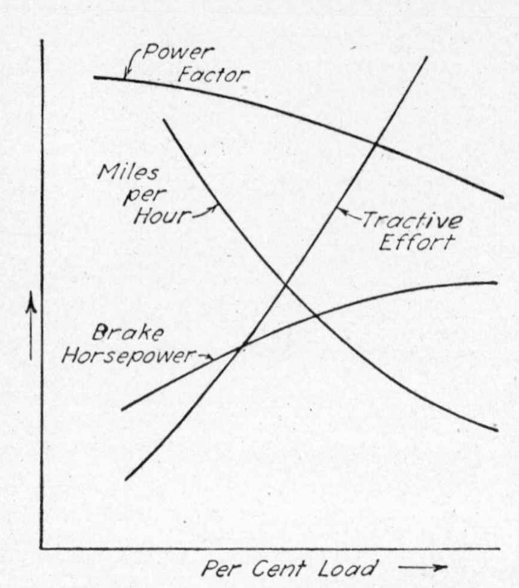

FIG. 25–8. Characteristic curves for a single-phase series railway motor.

In the smaller sizes, the motor is used where the attached load controls the upper speed limit, as in sewing machines, ironers, vacuum cleaners, mixers, and fans. The motor used in these applications is the universal type of motor which may be operated on either a-c or d-c systems. The larger sizes of series motors are used in railway service, where the voltage is reduced from the line by transformers on the car and the machine operates at a reduced voltage, the commutation being improved in this way. The series motor, when properly designed and operated, is a competing motor for electrical railway service, which is now, for the greater part, operated on d-c voltages from 600 to as high as 3000 volts with the motors on the trucks connected electrically in series. Figure 25–8 shows the characteristic curves for a single-phase series railway motor.

29. Repulsion Motor. This single-phase motor has the same objectionable commutation characteristics as the series motor. If the brushes of a d-c motor are short-circuited and the armature placed into an a-c field with relatively low inductance, the result is a repulsion motor. The brushes on this motor must be so placed that the armature reaction will form poles upon which the main field may act to produce torque. This is accomplished by shifting the brushes from the axis. By setting the brushes in the position which gives maximum current, the armature poles are so located that they will not be acted upon by the main field and, conversely, if the brushes are in such a position that the current is zero in the armature and no armature poles exist, the arrangement is such that the main field cannot react.

An angle of approximately 18° from the neutral is the optimum position, and the main field will repel the poles formed on the armature. From this characteristic the name repulsion motor is derived. The motor may rotate in either direction, the direction being determined by the position of the brush with respect to the neutral axis.

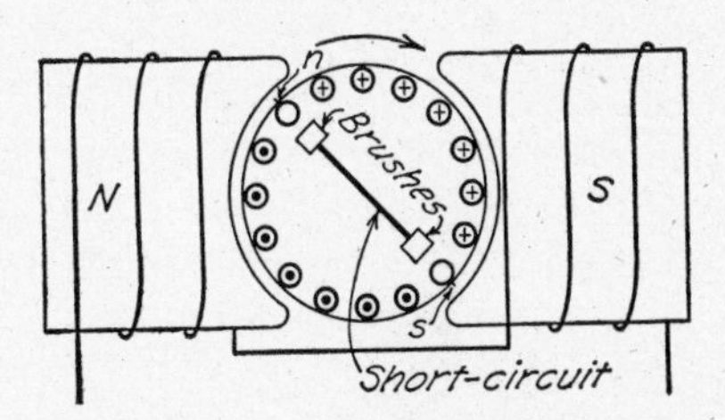

Fig. 26–8. The single-phase repulsion motor showing the brush position and the armature field.

The advantages of this type of motor lie in a partial speed control by brush shift, the ability to reverse rotation by brush shift, and a large starting torque with a low current. These motors fail because of poor commutation, because the sparking is excessive even in the best designs. However, its large starting torque is utilized by applying the principle to the single-phase induction motor as an auxiliary for starting purposes. Figure 26–8 shows the poles formed on the armature of the repulsion motor and the relative position of such poles to the main field.

30. Repulsion-Induction and Repulsion-Starting Induction-Running Single-Phase Motors. When the principles of the single-phase induction motor are combined with those of the repulsion motor, a very satisfactory single-phase motor results. However, this does not produce the cheapest type of motor, because commutators and windings are more expensive than the squirrel cage rotor.

The motor starts as a repulsion motor, with the brushes on the commutator, giving the characteristic heavy torque of the series motor. When the motor reaches a predetermined speed, a centrifugal device short-circuits the commutator bars and sometimes lifts the brush. These motors are usually built with radial instead of cylindrical commutators, thus permitting the segments to be short-circuited by placing a ring under pressure against the bars. The motor now operates as a single-phase induction motor and the commutator is safe against damage from sparking during all operating periods except starting. This type of motor finds extensive application in repair and manufacturing processes, especially where three-phase power is not available. The printing industry uses this type of motor on folding machines and small presses.

In the split-phase motor, another means is used for obtaining a larger starting torque. Single-phase induction motors are sometimes so arranged that the rotor is free to revolve on the shaft at low rotor speeds, under which condition a low starting torque is sufficient to drive the rotor though not sufficient to start the load attached to the shaft. When the rotor has attained the proper speed to produce considerable torque, a centrifugal device closes a friction clutch and the rotor transfers its speed to the load.

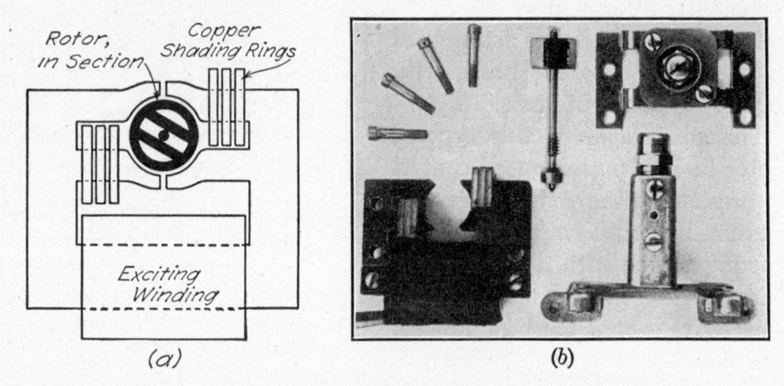

FIG. 27–8. (*a*) The schematic diagram of a Telechron timing motor. (*b*) Parts of a Holtz timing motor for a demand-meter register.

31. Single-Phase Clock and Timing Synchronous Motors. These types of motors have been developed for timing purposes. Though this motor runs at synchronous speed, it does not follow the principles of power motors.

With the constant frequency regulation of the large power networks, it is possible to use synchronous motors for constant average speeds and, if the operation of the single-phase motor is designed for some synchronous speed with the system frequency constant, the motor can be used for timing purposes. The design of timing equipment is such that the motors may be purchased on a basis of revolutions per minute.

Figure 27–8 shows the schematic diagram of one type of synchronous motor and the parts of another such motor. The motor shown in Fig. 27–8*a* consists of a laminated core, a coil, a shading coil, and a rotor made up of several disks pressed on a shaft. For this type of motor to run, it is necessary to proportion the field, air gap, and the rotor in order to establish a definite relationship with regard to the intensity and distribution of the magnetic flux.

The poles induced initially in the disks by the rotating magnetic field are present for part of a cycle and tend to follow the field. The reversal removes the exciting cause, but the rotor has moved in a definite direction for the interval and, if continued, such impulses will cause the rotor to gain speed (approaching synchronous speed). The starting torque is relatively strong, because there is large power loss in the disks and this must be supplied by the source. When the local poles are brought into synchronism, it is because of the low reluctance of the path through the metallic structure in the center of the disks; that is, the disk becomes permanently magnetized along this fixed diameter.

Many devices are used in producing synchronous motors but, in each instance, if the motor is self-starting, it starts as an induction motor. In some motors, it is necessary to bring the rotor up to synchronous speed by giving it an initial start.

Even though the synchronous motors are very small, they embody some of the most complicated electrical machine theory. The motor starts as a shaded pole motor having induction motor characteristics and then operates as a subsynchronous or synchronous motor. The torque analysis will be a combination of induction and synchronous motor torque. The induction motor action must develop enough torque to overcome the tendency of the rotor poles to lock in with the stator poles and, later, the stator-to-pole flux must overcome the induction motor torque. When the motor operates at a speed less than synchronous speed, these two types of torque are present.

PROBLEMS

1–8. Using unit power component of current and neglecting the resistance of the motor windings, develop the power factor characteristic of an induction motor.

2–8. At standstill a 4-pole, 60-cycle induction motor has a rotor reactance which per phase is 6 times the rotor resistance. The slip for the machine at full load is 5 per cent. Determine (*a*) the speed of the rotor when maximum torque is developed, (*b*) the ratio of the maximum to the full-load torque, assuming that the air-gap flux remains constant.

3–8. A 220-volt, 3-phase, 4-pole, 60-cycle induction motor, when operated at rated voltage and frequency on the stator, has a rotor voltage of 150 volts per phase at standstill. The rotor resistance is 0.2 ohm and the rotor reactance is 0.6 ohm per phase. With the air-gap flux remaining constant and a full-load slip of 5 per cent, determine the ratio of the starting torque to the full-load torque.

4–8. A 20-hp, 2300-volt, 3-phase, 8-pole, 60-cycle induction motor has a full-load slip of 6.5 per cent, a starting current of 550 per cent of full-load current, a starting torque 160 per cent of full-load torque, with the following load, power factor, and efficiency characteristics.

Load	½	¾	1	5/4
Power factor	72	82	86	88
Efficiency	86	87	87	86

Determine (*a*) full-load speed, (*b*) line current at full load, (*c*) full-load torque in pound-feet.

5–8. At standstill, an induction motor has 5 times its full-load current and develops 1.5 times full-load torque. An autotransformer is installed to reduce the starting current to give full-load torque at starting. Determine (*a*) the voltage on the motor at starting, (*b*) the motor current at starting, (*c*) the line current to the autotransformer, all in per cent.

6–8. A 15-hp, 220-volt, 3-phase, 6-pole, 60-cycle, wound-rotor induction motor has an efficiency of 82.6 per cent and a speed of 1140 rpm at full load. The wound rotor is replaced by a squirrel cage rotor of such a design that the slip for rated input is 3 per cent. What will be the efficiency when operating at rated input, if all losses except rotor copper losses are assumed to be constant?

7–8. A 15-hp, 230-volt, 3-phase, 1152-rpm, 60-cycle induction motor has rotor copper losses equal to 20 per cent of the total losses. What is the power input to the motor in kilowatts at full load?

8–8. An induction motor at maximum efficiency has equal rotor and stator copper losses and a slip of 3 per cent. Calculate the efficiency of the induction motor.

9–8. A 10-hp, 230-volt, 3-phase, 4-pole, 60-cycle induction motor has a full-load efficiency of 82.7 per cent with the stator and rotor copper losses equal and the copper losses one-half the total losses. Calculate the full-load speed of the motor.

10–8. A factory induction motor load requires 400 kw at 70.7 per cent lagging power factor. A 425-kva synchronous motor is installed to carry 147.5 hp and also used to improve the power factor of the plant. If the synchronous motor is operated at full rating and takes 35 kw in losses, what will be the power factor of the plant after the installation?

11–8. A 50-hp shaft load on a synchronous motor, with an energy component of 25 kw to supply the losses, is placed in parallel with a 1000-kva factory load which has a 60 per cent lagging power factor. What must be the synchronous motor rating if the final power factor is to be 80 per cent lagging?

12–8. A switchboard supplies three feeders: (1) 600 kva at 60 per cent lagging power factor; (2) 800 kva at 80 per cent lagging power factor; and (3) an energy demand of 200 kw. Determine (*a*) the total switchboard demand, (*b*) the power factor of the total load.

13–8. A 500-volt, 150-amp, 1-phase, 6-pole, 60-cycle synchronous motor has an armature reactance of 2 ohms and a negligible resistance. If the induced voltage is 400 volts, determine the power input to the motor.

14–8. A 150-hp, 4000-volt, 3-phase, wye-connected, 25-cycle synchronous motor has a full-load efficiency of 90 per cent and is operated at unity power factor. The synchronous impedance per phase is 100 ohms and the resistance can be neglected as compared to the synchronous reactance. Calculate the voltage induced, per phase, in the machine.

15–8. For a 1-phase synchronous motor the relationship between the induced voltage and the field current is expressed as $E_g = 1 + 100I_f$, and the stator impedance is considered equivalent to 1 ohm of inductive reactance. Determine (*a*) the field current necessary if the motor is to draw 15 kw from a 250-volt supply with a 60 per cent leading power factor, (*b*) the field current when the power demand is doubled and the power factor is unchanged.

CHAPTER 9

DIRECT-CURRENT GENERATORS

1. Generation of Voltage. The winding of a d-c generator is a closed-circuit winding with connections made to the commutator bars, as discussed in Chapter 1. The brushes make contact with the commutator at the proper places in order to include in the same armature path all the conductors which are generating voltages of a similar polarity. This means that many conductors are in series between adjacent brushes, some active and others inactive at a given instant in generating voltage. The active conductors (those cutting lines of flux) are generating voltages of different magnitudes, depending upon the strength of the field in the vicinity of the conductor.

The voltage generated by a conductor depends upon the rate at which the lines of flux are cut. The average voltage per conductor can be determined and, for Z conductors in series, the total voltage will be Z times as great as for a single conductor. Since all conductors cannot occupy the same position at the same time, the total voltage at every instant will become the sum of the instantaneous values generated in the various conductors. If the armature is rotated in a magnetic field, a constant average (commutator ripple) voltage will be generated in each armature circuit between adjacent brushes. This can be further explained by saying that there is always a constant number of conductors between adjacent brushes generating instantaneous voltages of different values but always adding to a constant value. This is shown in Fig. 1–9. The direction of the arrows on the conductors under a pole shows that the voltages generated are all in the same direction and that the total voltage between the brushes is the sum of the individual conductor voltages.

The voltage generated per conductor at any instant is proportional to the flux density in the region occupied by the conductor at that instant, the length, and the velocity of the conductor, and direction of motion in relationship to the magnetic field. This may be expressed as

$$e = Blv \times 10^{-8}$$

in which B is flux density, l is the length of the conductor, and v is the velocity of the conductor perpendicular to the flux. All values are expressed in the same system of units.

Referring to Fig. 1–9 the conductors under a pole generate a voltage which depends upon their position under the pole at that instant. The total voltage at every instant will be the same, since the conductors moving under the pole are the same and the group always generates the

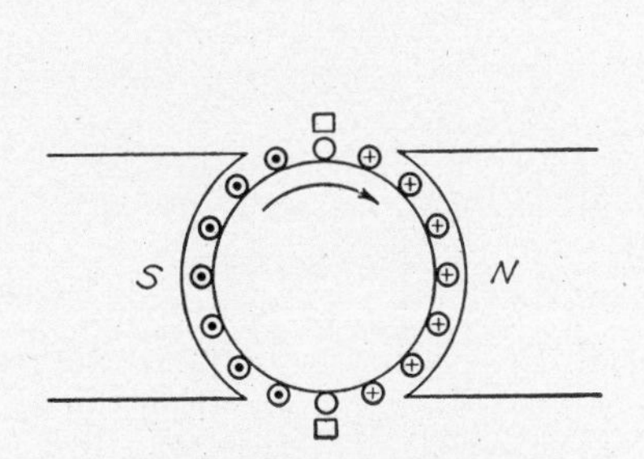

FIG. 1–9. Generated voltage in a group of conductors.

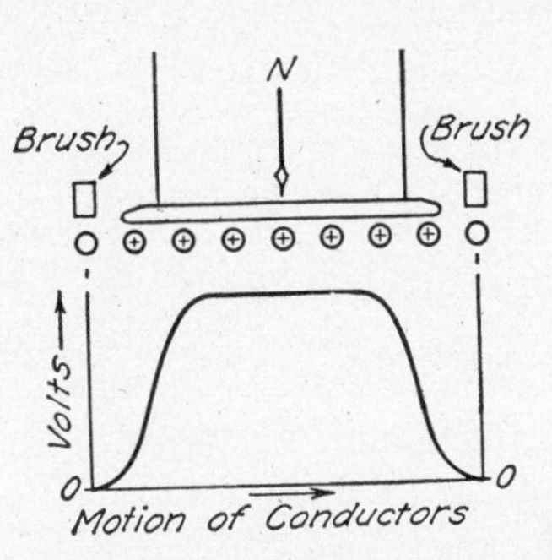

FIG. 2–9. Generated voltage under a north pole of Fig. 1–9.

same total voltage. Figure 2–9 shows the generated voltage in a conductor as it passes under a north pole.

The expression for the average voltage generated in a single conductor can be expressed in terms of the flux cut per pole as

$$E_{av} = \frac{\phi}{t} \times 10^{-8} \text{ volt}$$

where ϕ is the total flux per pole and t is the time in seconds for a conductor to move from under one pole to the adjacent pole. The voltage generated between the brushes in a generator is the total of the individual voltages generated by the conductors in that section. The total voltage at any instant is constant, since the same total number of conductors producing voltage is constant at all times. The general expression for the generated voltage in a generator can be stated as

$$E_{av} = \frac{Z}{P}\frac{\phi}{t} \times 10^{-8} \text{ volt}$$

where Z = total armature conductors
P = number of paths through the armature
ϕ = flux per pole
t = time in seconds for a conductor to travel from one pole to another.

Example a. A four-pole generator has 500 conductors on the armature. If the generator is running at 1200 rpm, find the average voltage generated between brushes for (*a*) a lap winding, (*b*) a wave winding. The total flux per pole is 10^6 lines.

For a simplex lap winding, there are as many paths through the armature as there are poles. Therefore, $P = 4$.

$$E = \frac{500 \times 10^6 \times 10^{-8}}{4 \times \frac{60}{4800}} = 100 \text{ volts}$$

For the simplex wave winding, there are only two paths, regardless of the number of poles. Therefore, $P = 2$.

$$E = \frac{500 \times 10^6 \times 10^{-8}}{2 \times \frac{60}{4800}} = 200 \text{ volts}$$

2. Generator Excitation. The magnetic fields of a d-c generator are produced by magnetomotive forces supplied by coils placed on the field poles and designed to carry the necessary exciting current. The diverse methods used to excite these field coils determine the various types of d-c generators. The different kinds of excitation can be listed as follows:

a. Shunt excitation { separate / self

b. Series excitation

c. Compound excitation { cumulative / differential

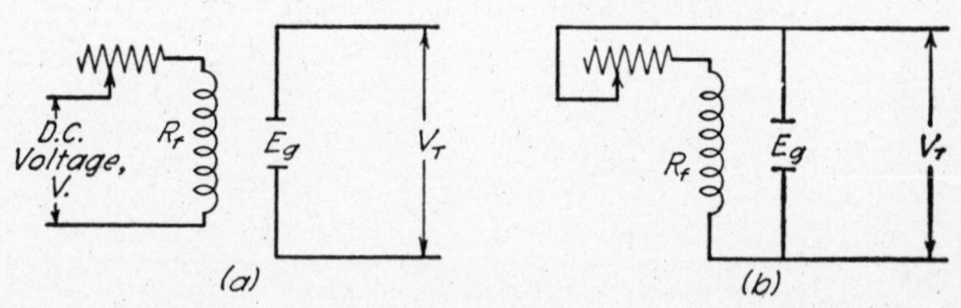

FIG. 3–9. Circuit diagram of a shunt generator: (*a*) separate excitation; (*b*) self-excitation.

a. Shunt Excitation. Figure 3–9 shows the two methods of supplying excitation under this classification. The resistance of the field circuit is sufficient to allow the connection of the circuit to a separate voltage source (or the machine armature) without excessive current flow, which means that the shunt field coils must consist of many turns of small wire in order to obtain sufficient ampere turns. In most instances, a separate source does not exist and self-excitation must be used.

b. Series Excitation. The field coils are connected in series with the armature in this type of excitation. The field current is the same as the armature current, and any variation in armature current will produce a corresponding change in field excitation. With a variable field current, and a variable flux, a variable generated voltage will exist. The field circuit for this type of excitation has a very low resistance. The field coils consist of a few turns of wire capable of carrying the armature current of the machine. Figure 4–9 shows the circuit diagram of the series generator.

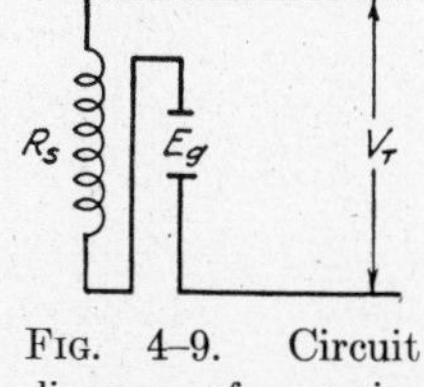

FIG. 4–9. Circuit diagram of a series generator.

c. Compound Excitation. Compound excitation is a combination of series and shunt excitation. The use of both shunt and series field windings makes it possible to combine the characteristics of both types.

The way in which the magnetomotive forces, caused by the shunt and series field windings, are combined determines whether the generator is cumulatively or differentially connected. If the series field ampere turns add to those of the shunt field, the connection is cumulative; but, if the series field ampere turns oppose those of the shunt field, the connection is differential. Therefore, the total field magnetomotive force increases with load for a cumulative compound connection, whereas the total field magnetomotive force decreases with load for a differential

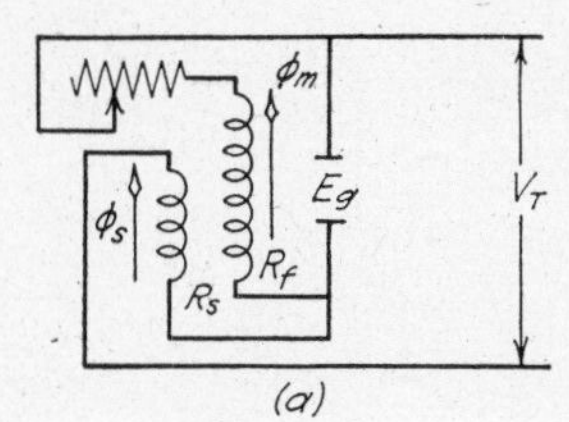

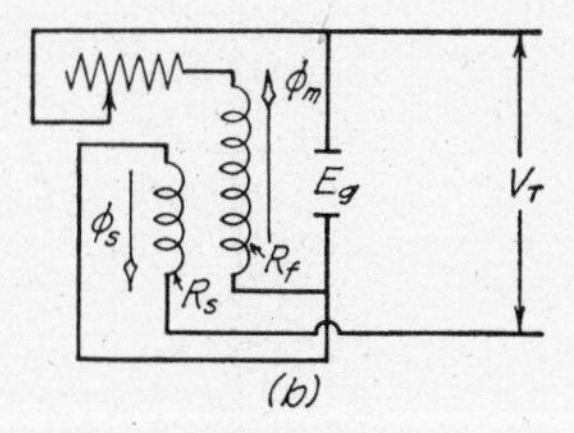

FIG. 5–9. Circuit diagrams of short shunt compound generators: (*a*) cumulative compound; (*b*) differential compound.

compound connection. Figure 5–9 shows the circuit diagrams for the cumulative and differential connections.

3. Magnetization Curve of a Generator. If the expression for the generated voltage between brushes $E = (Z/P)(\phi/t) \times 10^{-8}$ is reduced by grouping the machine constants, it is seen that the voltage for a given machine varies directly with the speed and flux. The generated voltage then may be expressed as $E = k\phi N$, in which k is the constant for the particular generator (includes all constants, conductors, and paths through the armature), ϕ is the flux per pole, and N is the speed.

From the equation $E = k\phi N$, it follows that the voltage generated is a direct measure of the air-gap flux of the generator for a constant speed N. The flux depends upon the field magnetomotive force or ampere turns NI_f, and the relationship between the ampere turns and generated voltage is the same as the magnetic circuit relationship between field magnetomotive force and air-gap flux. This relationship $[\phi = (f)NI_f]$ is called the magnetization curve. The data for the curve between the no-load generated voltage and field current are obtained with the armature rotating at constant speed. Figure 6–9 shows the circuit diagram for this test and the general shape of the magnetization curve.

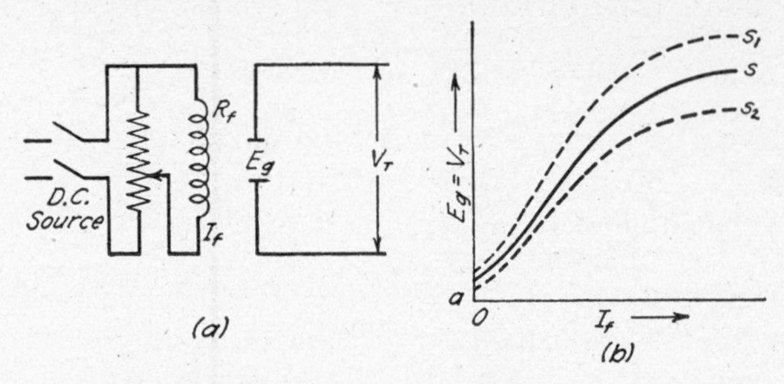

FIG. 6–9. (a) Circuit diagram for a separate excited shunt generator with potentiometer field control. (b) Magnetization curve.

As the field current is increased, the generated voltage increases approximately uniformly until the iron portion of the magnetic circuit becomes saturated. After this, the generated voltage no longer holds the same relationship to the field magnetomotive force and the voltage does not increase proportionally with the field current. If the iron has never been magnetized or is thoroughly demagnetized, the voltage is zero when I_f is zero but, if the field has previously been magnetized, the voltage oa exists because of the residual magnetism in the magnetic circuit.

The magnetic circuit relationships for a particular generator are fixed, but the speed can be varied to produce many different magnetization curves. The expression $E = k\phi N$ shows that a variation in speed will produce a corresponding variation in generated voltage. The magnetization curve (Fig. 6–9b) is for a definite speed N, and for speeds $N_1 > N$ and $N_2 < N$ the curves would be those indicated by the dotted lines. It is possible from this relationship to construct the magnetization curve for any speed, the curve at one speed having been determined.

Experimental tests have shown that the flux density in a magnetic circuit and the magnetomotive force have different relationships, depending upon whether the magnetomotive force is increasing or decreasing. Figure 7–9 shows a characteristic magnetization loop for a magnetic circuit. The arrows on the curve indicate the direction of field current change. The value *oa* is called *remanence* * (or the residual magnetism).

The operation of a d-c generator depends upon the control of field magnetomotive force, which, in turn, depends upon the control of field current. Most of the d-c generators in use are of the constant voltage type, having fields which do not depend entirely upon load currents. These machines are classified as either a shunt or a compound generator.

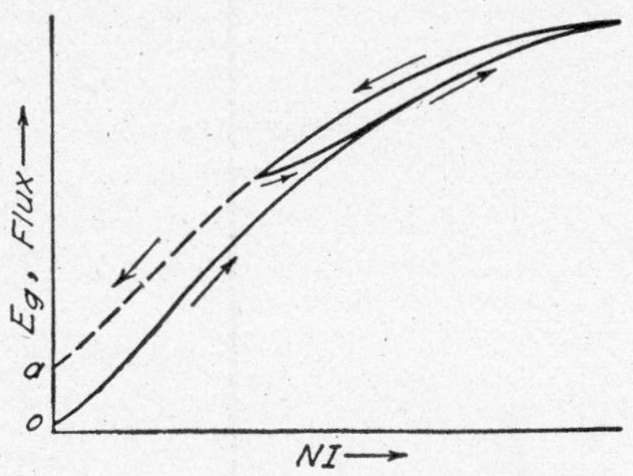

FIG. 7–9. Magnetization loop. The value *oa* is the remanence.

The magnetic circuit of the generator has some residual flux after the magnetic field has once been energized. The generator will produce a small voltage in the armature as a result of this residual flux, without the shunt field being connected to the armature. If this generated voltage caused by the residual flux is connected to the shunt field circuit, a current will flow. If this current flows in such a direction as to aid the residual magnetomotive force, a cumulative action exists, and the generated voltage can be increased to the desired voltage. This method of supplying the shunt field excitation is called self-excitation. The generated voltage at no load which can be obtained from the generator is determined by the magnetization curve of the machine and its shunt field circuit resistance. The ohmic resistance of the shunt field circuit must be of such a value that it will permit the proper field current to flow in order to give the desired generator terminal voltage for the shunt field circuit. The relationship between the generator magnetic circuit and electrical circuit in the shunt field can be tabulated as follows:

MAGNETIC CIRCUIT	SHUNT FIELD CIRCUIT
$E_g = K\phi N$	$I_f = \dfrac{V_T}{R_f}$
ϕ depends upon I_f	$V = E_g$ at no load
N is constant	
$\therefore E_g = K'I_f$	$\therefore I_f = \dfrac{E_g}{R_f}$

* Remanence is the magnetic induction which remains in a magnetic circuit after the removal of an applied magnetomotive force. (05.25.130) American Standard Definitions of American Institute of Electrical Engineers.

The value of I_f must be the same for both circuits. The diagram in Fig. 8–9 shows a magnetization curve and field resistance lines of a shunt generator. The resistance lines are shown for three conditions. If the

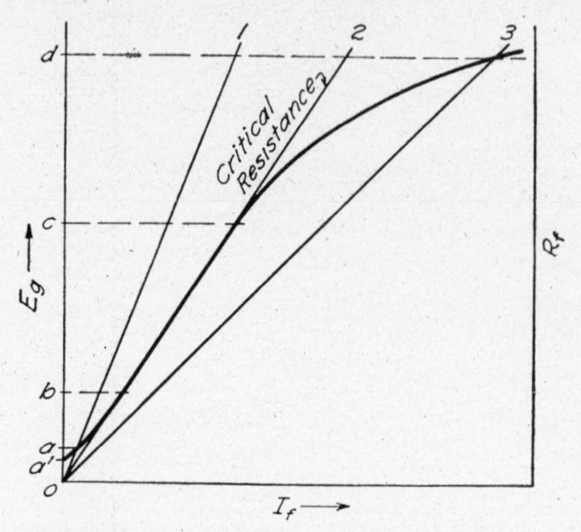

FIG. 8–9. Effects of shunt field resistance.

field resistance line is at *o1*, the generated voltage will not exceed the value *oa*. If the resistance line is at *o2*, the voltage may be any value from *ob* to *oc* and will not be stable. This value is called the *critical field resistance*. If the resistance value is at *o3*, the voltage will be *od*. All values of resistance greater than the critical field resistance value will give a voltage slightly above the residual voltage *oa'*. To obtain a stable voltage, a resistance less than the critical field resistance must be used.

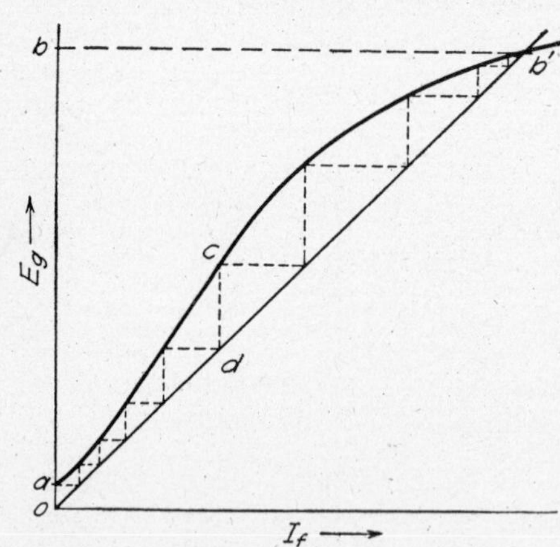

FIG. 9–9. "Building up" of a shunt generator.

The "*building up*" process in a d-c generator can occur only when the field resistance is less than the critical value and the field is connected to the armature circuit so that the field magnetomotive force aids the residual magnetism. If the first condition is not satisfied, the results for both magnetic circuit and electric circuit produce a voltage but little greater than residual voltage. If the second condition is not satisfied, there is a tendency to reduce the generated voltage below the residual voltage. The "*building up*" process can be illustrated by a diagram (Fig. 9–9) for both the magnetic circuit and electric circuit, indicated by dotted lines. The final value of generated voltage occurs at that value which satisfies both the magnetization curve and the shunt field circuit resistance line.

With the residual voltage, *oa*, as a starting value, the generated voltage continues to increase until the voltage, *ob*, is reached. At *ob* the magnetization curve, *ab′*, and the field resistance line, *ob′*, intersect, this value of voltage being necessary to satisfy the field circuit. The generated voltage cannot exceed *ob*, because the field circuit would require a terminal voltage greater than can be generated for the corresponding value of field current. The dotted lines in Fig. 9–9 show the effect of the inductance in the magnetic circuit. For example, the difference between the generated voltage and the voltage across the field resistance, for a definite field current, is indicated by the amount *cd*. Since the current is varying in the field circuit, an additional voltage drop caused by the field inductance must be supplied by the generator. This difference in voltage, *cd*, includes the armature resistance drop (which is almost negligible) and the field reactance drop. The relationship between the magnetization curve and the field resistance at any value of field current during the process of building up can be expressed as

$$E_g = V_T + I_a R_a + \mathcal{L}\left(\frac{di}{dt}\right)_f$$

or

$$E_g = I_f R_f + I_f R_a + \left(\mathcal{L}\,\frac{di_f}{dt}\right)$$

At the point b' the field current is not changing and, at this value of field current, $\mathcal{L}(di_f/dt) = 0$; also, since the value of $I_f R_a$ is practically negligible, $E_g = I_f R_f = V_T$.

From the discussion of the *building up* of a generator it follows that the generator may fail to *build up* because of any one of three reasons. Although any one of the three will prevent the generator from functioning, the order of importance has been considered in discussing them.

1. *No Residual Magnetism.* In order to obtain any shunt field current, a residual voltage must give the field its initial current. If the machine is new or has not been in use for a considerable period of time, it may be necessary to excite the field from some d-c source.

2. *Reversed Shunt Field Connection.* In order that the residual voltage may be able to cause a cumulative action in the magnetic circuit, it is

necessary that the shunt field be connected to the armature so that the current flowing in the shunt field winding produces a magnetomotive force which will aid the residual magnetomotive force.

3. *Shunt Field Circuit Resistance Too Great.* As indicated in Fig. 8–9, a value of field resistance less than the *critical* value is necessary. It is apparent that a high flux density is desirable in order to prevent large changes in voltage if the field current fluctuates.

4. Effect of Armature Reaction. In Chapter 3, it has been shown that the armature conductors (when current exists in them) will produce a magnetomotive force which reacts with the main-field magnetomotive force in order to produce the resultant field for the machine. This armature magnetomotive force has two components: (1) cross-magnetizing and (2) demagnetizing. The action of the armature magnetomotive force is along the brush axis, and the brush axis must be approximately at right angles to the resultant field of the machine. This latter condition is necessary if the coils being commutated are in zero field at the time of commutation. If the machine is a generator and the previous conditions are satisfied, the brushes must be shifted in the direction of rotation of the armature as the load increases. This may be seen from a study of the magnetomotive force relationship of a dynamo when used as a generator.

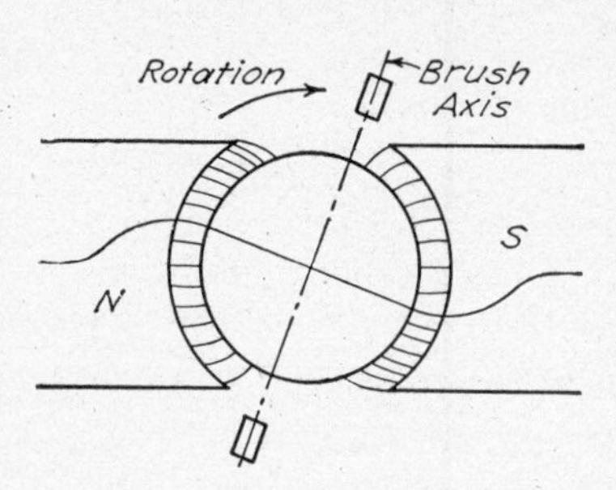

FIG. 10–9. Uneven flux distribution in the air gap of a generator when loaded.

It has been shown in Chapter 6 that the addition of interpoles makes it unnecessary to shift the brushes to get good commutation. The modern generators have interpoles to improve commutation and, as a result, they improve the performance of the machine. The addition of the interpoles gives a slightly different air-gap flux distribution from that indicated in the next paragraph in which the flux distribution in the air-gap of the generator is discussed.

The poles are always stationary in space, and the resultant magnetomotive force produces an uneven flux distribution over the pole face. This is caused by two things: (1) a non-uniform magnetic path for the flux and (2) saturation of the iron in certain sections of the pole causing changes in the permeability of the magnetic circuit. Figure 10–9 shows a sketch of a two-pole machine with an uneven flux distribution in the air-gap. Figure 11–9 shows a developed diagram of the air-gap flux distribution for no load and full load on a d-c generator.

Figures 10–9 and 11–9 show that the air-gap flux distribution at no load and full load are different. Because of the uneven distribution, the resultant magnetomotive force may not be able to produce the same total air-gap flux under load as it can at no load. This is caused by the new flux densities in the different sections of the pole faces, which require more total magnetomotive force than the amount required under no-load flux condition. The reduction in total air-gap flux gives a reduced generated voltage per path and a corresponding reduction in terminal voltage.

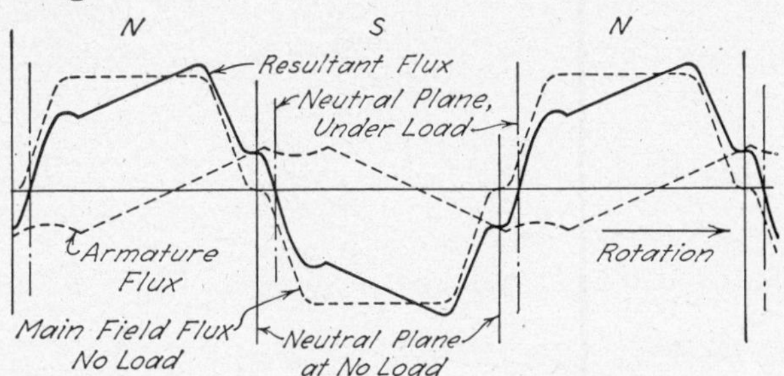

FIG. 11–9. Air-gap flux distribution for no load and full load on a generator.

The effects of armature reaction are, therefore, twofold in a d-c generator:

1. New air-gap flux distribution which is not uniform since the load current fluctuates.

2. A shifting of the brush axis in the direction of rotation of the armature is required to obtain good commutation. This brush shift increases, in turn, the effects stated under (1) unless the machine has interpoles.

Compensating windings, series field windings, and interpoles are used to compensate for the effects of armature reaction. These have been discussed in Chapter 6, but a summary of these discussions will show the part that each plays in influencing the generator performance.

The compensating winding is placed in the pole face and the armature or load current passes through them in such a direction as to oppose the armature magnetomotive force. This reduces to a minimum the shifting of the air-gap flux which is caused by armature reaction.

The series field also carries the armature or load current and can supply an additional magnetomotive force to the main field. This additional magnetomotive force increases the generated voltage to an amount which can compensate for the voltage drops caused by the armature and series field resistances.

The interpole (or commutating pole) is used to eliminate the necessity of shifting the brush axis and to insure good commutation.

Although each one is a correcting influence, these do not eliminate armature reaction, but simply aid in reducing its ultimate effect.

5. External Characteristics of a Shunt Generator. Figure 12–9 shows the circuit diagrams for separately excited and self-excited shunt generators. The only difference between these two generators is in the source of excitation for the shunt field.

The external characteristic of a shunt generator is the relationship between terminal voltage and load current. The terminal voltage will

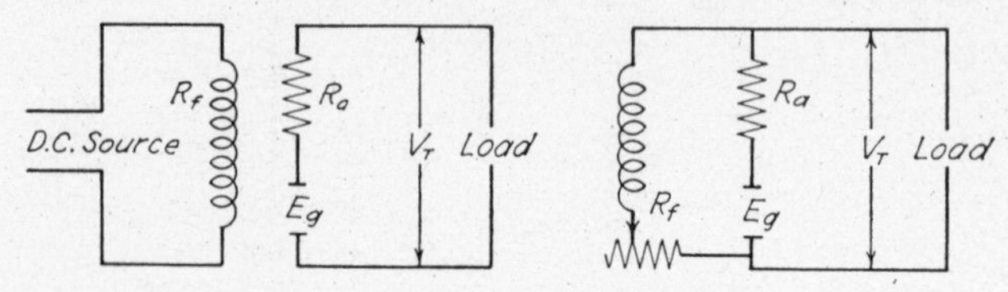

FIG. 12–9. Schematic circuit diagrams of shunt generators.

decrease as the armature current increases and will differ from the generated voltage by the voltage drop caused by the armature resistance. This may be written as

$$V_T = E_g - I_a R_a$$

The generated voltage E_g depends upon the rate at which the flux is cut and, for a constant speed machine, depends only upon the variations in flux:

$$E_g = k\phi N$$

and for constant speed

$$E_g = k_1\phi$$

The net flux in the air gap is a resultant flux caused by the magnetomotive forces of the main field and of armature reaction. If the main-field magnetomotive force remains constant for all loads, the net field strength varies only with the effects of armature reaction. If the main-field magnetomotive force does not remain constant, the net field strength varies with both the main-field magnetomotive force and the magnetomotive force caused by the armature current.

The factors affecting the terminal voltage of a shunt generator as the machine is loaded are (1) voltage drop caused by armature resistance, (2) effects of armature reaction changing the net air-gap flux, and (3) change in the main-field strength caused by a change in shunt-field current. The schematic circuit diagrams of the separately excited and self-excited shunt generators are shown in Fig. 12–9. A careful study of these circuit diagrams will show that the factors (1) and (2) will control the external characteristic of a separately excited shunt generator and that factors (1), (2), and (3) will control the external characteristic of a self-excited generator. The relative magnitude of each controlling

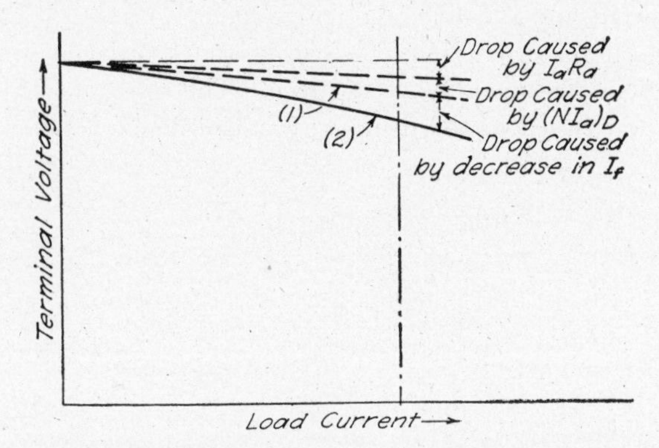

FIG. 13–9. External characteristic curves of a shunt generator: (1) separately excited; (2) self-excited.

factor will determine the final shape of the external characteristic curve. Figure 13–9 shows the external characteristic curves for a shunt generator when it is operating as a separately excited or as a self-excited generator.

If the generator is operated at some speed other than the rated speed, the external characteristic curve will be altered. The rated speed is determined by the designer as the most economical speed for generator operation. Any deviation from this speed means that the generator is operated at a different point on the magnetization curve with corresponding effects on its characteristic. On Fig. 6–9*b* the effect of speed on the no-load generated voltage is indicated and it follows that the smaller the flux, the higher the speed required to give the same voltage. Figure 14–9 shows the external characteristic curves for a shunt generator, operated at two different speeds. The speed for curve (*b*) is greater than the speed for (*a*). The factors causing the terminal voltage to decrease have a greater effect at the higher speed, since the initial flux of the magnetic circuit is lower.

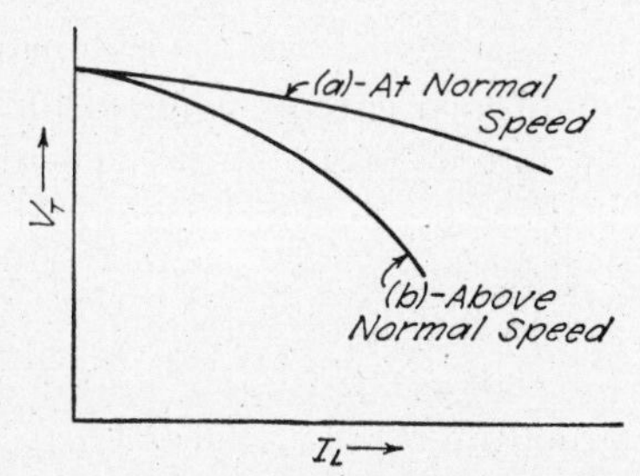

FIG. 14–9. External characteristic as influenced by speed.

It has been shown that the terminal voltage of a generator decreases as load is applied and that the factors causing the decrease in voltage are a voltage drop in the resistance and changes in air-gap flux produced by changes in the magnetic circuit conditions. If the resistance of the armature circuit and the demagnetizing effect of armature reaction are determined, the external characteristic of the shunt generator can be calculated from the magnetization curve. The resistance of the armature can be measured in the usual way. The demagnetizing effects of

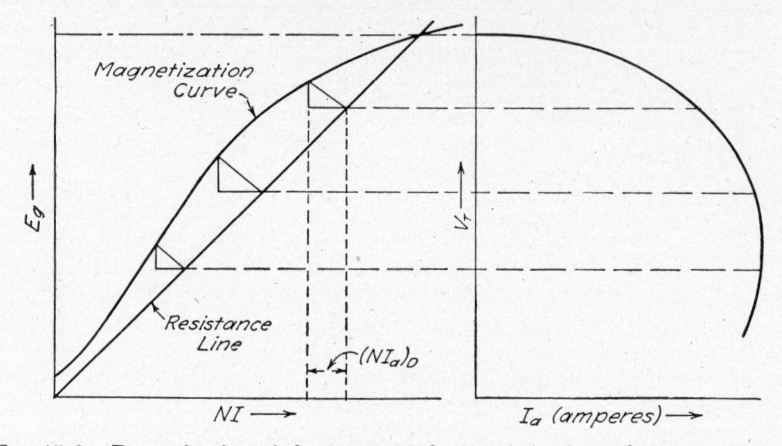

FIG. 15–9. Determination of the armature characteristics from the magnetization curve and field resistance line.

armature reaction can be determined by operating the generator separately-excited and short-circuited at rated armature current. The shunt-field current required for this short-circuit condition generates a definite no-load voltage. The difference between the generated voltage and the terminal voltage for this test (which is zero) is caused by the voltage loss in the armature (I_aR_a) and the effect of armature reaction. From this information, it follows that the resultant magnetomotive force differs from the no-load magnetomotive force by the effects of armature reaction and the decrease in shunt-field current.

Figure 15–9 shows the relationship between the armature characteristic curve and the no-load magnetization curve.

Figure 16–9 shows an enlarged diagram of the top section of Fig. 15–9. The effect of each component part is to reduce the terminal voltage of the generator. The size of the triangle, consisting of a voltage component (I_aR_a) as the vertical side and the magnetomotive force component (demagnetizing effects of armature reaction) as the horizontal side, is a function of the value of the armature current. This means that, for all practical considerations, the size of the triangle will vary directly as the armature current. The triangle must fit in the space between the magnetization curve and the field resistance line in order to satisfy the two relationships previously mentioned.

This method of determining the external characteristics is influenced by two factors which will cause inaccurate calculations. The first factor is the variation in armature circuit resistance which is caused by variation in temperature and the change in brush contact resistance with increased current density. The second factor is the inability to deter-

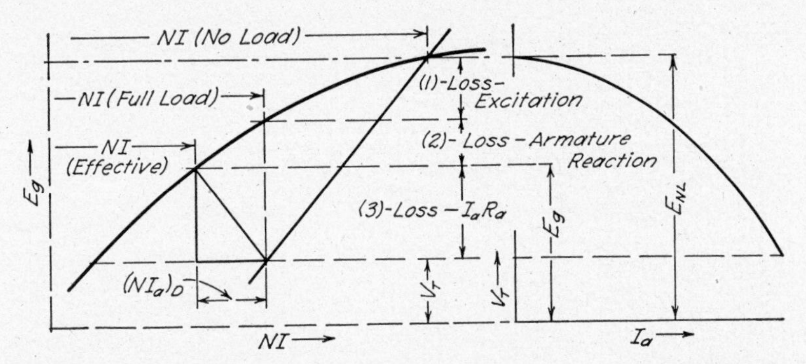

Fig. 16–9. Component parts of the armature characteristic: (1) decrease in generated voltage caused by a decrease in I_f; (2) decrease in generated voltage caused by the effects of armature reaction; (3) decrease in terminal voltage caused by armature current and resistance.

mine the effect of armature reactions. The increase in demagnetizing and cross-magnetizing ampere-turns does not produce a straight line variation in air-gap flux.

6. Characteristics of Compound Generators. The compound generator (Fig. 5–9) consists of the shunt generator with a series field added. The series field carries the armature current or line current and is placed on the main-field structure to furnish additional magnetomotive force to the magnetic circuit. Although it is possible to have the series-field ampere turns oppose the shunt-field ampere turns, this is seldom done, since the result would be a generator with a characteristic poorer than the shunt generator alone. A generator connected in this way is called a differential compound generator. In the usual connection, the series-field ampere turns aid the shunt-field ampere turns, and an improvement over the shunt generator characteristic results. A generator connected in this way is called a cumulative compound generator.

The strength of the series field relative to the shunt field determines the degree of *compounding* of the generator. If the series-field ampere turns do not compensate for all the factors and the terminal voltage at full load is less than the no-load terminal voltage, the generator is under-compounded. If the terminal voltage increases with load current, the generator is overcompounded and, if the no-load and full-load voltages

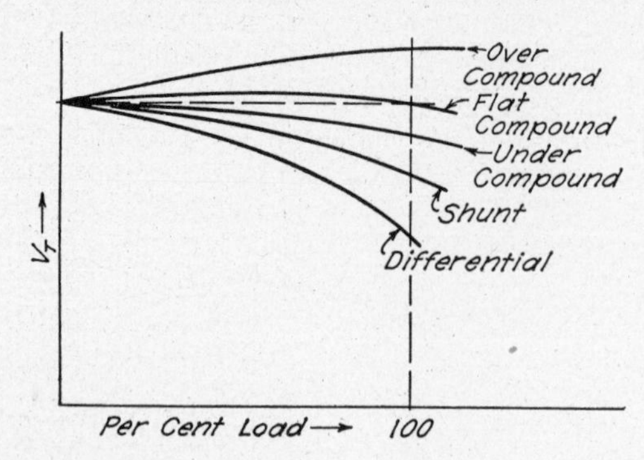

FIG. 17–9. Typical load curves for various degrees of compounding.

are the same, the generator is flat-compounded. Figure 17–9 shows typical load curves for the differential compound and the three classes of cumulative compound generators.

The effect of increase in speed is to give the generator a more rising voltage characteristic with the addition of load. This is different from

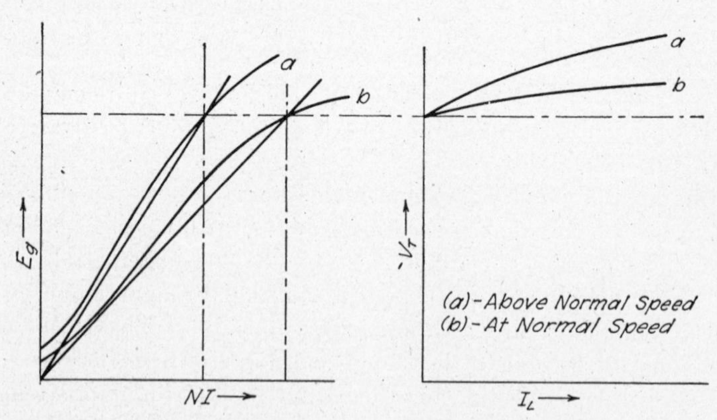

FIG. 18–9. External characteristics of an over-compound generator for two different speeds; (a) is for a speed greater than (b).

the effect on a shunt generator (Fig. 14–9), which gave a poorer characteristic for increased speed. A study of the effect of series-field turns on the external characteristic, when the generator is operated at two different speeds, is shown in Fig. 18–9. The higher speed requires a lower saturation at no-load voltage and, as a result, the series-field turns give a greater percentage change in total flux and the terminal voltage increases more as the load current is increased.

The factors influencing the external characteristic of a compound generator are the same as those for a shunt generator. The addition of the series field, however, brings additional magnetomotive force to the main magnetic circuit and the final characteristic differs from that of a shunt generator by the series-field influence. In practice, the series field is usually made strong enough to compensate for all the factors reducing the terminal voltage and to furnish an additional magnetomotive force

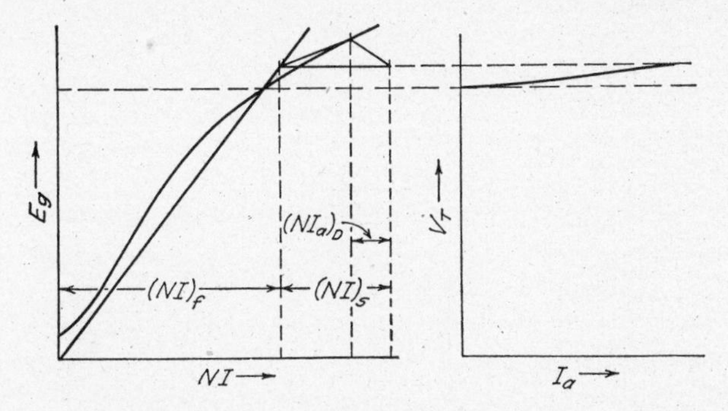

FIG. 19–9. Determination of the armature characteristic of an over-compound generator from the magnetization curve and field resistance line.

component to increase the terminal voltage and, thereby, compensate for transmission line losses. In this way, the generator can maintain a constant voltage at the end of a line.

The determination of the external characteristic of a compound generator, from its magnetization curve and field resistance line, can be made in the same general way as it can be made for a shunt generator. The horizontal (or base) side of the construction triangle has two magnetomotive force components which have opposing effects on the generator performance characteristic. The components are the series-field ampere turns, which aid the main field, and the demagnetizing ampere turns of armature reaction, which oppose the main field. Like that of the shunt generator, the construction triangle of the compound generator must touch both the field resistance line and the magnetization curve. Figure 19–9 shows how the armature characteristics of an overcompound generator may be determined from its magnetization curve and field resistance line.

Figure 20–9 shows an enlarged diagram. The no-load terminal voltage is $o'x'$ for which the shunt-field ampere turns (oa) are required. If the compound generator is loaded to an armature current $o'G$, the series-field turns furnish additional ampere turns (bd) and the demagnetizing effect of armature reaction is (dc) ampere turns. The additional ampere turns (ab) are caused by the increased terminal voltage which, in turn,

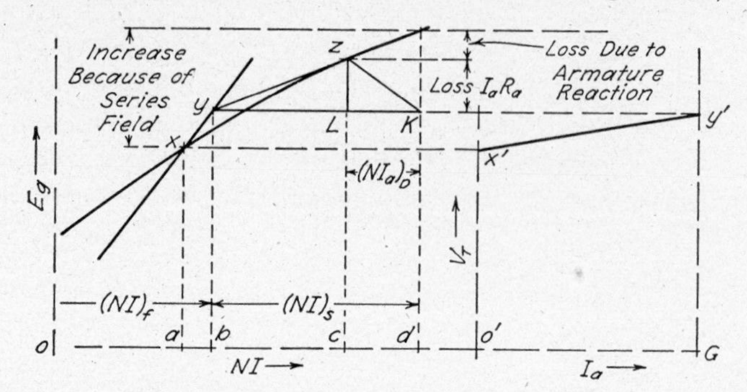

FIG. 20–9. Enlarged diagram of Fig. 19–9 showing the component parts in the construction of the armature characteristic.

increases the shunt-field ampere turns from oa to ob. The voltage ZL is the voltage drop in the armature and series-field circuit. (*Note:* This is for a long shunt compound generator.) The difference between a long shunt and short shunt compound generator is discussed in the next article. On Fig. 20–9, it will be seen that each component which can influence the armature characteristic has been considered. The components in this, as in the shunt generator diagram, are drawn vertically for voltage and horizontally for magnetomotive force.

7. Long and Short Shunt Compound Generators. The main classification of compound generators are cumulative and differential com-

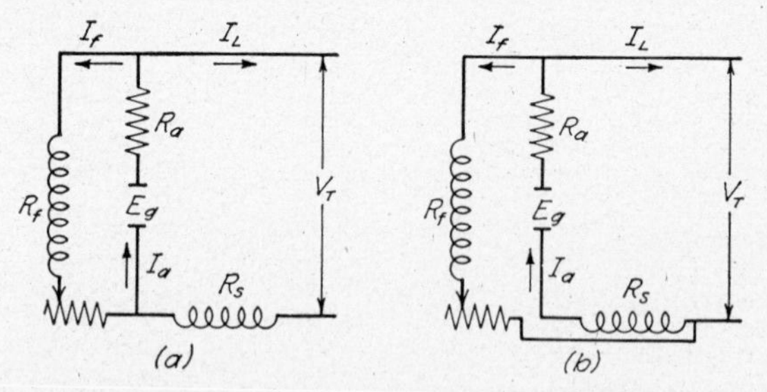

FIG. 21–9. Compound generator connections: (*a*) short shunt; (*b*) long shunt.

pound. The differential compound generator, because of its extremely poor external characteristic, is used only in special cases. The degree of compounding has been discussed but the possible ways of connecting the shunt and series fields have not. Figure 21–9 shows the two ways of connecting the shunt and series fields of compound generators. In the short shunt compound connection (Fig. 21–9*a*), the following current and voltage relationships exist:

$$I_s = I_L$$

$$I_a = I_f + I_L = I_f + I_s$$

$$V_T = E_g - I_a R_a - I_L R_s$$

$$V_f = V_T + I_L R_s$$

For the long shunt compound connection (Fig. 21–9*b*) these relationships exist:

$$I_s = I_a$$

$$I_a = I_s = I_f + I_L$$

$$V_T = E_g - I_a(R_a + R_s)$$

$$V_f = V_T$$

A careful study of these voltage and current relationships will show that there is a difference in these two connections whereas, practically, little difference will exist between their external characteristics. The long shunt compound connection is usually used. The interpole windings can be considered electrically as part of the armature circuit in making calculations. The shunt field and control rheostat are connected externally across the armature and series-field circuit in order to make the long shunt compound connection.

8. Determination of Series Turns. It is often desirable to determine by experiment the number of series turns necessary to give a shunt generator a definite voltage characteristic or to change the degree of compounding of a compound generator. The procedure is as follows.

1. Determine the shunt-field current necessary to give rated no-load terminal voltage.

2. Determine the shunt-field current necessary to give the desired full-load terminal voltage.

3. From tests (1) and (2), the change in shunt-field current can be determined and the increase in ampere turns calculated when N_{sh} (shunt-field turns) is known. If I_{FL} is the full-load armature current,

$$I_{FL} N_s = (I_{fFL} - I_{fNL})\, N_{sh}$$

and

$$N_s = \frac{(I_{fFL} - I_{fNL})}{I_{FL}}\, N_{sh}$$

If the calculations give fractional turns, complete turns must be placed on the field poles and a shunt (diverter) must be placed across the series-field winding to proportion the current through the winding and give the correct ampere turns. The resistance of the shunt relative to the series-field resistance must be in inverse ratio to the desired current division. Figure 22–9 shows a circuit diagram of a series field with a shunt across it. The series field is to furnish 150 ampere turns with a total armature current of 70 amperes. Three turns are used in the series field and only 50 amperes are necessary. The shunt must carry the 20 remaining amperes.

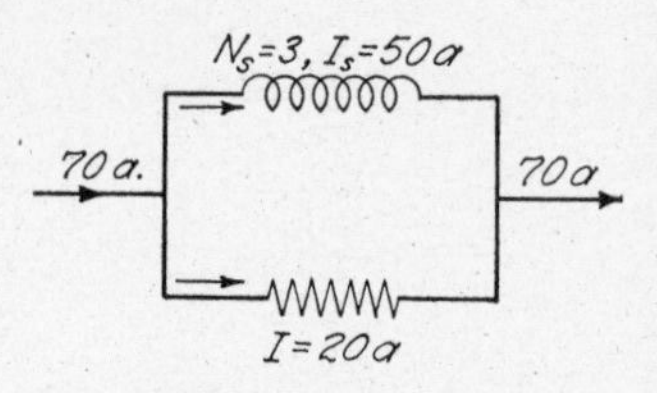

FIG. 22–9. Series field with a shunt (diverter).

Example b. If the resistance of the series field is 0.05 ohm, what must be the resistance of the shunt to give the current division for Fig. 22–9.

$$\frac{I_{\text{series}}}{I_{\text{shunt}}} = \frac{R_{\text{shunt}}}{R_{\text{series}}}$$

$$\frac{50}{20} = \frac{R}{0.05} \qquad R = \frac{50 \times 0.05}{20} = 0.125 \text{ ohm}$$

9. Series Generators. The series generator was formerly used to supply a fairly constant current at a variable voltage for loads such as street lighting. The magnetization curve is similar to that of the shunt and compound generators and the terminal voltages differ from the generated voltages by the voltage drop in the armature and series field. Figure 23–9 shows the circuit diagram and the external characteristic as determined from the magnetization curve and field resistance line. The generator is usually operated on the part (Wy) of its characteristic curve. Beyond the point x on the external characteristic curve, the terminal voltage decreases as the load is increased. This decrease in voltage is caused by the demagnetizing effects of armature reaction decreasing the resultant magnetomotive force.

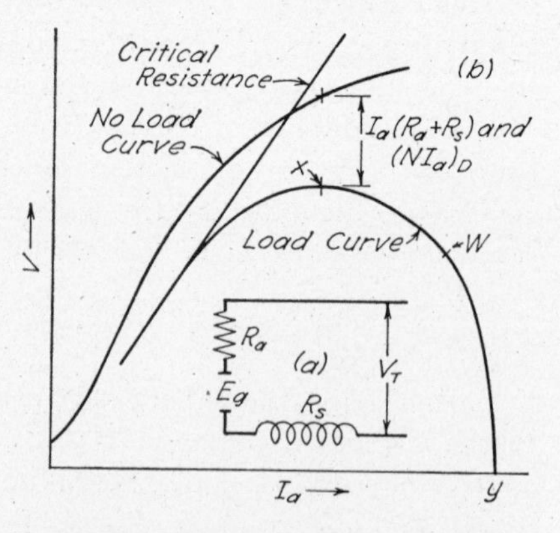

FIG. 23–9. Series generator: (*a*) circuit diagram; (*b*) determination of the external characteristic curve from the maganetization curve and field resistance line.

The series generator has been replaced by the constant current transformer for street lighting circuits, but it is still used as a voltage booster on d-c systems. The booster generator is connected in series with the load and the load current passes through its armature and series field. If the machine is rotated by a prime mover, it will generate a voltage and increase the system voltage on the output side of the generator as the load current increases. The increase in voltage for the same current represents additional power supplied to the system by the series generator. Figure 24–9 shows the circuit diagram of a series generator used as a booster.

Example c. A series generator used as a booster raises the line voltage from 500 volts to 650 volts when the line current is 125 amp. What are the voltage, current, and power outputs of the series generator? Use the circuit diagram of Fig. 24–9.

$$V_A = 500 \text{ volts}$$

$$V_B = 650 \text{ volts}$$

Then

$$V_G = 150 \text{ volts}$$

$$I_G = I_L = 125 \text{ amp}$$

$$\text{The power output} = 150 \times 125 = 18{,}750 \text{ watts}$$

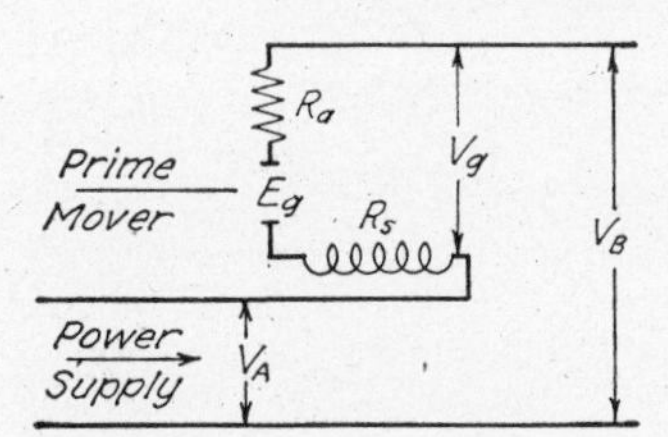

Fig. 24–9. Series generator as a booster.

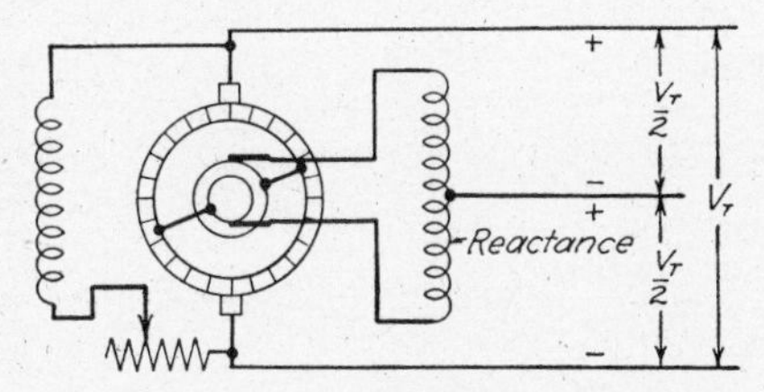

Fig. 25–9. Circuit diagram of a three-wire generator.

10. Three-Wire Generator. The three-wire generator principle is a convenient way to obtain the neutral or midpoint for the three-wire system. An a-c voltage is generated in the armature of every machine and, if this armature winding is tapped at equidistant points and these taps are brought to the outside through slip rings, an alternating voltage is available. If a high reactance is connected across these slip rings, only a small amount of alternating current will flow; and, if this high reactance is tapped at the middle point of the winding, the point will be at equipotential with respect to all generated voltages. The potential difference between the d-c terminals and the center tap on the reactance coil will be constant at all times and equal to one-half the line voltage. The circuit diagram of the three-wire generator is shown in Fig. 25–9.

If the loading between the lines and the neutral is not balanced, a current will flow in the neutral back through the reactance into the armature winding.

11. Voltage Regulation. "The voltage regulation of a direct current generator is the final change in voltage with constant field rheostat setting when the specified load is reduced gradually to zero, expressed as a per cent of rated load voltage, the speed being kept constant." †

The expression for percentage voltage regulation is $[(V_{NL} - V_{FL})/V_{FL}] \times 100$.

The performance of a generator is judged by its percentage voltage regulation. A machine with a low percentage regulation is designed so that the effects of armature reaction, change in shunt-field current, and voltage drop in the armature and series field are of negligible effect. If the percentage voltage regulation is positive in sign, the external characteristic is drooping and, if negative in sign, it is rising. The voltage regulation of a series generator would have no meaning since the voltage at no-load current would be only that produced by the residual magnetism.

Example d. A shunt generator supplies 200 amp at 125 volts. When the load is removed and the speed held constant, the terminal voltage is 140 volts. What is the percentage regulation?

$$V_{FL} = 125 \text{ volts} \qquad V_{NL} = 140 \text{ volts}$$

$$\text{Regulation in percentage} = \frac{140 - 125}{125} \times 100 = 12 \text{ per cent}$$

Example e. The terminal voltage of a compound generator changes from 125 volts at no-load to 140 volts at full load. What is the percentage voltage regulation?

$$V_{NL} = 125 \text{ volts} \qquad V_{FL} = 140 \text{ volts}$$

$$\text{Regulation in percentage} = \frac{125 - 140}{140} \times 100 = -10.7 \text{ per cent}$$

12. Automatic Voltage Control, Tirrill Regulator. The Tirrill regulator is a mechanical device which automatically changes the shunt-field current of the generator as the load changes and aids in keeping the terminal voltage V_T constant for the load variations. Figure 26–9 shows a simplified circuit diagram of a Tirrill regulator. The adjustments are the spring tensions on the main contacts and relay contacts. The principle of operation is to short-circuit the shunt-field rheostat resistance R in this way, permitting the generated voltage to increase.

† American standard definitions, American Institute of Electrical Engineers (10.95.120).

This in turn will increase the terminal voltage V_T to the required value. For balanced conditions both the main contacts and relay contacts are open. The sequence of operations is as follows: If the terminal voltage decreases, the current through the holding coil for the main contacts will decrease and the spring will close the main contacts. Current will flow through the differentially wound relay magnet and the demagnetizing effect will permit the spring to close the relay contacts. The closing of the relay contacts will short-circuit the shunt-field rheostat R and the shunt-field current will increase, increasing the generated voltage and

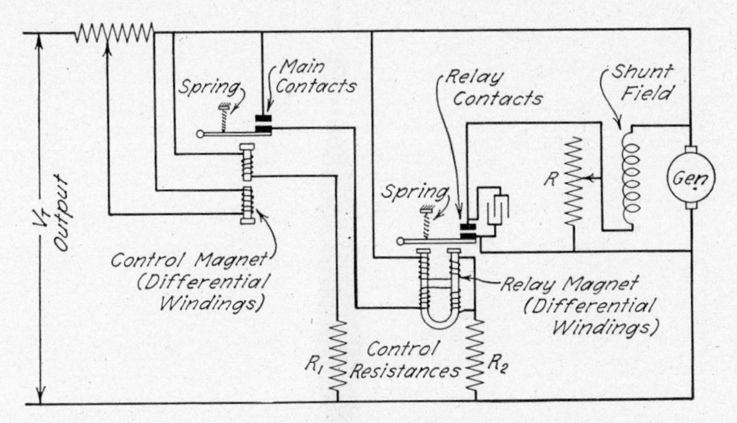

FIG. 26–9. Circuit diagram of an automatic voltage regulator.

terminal voltage. When the generated voltage has increased sufficiently the reverse action occurs. This means that the main contacts are opened, the relay magnet is operative, opening the contacts, and the field rheostat is inserted in the shunt-field circuit.

The differential action of the control magnet is obtained by using the voltage drop across the compensating shunt placed in the load circuit. Thus a higher voltage will be required to operate the main contacts as the load current increases, and the terminal voltage can be increased and at the same time regulated. This scheme makes it possible to compensate for line voltage drops to a distant load if desired. The effect of current compensation can be changed by adjustment along the compensating shunt to give the desired effect through the auxiliary coil on the main control magnet.

13. Rotary Synchronous Converters. In a d-c machine, the induced voltage in the armature conductors is alternating and, by using brushes and a commutator, the voltage and current in the external circuit may be made unidirectional. If the winding of a d-c generator is tapped symmetrically and the connections brought out through slip rings, both direct current and alternating current are available from the same winding. The machine, in this event, is called a double-current generator. The real advantage of this arrangement is not that the machine is a double-current source, but that it is possible to operate from the a-c side as a motor and the d-c side as a generator at the same time. This machine is called the rotary or synchronous converter, and its purpose is to change alternating current to direct current. It is possible, however, to operate the machine in the reverse order, that is, direct current to alternating current. When the machine is operated in this manner, it is called an inverted converter. Since this book cannot consider all the possible operating conditions, it is sufficient to state that operating the machine as an inverter may be dangerous. This danger is caused by the demagnetizing effects of armature reaction of low-power factor loads.

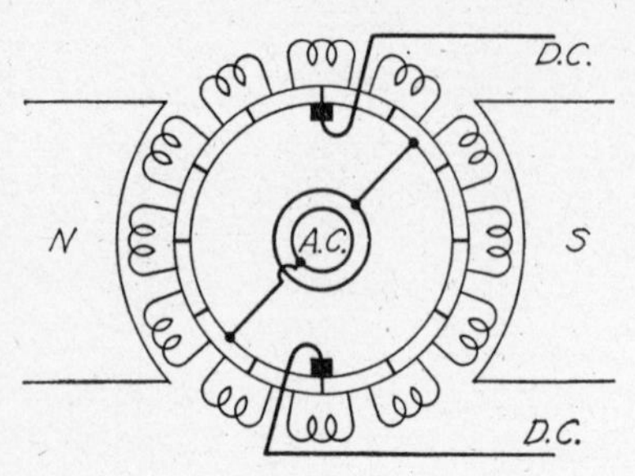

FIG. 27–9. Schematic circuit diagram for a single-phase synchronous converter.

The real advantage of a rotary converter is its improved efficiency over the motor-generator set and lower first cost. The iron and friction and windage losses are reduced, since there is only one magnetic circuit and one set of bearings. Since the armature current is a resultant current (alternating current and direct current) of motor and generator action, the armature current is usually smaller than that in a generator of equivalent rating. This decreased armature current gives a lower armature copper loss. The voltage and current ratios for a converter are fixed and, as a result, the output voltage of the d-c generator is determined by the input a-c voltage. This results in a definite input transformer voltage for a predetermined d-c output voltage of the converter. The rotary converter installation includes the group of transformers having the proper secondary voltage rating to give the desired d-c output voltage.

a. Single-Phase. Although most rotary converters are of the polyphase type, the voltage and current relationships will be developed for the single-phase machine to show more clearly these fundamental relationships. Figure 27–9 shows the schematic circuit diagram of a single-phase synchronous converter. The a-c voltage in the winding varies from zero to maximum value and the d-c voltage is a constant value which is the maximum value of the alternating voltage. The voltmeter reads the effective value of voltage at every instance and the ratio of voltages (assuming sine waves) is

$$V_{DC} = \sqrt{2}V_{AC} \quad \text{or} \quad V_{AC} = 0.707V_{DC}$$

If the machine losses are neglected (power input equals power output), the ratio of currents can be determined from the expression

$$V_{DC}I_{DC} = V_{AC}I_{AC}\cos\theta$$

since

$$V_{DC} = \sqrt{2}V_{AC}$$

Then

$$I_{DC} = \frac{I_{AC}\cos\theta}{\sqrt{2}}$$

and

$$I_{AC} = \frac{\sqrt{2}I_{DC}}{\cos\theta}$$

If the power factor is unity, the ratio of I_{AC} to I_{DC} becomes

$$I_{DC} = \frac{I_{AC}}{\sqrt{2}} = 0.707I_{AC}$$

When the losses are considered and the efficiency is η, the expression for power output becomes

$$V_{DC}I_{DC} = V_{AC}I_{AC}\eta\cos\theta$$

and the current relationship is

$$I_{DC} = \frac{I_{AC}\,\eta\cos\theta}{\sqrt{2}}$$

or

$$I_{AC} = \frac{\sqrt{2}I_{DC}}{\eta\cos\theta}$$

b. Three-Phase. For the three-phase, three-wire a-c input, the machine winding is tapped at three equidistant points per pair of poles and, for the same d-c voltage output, the a-c line voltage input is less than it is in the single-phase converter. Figure 28–9 shows the schematic circuit diagram for the three-phase synchronous converter. The three-phase line voltage is 86.6

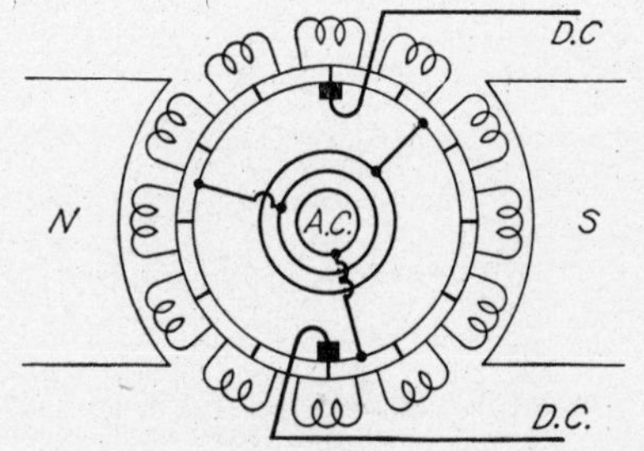

Fig. 28–9. Schematic circuit diagram for a three-phase synchronous converter.

per cent of the single-phase line voltage required to maintain similar conditions in the armature circuit, and the ratio of line voltages for the three-phase supply is

$$V_{DC} = \frac{\sqrt{2}V_{AC}}{0.866} = 1.63V_{AC}$$

or

$$V_{AC} = 0.612V_{DC}$$

When the losses are considered and the efficiency is η, the power expression for the three-phase converter becomes

$$V_{DC}I_{DC} = \sqrt{3}V_{AC}I_{AC}\eta \cos \theta$$

And, by substituting the value $V_{DC} = 1.63\ V_{AC}$, the ratios of currents are

$$I_{DC} = \frac{\sqrt{3}}{1.63} I_{AC}\eta \cos \theta$$

or

$$I_{DC} = 1.06I_{AC}\eta \cos \theta$$

and

$$I_{AC} = \frac{0.943I_{DC}}{\eta \cos \theta}$$

c. N-Phase. Figure 29–9 shows the voltage ratio between the d-c voltage output and the polyphase voltage input. Following the same

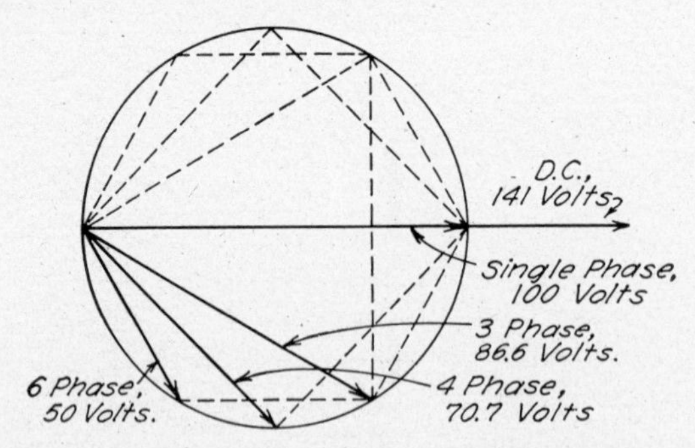

FIG. 29–9. Diagram of the voltage ratio between the d-c voltage and the polyphase a-c voltage.

procedure as for the single-phase and three-phase inputs, the ratios for any number of phases can be determined. Multiphase synchronous converters are used in many installations, and the six-phase converter is quite common. The following table gives the voltage and current ratios for the most common polyphase installations (assuming unity power factor and 100 per cent efficiency). The six-phase supply for a synchronous converter may be obtained by the connections shown in Fig. 30–9. Most transformers have two secondary windings, and the three-phase

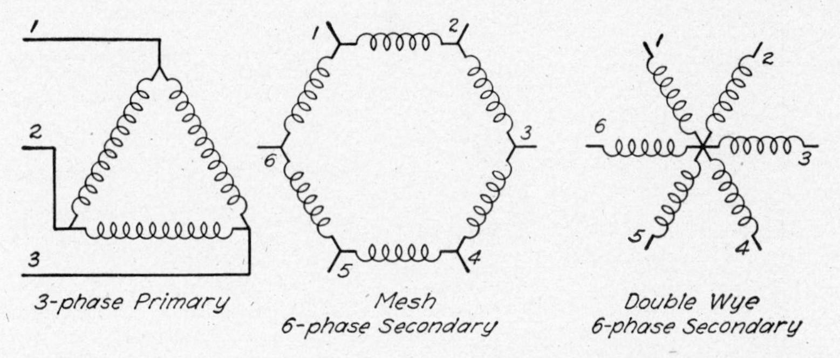

FIG. 30–9. Schematic circuit diagrams of a six-phase mesh circuit and double wye.

source may be connected into a six-phase mesh or into a double wye secondary connection. This last type of connection is used frequently for converters.

TABLE I–9

Number of Slip Rings	Number of Phases	Line Values: Current Ratio $\frac{I_{AC}}{I_{DC}}$	Line Values: Voltage Ratio $\frac{V_{AC}}{V_{DC}}$
2	1	1.414	0.707
3	3	0.943	0.612
4	4	0.707	0.500
6	6 (mesh)	0.471	0.354
6	6 (diametrical)	0.471	0.707

The resultant current in the converter winding is not uniform in all coils but varies with the position of the coil relative to the a-c taps on the winding. The coils nearest the taps carry the largest current. As a result, the heating in the winding is not uniform and hot spots occur near the a-c connections. To reduce this difficulty, the six-phase converter is used. The twelve-phase converter would further reduce this difficulty, but the additional cost of equipment and the complicated connections make it undesirable. The converter is rated in the same way as any piece of electrical equipment and it is important that the machine be operated as near unity power factor as possible to avoid excessive heating in the windings.

A synchronous converter may be started by any of the methods employed in starting synchronous motors, or it may be started as a d-c motor and, at the correct speed, synchronized with the a-c input. If the converter is started from the a-c side, the shunt-field winding of the machine must be opened in several places to protect the insulation from damage, which might result from the high voltage induced in this winding at starting.

Example f. The power for a 100-kw, 250-volt, d-c load is to be furnished by a three-phase rotary converter from a 2300-volt, three-phase supply. If the rotary converter efficiency is 95 per cent for unity power factor operation, determine the rotary converter input and the transformer ratings. (Assume the transformer bank connected in delta-delta.)

D-c side:

$$I_{DC} = \frac{100,000}{250} = 400 \text{ amp} \qquad V_{DC} = 250 \text{ volts}$$

A-c side:

$$V_{AC} = 0.612\ V_{DC} = 0.612 \times 250 = 153 \text{ volts}$$

$$I_{AC} = \frac{0.943\ I_{DC}}{\eta \cos \theta} = \frac{0.943 \times 400}{0.95 \times 1.00} = 397 \text{ amp}$$

Rotary converter input:

$$V_{AC} = 153 \text{ volts} \qquad I_{AC} = 397 \text{ amp}$$

Current per transformer secondary:

$$\frac{397}{\sqrt{3}} = 229 \text{ amp}$$

Kilovolt-ampere rating:

$$\frac{229 \times 153}{1000} = 35.0 \text{ kva}$$

Three transformers, each having a rating of 2300/153 volt 35.0 kva are required.

This can be checked easily since the efficiency and power factor are given. Input is 100/0.95 = 105 kw at unity power factor. Transformer bank is 105 kva, which is 35 kva per transformer.

PROBLEMS

1-9. A 4-pole lap-wound, d-c generator is running at 1500 rpm. If there are 400 active armature conductors and the flux per pole is 1.25×10^6 lines, what is the generated voltage?

2-9. There are 540 conductors on a wave-wound armature of a 6-pole, 50-kw, 250-volt, d-c generator. As a result of shifting the brushes from the no-load neutral, there are 600 demagnetizing ampere turns per pole of armature reaction at full load. (*a*) What is the angle of brush shift, in electrical degrees? (*b*) Determine the cross-magnetizing ampere turns per pole.

3–9. The saturation curve of a d-c shunt generator is represented by the equation $E_g = 180 + 40I_f$, where I_f is the field current. The armature resistance is 0.2 ohm, the shunt-field circuit resistance is 120 ohms and the effect of armature reaction is negligible. (*a*) What is the no-load terminal voltage of this generator (neglecting the voltage drop in the armature caused by the shunt-field current)? (*b*) When the machine has been loaded until the terminal voltage is 240 volts, what is the load current?

4–9. A 15-kw, 250-volt, d-c shunt generator has a voltage regulation of 12 per cent. The armature resistance is 0.075 ohm and the shunt-field circuit resistance is 80 ohms. Determine the ratio of flux per pole at no load to flux per pole at full load.

5–9. A 25-kw, 250-volt, self-excited shunt generator has an armature resistance of 0.098 ohm. With the speed constant at 1200 rpm and the shunt-field current held constant at 3 amp the terminal voltage is 250 volts at full load and 274 volts at no load. (*a*) What is the full-load flux, expressed in per cent of no-load flux? (*b*) What change in field circuit resistance is required to maintain the field current constant from no load to full load?

6–9. A separately excited d-c generator is rated at 250 volts and 100 amp. It has a voltage regulation of 6 per cent and its external characteristic is assumed to be a straight line. If the load resistance is changed from 2.5 ohms for full-load condition to 4 ohms, find the terminal voltage and kilowatt load of the generator. The armature resistance is 0.15 ohm.

7–9. A short shunt, overcompound, d-c generator has the following rating: 100 kw, 250 volts, 1200 rpm. The machine constants are: $R_a = 0.012$ ohm, $R_s = 0.015$ ohm, and $R_f = 50$ ohms. Determine the generated voltage of this machine when the load current is 50 per cent of the full-load current and the terminal voltage is 250 volts.

8–9. A 25-kw, 250-volt, 4-pole shunt generator has its field connected to a storage battery. To obtain 250 volts at no load, the field current is 4 amp. At full load the field current must be increased to 4.5 amp for a terminal voltage of 250 volts. The field has 2000 turns per pole. How many series-field turns per pole should be used to make this generator a flat-compound generator? Neglect the effects of armature resistance.

9–9. A compound generator has a saturation curve of such a type that the operating portion of it may be expressed by the equation $E_g = 80 + 0.01NI$ where NI is the total ampere turns of the magnetic circuit, whether furnished by the shunt field, or the series field, or by armature reaction.

$$NI \text{ of the shunt field} = 1000I_f$$

$$NI \text{ of the series field} = 10I_s$$

$$NI \text{ of armature reaction (demagnetizing)} = 5I_a$$

If the generator is separately excited and has the series field connected additively find (*a*) the shunt-field current for a no-load terminal voltage of 120 volts, (*b*) the shunt-field current for a terminal voltage of 120 volts when $I_a = 100$ amp. $R_a = 0.1$ ohm and $R_s = 0.05$ ohm.

10–9. A 25-kw, 250-volt, d-c shunt generator is to be converted into a short shunt flat-compound generator by the addition of a series field (using a diverter if required). When operating as a shunt generator,

(1) The field current to give a terminal voltage of 250 volts at no load is 3 amp.
(2) The field current to give a terminal voltage of 250 volts at full load is 3.48 amp.
(3) Shunt-field turns per pole is 500.

How many series-field turns per pole are required? (Neglect the voltage drop in the series-field turns.) If the resistance per·turn of the series field is 0.01 ohm determine the resistance of a diverter if one is required.

11–9. An overcompound short shunt, d-c generator is rated at 250 kw at 250 volts and 1000 rpm. The armature resistance is 0.01 ohm, the series-field resistance is 0.012 ohm, and the shunt-field circuit resistance is 10 ohms. If the air-gap flux under full load is 115 per cent of the no-load flux, what is the generated voltage at no load?

12–9. A d-c shunt generator is rated at 50 kw, 125 volts, 1200 rpm. The armature resistance is 0.03 ohm and the shunt-field circuit resistance is 12.5 ohms. If the air-gap flux under load is 95 per cent of the no-load air-gap flux, determine the per cent voltage regulation for this machine.

13–9. A 10-kw, 125-volt, 1750-rpm, flat-compound, long shunt generator is driven by a motor which runs at 1750 rpm for full load on the generator and 1800 rpm for no load on the generator. The generator constants are $R_a = 0.025$ ohm, $R_s = 0.02$ ohm, and $R_f = 100$ ohms. Neglecting the effect caused by the field current, determine the generator voltage at no load. What is the ratio of no-load air-gap flux to full-load air-gap flux?

14–9. A long-shunt cumulative compound generator has these constants: $R_a = 0.025$ ohm, $R_s = 0.02$ ohm, and $R_f = 100$ ohms. Terminal voltage at full load is 125 volts and at no load is 133 volts. The generator is driven by a motor which drives the generator at 1150 rpm at full load and 1190 rpm at no load. Determine the power rating of the generator if the air-gap flux is constant at no load and at full load.

15–9. A 3-phase rotary converter supplies 125 amp at 575 volts d-c. The a-c supply to the converter is from a 3-phase wye-delta bank of transformers which in turn is supplied by a 2300-volt, 3-phase, 3-wire line. Assuming a rotary efficiency of 96 per cent, determine the voltage, current, and kilovolt-ampere rating of the supply transformers. Assume unity power factor and neglect the voltage drop in the converter.

CHAPTER 10

DIRECT-CURRENT MOTORS

A motor has been defined as a machine for converting electrical energy to mechanical energy; the d-c dynamo becomes a motor when energy transfer occurs in this way.

1. Torque Curves. For mechanical power to be delivered by any machine, it is necessary to have both torque and rotation. In the chapter on motor theory (Chapter 5), it was shown that the torque developed by a given machine is proportional to the armature current and the air-gap flux.

The armature winding of a motor is connected in such a way that the current in each active conductor reacts with the air-gap flux to produce torque acting in the same direction at every instant. As any single conductor moves from under one pole to the adjacent pole, the current is reversed in that conductor (by the commutator) so that the torque is always in the same direction.

In the d-c motor, the strength of the magnetic field (air-gap flux) is a resultant of several magnetomotive forces all acting in a common magnetic system. It will be shown for each type of d-c motor that the air-gap flux is influenced by different magnetomotive forces and, for that reason, is not necessarily constant for all conditions of motor operation.

The torque developed by a d-c motor is

$$T = KZI_a\phi \qquad (a\text{–}10)$$

where K is a constant, depending upon the number of parallel paths through the armature winding, the selection of units, the diameter of the armature, and the percentage of active conductors, Z is the number of conductors in the winding, I_a is the armature current in amperes, and ϕ is the air-gap flux per pole.

The torque for a given d-c machine becomes

$$T = K_T\phi I_a \qquad (b\text{–}10)$$

where K_T is the constant including KZ from equation (a–10), ϕ is the total air-gap flux per pole, and I_a is the armature current.

a. Shunt Motor. The shunt motor is connected in the same manner as the shunt generator, with its field connected directly across the armature terminals. The armature and field circuits are separate electrical circuits with the main-field current and flux substantially constant at all times. The armature current increases as the motor load increases. The characteristic torque curve for a shunt motor is shown in Fig. 1–10. The characteristic is practically a straight line within its working range, since one of the controlling factors (the air-gap flux) remains approximately constant for all loads. The change in the shape of the curve at values of current above normal is caused by the effects of armature reaction, which decreases the air-gap flux.

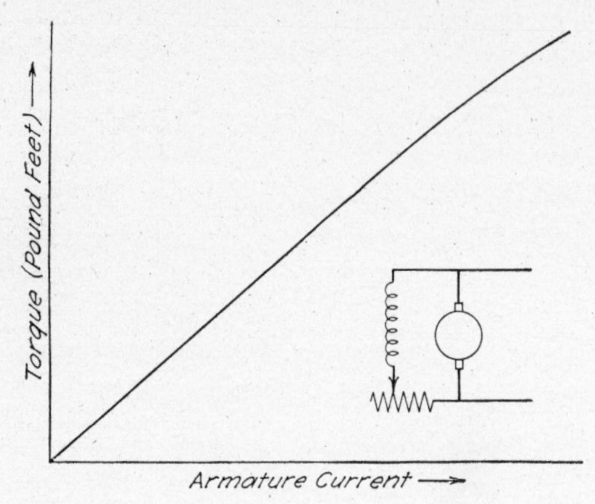

FIG. 1–10. Shunt motor torque characteristic curve.

b. Series Motor. The field circuit of a series motor is in series with the armature and, in this way, the field flux is dependent upon the armature current. From equation (*b*–10),

$$T = K_T\phi_s I_a$$

and, since ϕ_s varies with the armature current,

$$T = K_T I_a^2$$

This assumes that the reluctance of the magnetic circuit is constant, an assumption true for most practical considerations.

Figure 2–10 shows the torque characteristic curve of a series motor. This curve is a second-degree curve, and a small variation in armature current produces a large variation in torque.

c. Compound Motors. The compound motor has both a shunt field and a series field. There are two possible field arrangements in the magnetic system of a compound motor. These depend upon whether the series-field ampere turns aid or oppose the shunt-field ampere turns. The first condition is called the cumulative compound arrangement and the second the differential compound arrangement.

The air-gap flux of a compound motor is produced by a resultant magnetomotive force acting on the magnetic system. This resultant magnetomotive force is the resultant of the main-field, armature, and

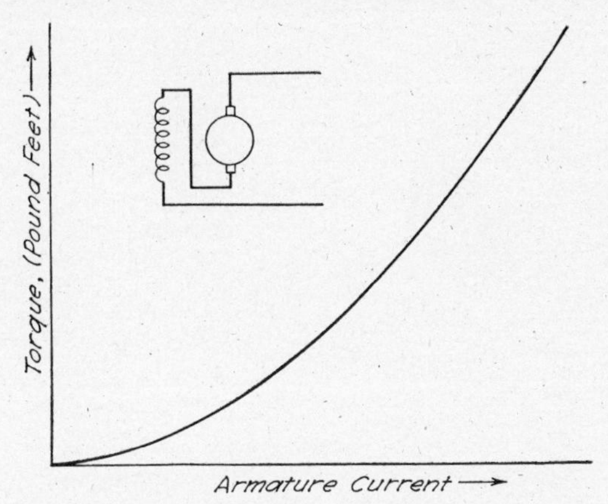

FIG. 2–10. Series motor torque characteristic curve.

series-field magnetomotive forces. The torque expression for the compound motors becomes

$$T = K_T \phi_R I_a$$

where ϕ_R is a varying factor, depending upon the effects of armature reaction, strength of the series field as compared to the shunt field, and

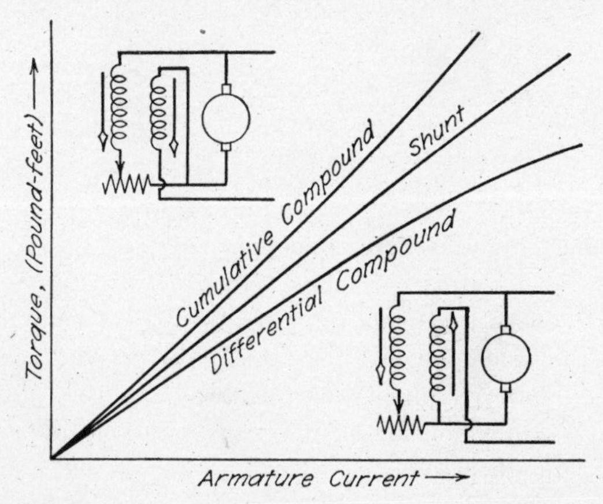

FIG. 3–10. Characteristic torque curves of the compound and shunt motors.

the connection of the series field to aid or oppose the shunt field. Figure 3–10 shows the torque characteristics of the cumulative and differential compound motors. The characteristics of the long or short shunt compound motor are practically the same for either type of connection. This discussion will not attempt to differentiate between the two connections.

Example a. A shunt motor is running at 1200 rpm and the armature current is 50 amp for a given load. If the load is changed so that the armature current is 30 amp, compare the motor torques developed for the two armature currents. Assume the air-gap flux to remain constant.

$$T = K_T \phi I_a$$

Then

$$\frac{T_1}{T_2} = \frac{K_T \phi 50}{K_T \phi 30} = \frac{50}{30} = \frac{5}{3} = 166.7 \text{ per cent}$$

The torque for $I_a = 30$ amp is 60 per cent of the torque for $I_a = 50$ amp.

Example b. A street car motor (series motor) requires 160 amp when starting and 60 amp for a given load. What is the ratio of starting torque to running torque? Assume the saturation curve to be a straight line.

$$T = K_T I_a^2$$

Therefore

$$\frac{T_{\text{starting}}}{T_{\text{running}}} = \frac{K_T(160)^2}{K_T(60)^2} = \frac{256}{36}$$

The ratio is 7.11 to 1.

Example c. A cumulative compound motor has a varying load upon it which requires a variation in armature current from 50 amp to 100 amp. If the series-field current causes the air-gap flux to change by 3 per cent for each 10 amp of armature current, give the ratio of torques developed for the two values of armature current.

$$T = K_T \phi_R I_a$$

$$T_{50} = K_T(115)(50)$$

$$T_{100} = K_T(130)(100)$$

$$\frac{T_{100}}{T_{50}} = \frac{K_T(130)(100)}{K_T(115)(50)} = \frac{260}{115} = \frac{2.26}{1}$$

2. Counterelectromotive Force and Speed Relations. The torque developed by the conductors carrying current when in the presence of a magnetic field causes the armature to rotate. The commutator is so connected to the armature windings that the current flowing through the conductors under a given pole is always in the same direction. Therefore, the torque developed in each conductor under the pole is always in the same direction.

Since the armature rotates in the magnetic field, the same conductors that carry current and develop torque are also cutting the magnetic field and have an electromotive force generated in them. The direction of this generated voltage is such as to oppose the impressed voltage. The current, which flows in the armature circuit of a motor, depends upon two factors: (1) the ohmic resistance of the armature circuit and (2) the resultant voltage acting on the armature circuit, which is the difference between the terminal and generated voltages of the armature. This generated voltage in the armature of a motor, since it is in opposition to the impressed voltage, is called the *counterelectromotive force* or *back electromotive force*. The same factors which control the generated voltage of a d-c generator also control the counterelectromotive force in a d-c motor. The expression for the counterelectromotive force is

$$E_c = K\phi N$$

where E_c = counterelectromotive force
K = a constant for the machine (including the factor 10^{-8})
ϕ = air-gap flux per pole
N = speed.

The voltage acting on the armature circuit of a motor is the algebraic sum of the terminal voltage and the counterelectromotive force, whereas the current flowing in the armature is determined by this resultant voltage and the resistance of the armature circuit. These relationships can be expressed as

$$V_T + (-E_c) = I_a R_a$$

$$V_T = E_c + I_a R_a$$

$$E_c = V_T - I_a R_a$$

If these relationships are compared with those for a d-c generator, it will be seen that the generated voltage is less than the terminal voltage for a motor; the reverse is true for the generator. This expression may be written in several ways and, if the factors controlling the counterelectromotive force are considered, the following relationships exist.

$$V_T = K\phi N + I_a R_a$$

$$N = \frac{V_T - I_a R_a}{K\phi} \qquad (c\text{–}10)$$

$$\phi = \frac{V_T - I_a R_a}{KN} \qquad (d\text{–}10)$$

The relationships shown in equations (c–10) and (d–10) are analytical and, in order to get a correct value for the speed or flux for a motor, it is necessary to determine accurately the numerical values for the factors K, ϕ, and N.

If these relationships are to be used for specific motors, it is necessary to modify the expressions to include the effects of series, shunt, and interpole fields and windings, and the type of series-field connection (long or short shunt). For specific motors, the following relationships exist.

Shunt motor:

$$V_T = E_c + I_a R_a$$

Series motor:

$$V_T = E_c + I_a(R_a + R_s)$$

Compound motor, long shunt:

$$V_T = E_c + I_a(R_a + R_s)$$

Compound motor, short shunt:

$$V_T = E_c + I_a R_a + (I_a + I_f)R_s$$

The resistance of the interpoles can be included in the value of R_a. It is possible, by substitution in the preceding expressions, to get the expressions (*c*–10) and (*d*–10) for any d-c motor.

Example d. A shunt motor is running at 1200 rpm and the armature requires 50 amp from a 230-volt source. If the load is changed so that the armature current is 25 amp, determine the motor speed. The value of armature resistance is 0.15 ohm and the air-gap flux is assumed to be constant.

$$1200 = \frac{230 - 50(0.15)}{K\phi} \quad \text{initial condition}$$

$$N = \frac{230 - 25(0.15)}{K\phi} \quad \text{final condition}$$

$$\frac{N}{1200} = \frac{230 - 25(0.15)}{230 - 50(0.15)} = \frac{230 - 3.75}{230 - 7.50} = \frac{226.25}{222.50}$$

$$N = 1200 \times \frac{226.25}{222.50} = 1219 \text{ rpm}$$

3. Determination of Mechanical Power Developed. The total power input to a motor for a given load must include the various electrical losses plus the mechanical power developed. Since this mechanical power is developed by the rotating armature, the power input to the armature circuit minus the copper losses must be this developed power, which is the product of the counterelectromotive force and armature current. This can be shown by the following relationships for voltage and current. Consider the most general case of a long shunt compound motor. The voltage relationship for the armature becomes

$$V_T = E_c + I_a(R_a + R_s)$$

Multiplying by I_a gives this power relationship:

$$V_T I_a = E_c I_a + I_a^2(R_a + R_s)$$

and

$$E_c I_a = V_T I_a - I_a^2(R_a + R_s)$$

or

$$P_M = P_I - I_a^2(R_a + R_s)$$

where P_M = mechanical power developed
P_I = power input to the armature circuit.

Although this gives the magnitude of the developed power, the actual power available will obviously be less than this value by an amount equal to the rotational losses of the armature. The division of losses in a motor is discussed in Chapter 11.

Example e. A series motor having an armature resistance of 0.10 ohm and series-field resistance of 0.12 ohm requires 60 amp from a 250-volt supply. What is the mechanical power developed in the armature?

$$E_c = 250 - 60(0.10 + 0.12) = 250 - 13.2 = 236.8 \text{ volts}$$

$$P_M = E_c I_a = 236.8 \times 60 = 14{,}208 \text{ watts}$$

4. Factors Controlling the Direction of Rotation. A self-excited d-c generator, for a given field connection, must be rotated in a definite direction to cause the generator to function, and the same air-gap flux and armature current relationship determine the direction of rotation of the machine when operated as a motor. The direction of rotation of a motor for a given field connection is the same, regardless of the polarity of the supply, because the reversal of the supply current reverses the direction of the current in both the armature and field circuits and a reversal of both does not reverse the direction of armature rotation. To reverse the direction of rotation, it is necessary to reverse the direction of either the main field or the armature current. In reversing the direction of rotation of a compound motor, care must be exercised to maintain the same relationship between the main-field magnetomotive force and the series-field magnetomotive force. In order to keep this relationship the same for both directions of rotation, it is better to reverse the armature current rather than the shunt-field current.

5. Effects of Armature Reaction. The effects of the armature magnetomotive force and its reaction on the magnetic systems of machines have been discussed in Chapter 3. The effects on the d-c generators have been shown in Chapter 9, and the same theory applies to d-c motors with only minor modification. In Figs. 10–9 and 11–9 (a simple two-pole generator), the directions of the main field, of the rotation, and of the armature current for a shunt generator are shown. The direction of the armature current (Lenz's Law) is such that the torque it produces opposes the rotation supplied mechanically by the generator's prime mover. If the machine is changed to a motor with identical conditions of main-field and armature current, the armature will rotate in the opposite direction, which is counterclockwise. This is shown in Fig. 4–10, the arrows indicating the direction of rotation for the two conditions.

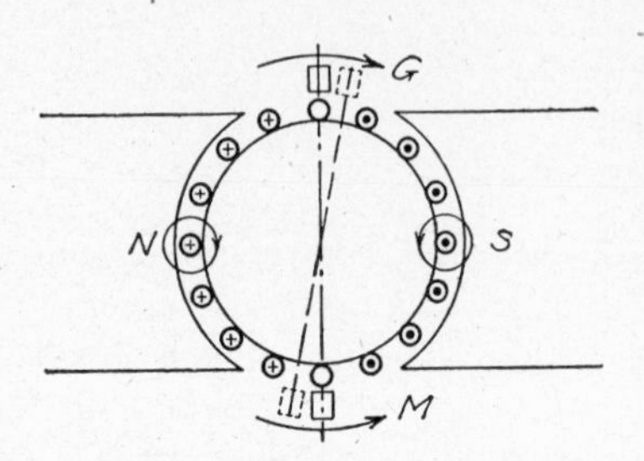

FIG. 4–10. Direction of rotation of the armature of a dynamo when operating as a generator and motor for the same direction of armature current.

The main field and the armature magnetomotive forces added vectorially give a resultant magnetomotive force which produces an uneven flux distribution in the air gap along the pole face because of the cross-magnetizing effects of armature reaction. Unless interpoles are used, this requires that the brushes be shifted in order to obtain good commutation. As shown in Fig. 4–10, for generator action the brushes are shifted in the direction of rotation, and for motor action the brushes are shifted against rotation. In the particular example shown, the magnetic circuit conditions are identical for both motor and generator operation, and the brushes are on the electrical neutral axis. The fact that the mechanical rotation is different in the two situations makes it unnecessary to change the brush position. It may be stated, therefore, that in all d-c machines without interpoles the brushes are always shifted in the same direction as the resultant field.

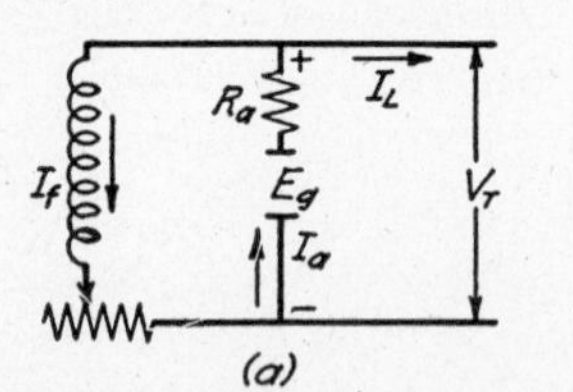

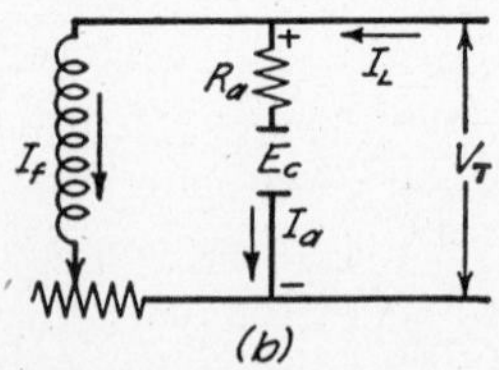

FIG. 5–10. Current relationships for the same armature rotation: (*a*) generator; (*b*) motor.

In Art. 4 it is stated that, to reverse the direction of rotation of a motor, the direction of the field or armature current must be reversed. The current relationships of a shunt machine operating as a generator and motor are indicated by diagrams in Fig. 5–10. For the same circuit polarity, the only difference between *a* and *b* is the direction of armature current. The reversed armature current causes a shift in the air-gap flux and, with the armature rotating in the same direction, it is necessary in *b* to shift the brush axis against rotation if there are no interpoles.

The shifting of the brushes from the mechanical neutral in the motor gives the demagnetizing and cross-magnetizing components of armature magnetomotive force. The band of conductors within twice the angle of brush shift are the demagnetizing conductors and the remaining ones are cross-magnetizing. The component effect of these, as has been shown in Chapter 3, is to reduce the resultant magnetomotive force acting on the magnetic circuit and to give an uneven flux distribution in the air gap. The same methods of compensating for these effects are used in d-c motors as in d-c generators. Interpoles and compensating windings are commonly used to aid commutation, and series windings are used to give desired speed characteristics.

From the relationships expressed in equations (*b*–10) and (*c*–10)

$$T = K_T \phi I_a \quad \text{and} \quad N = \frac{V_T - I_a R_a}{K\phi}$$

The effects of armature reaction will be:

1. The torque will be affected in proportion to the demagnetizing effect of armature reaction, which varies as the motor load.

2. The speed will tend to increase, depending upon the net reduction in air-gap flux, as the motor load increases.

Example f. A shunt motor is running at 1200 rpm for a load which requires an armature current of 50 amp from a 230-volt source. At no load the armature current is 5 amp. If the effect of armature reaction has reduced the air-gap flux 2 per cent from no load to full load, determine the no-load speed. The armature resistance is 0.15 ohm.

Full load:

$$1200 = \frac{230 - 50(0.15)}{K(0.98\phi)}$$

No load:

$$N = \frac{230 - 5(0.15)}{K\phi}$$

$$\frac{N}{1200} = \frac{\dfrac{230 - 5(0.15)}{K\phi}}{\dfrac{230 - 50(0.15)}{K\phi(0.98)}}$$

$$N = \frac{1200[230 - 5(0.15)]0.98}{230 - 50(0.15)}$$

$$N = \frac{1200(229.25)(0.98)}{222.50} = 1211 \text{ rpm}$$

6. Shunt Motor Characteristics. For a shunt motor

$$T = K_T \phi I_a$$

and

$$N = \frac{V_T - I_a R_a}{K\phi}$$

Since the voltage drop in the armature circuit at full load is only 3 to 8 per cent of the impressed voltage, the numerator of the expression for speed changes but a small amount, and the motor speed is essentially constant from no load to full load. At no load, the counterelectro-

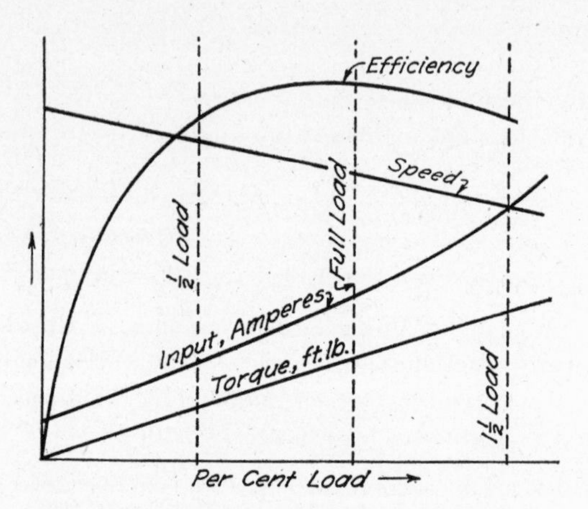

FIG. 6–10. Performance curves of a shunt motor.

motive force is almost equal to the impressed voltage and the motor speed is a maximum. The difference in these two voltages permits an armature current of sufficient value to react with the air-gap flux so that the torque necessary for the no-load mechanical losses may be produced.

When mechanical load is applied to the motor, the speed decreases, causing the counterelectromotive force to decrease and permitting the armature current to increase. The point of equilibrium is reached when the speed has decreased sufficiently to permit the torque increase, dependent upon the increase in current, to balance the load torque. If the effect of armature reaction with the increased current reduces the air-gap flux, the motor speed may increase with load and, if the increase in speed causes the armature current to increase, the motor will be unstable. Figure 6–10 shows the performance curves of a shunt motor.

7. Series Motor Characteristics. For a series motor, a straight line saturation curve being assumed,

$$T = K_T I_a^2$$

and

$$N = \frac{V_T - I_a(R_a + R_s)}{K\phi}$$

Since for this assumption the air-gap flux varies directly with the armature current, the expression for speed can be rewritten in terms of the one variable, the armature current. The expression becomes

$$N = \frac{V_T - I_a(R_a + R_s)}{K_1 I_a}$$

An examination of the expression for speed shows that, at small loads, the armature current and air-gap flux are small and the motor runs at a speed considerably above that of full load. This speed may become

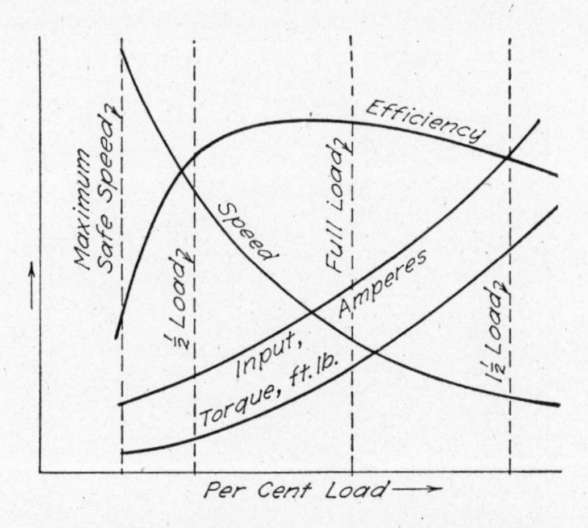

FIG. 7–10. Performance curves of a series motor.

dangerous if the load is too small and, for this reason, a series motor should not be operated at no load. There must be sufficient load on the motor at all times to keep the speed at a safe value.

As the load on the series motor is increased from a small value, the speed decreases along an exponential curve which approaches a straight line when the magnetic circuit becomes saturated. The series motor develops a large torque at low armature speed and a low torque at high armature speed. Figure 7–10 shows typical performance curves of a series motor.

8. Compound Motor Characteristics. For compound motors

$$T = K_T \phi I_a$$

and for a long shunt

$$N = \frac{V_T - I_a(R_a + R_s)}{K\phi}$$

where ϕ is the resultant flux in the air gap.

a. Cumulative Compound Motors. The speed of a cumulative compound motor will decrease with an increase in load. This can be seen from an analysis of the speed equation

$$N = \frac{V_T - I_a(R_a + R_s)}{K\phi}$$

The value of the flux ϕ depends upon the resultant magnetomotive force of the magnetic circuit. For the cumulative compound motor, the main-field and series-field magnetomotive forces add directly and, as the load current increases, the resultant magnetomotive force usually increases.

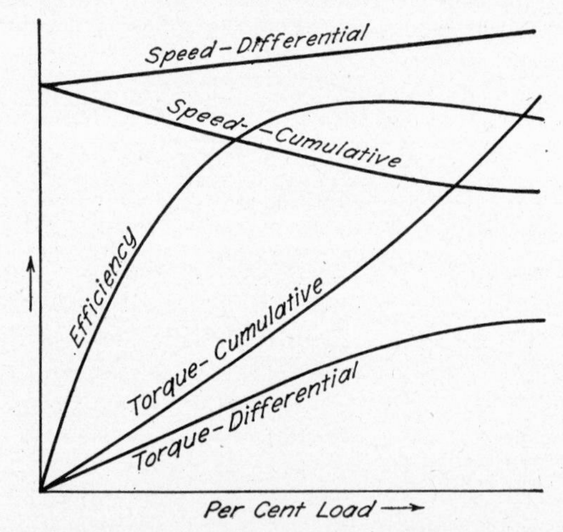

FIG. 8–10. Performance curves of cumulative and differential compound motors.

If the air-gap flux increases, the motor speed decreases. The counter-electromotive force will remain practically constant. The speed characteristic of the cumulative compound motor is poorer than that of the shunt motor but better than that of the series motor.

b. Differential Compound Motors. The series-field magnetomotive force opposes the main-field magnetomotive force in this motor, and the speed characteristic will be similar to that of a shunt motor with large armature reaction effects. If the air-gap flux is reduced at the proper rate as the armature current increases, the counterelectromotive force can decrease and the speed remain nearly constant. The object of the differential compounding is to maintain a better speed characteristic than in a shunt motor. It is possible to have an increase in speed as load is applied and an analysis of the speed relationship shows this fact. In the expression for the differential compound motor

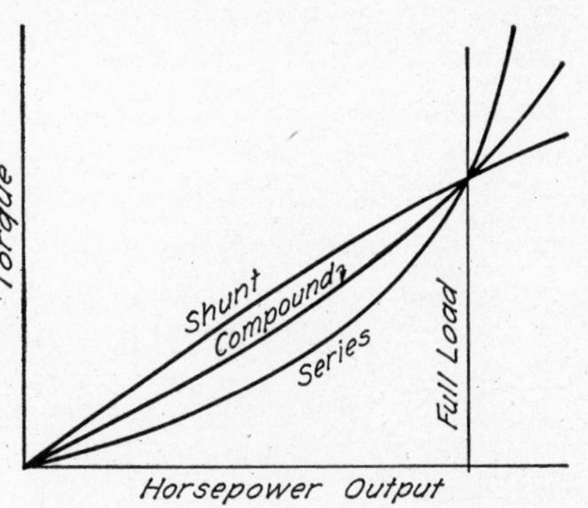

FIG. 9–10. Torque characteristics for shunt, series, and compound motors having the same full-load torques.

$$N = \frac{V_T - I_a(R_a + R_s)}{K\phi}$$

The value of ϕ will decrease as the load on the motor increases. For the differential compound motor, the main-field magnetomotive force and series-field magnetomotive force oppose each other. As the load increases, the resultant magnetomotive force and air-gap flux decrease, this decrease being further aided by the effects of armature reaction. Figure 8–10 shows the characteristic performance curves of cumulative and differential compound motors.

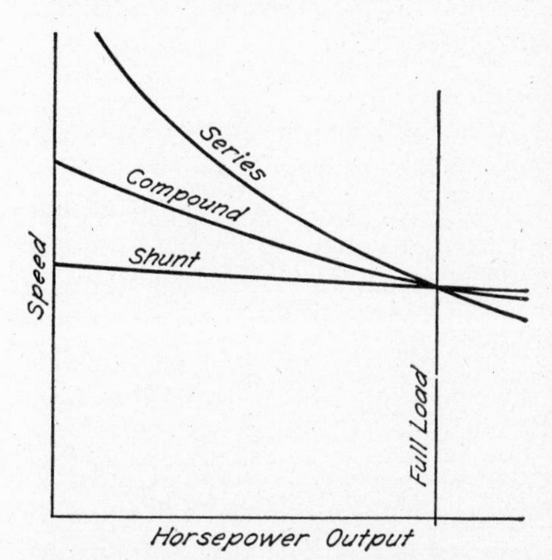

FIG. 10–10. Speed characteristics for shunt, series, and compound motors having the same full-load speed.

The use of long or short compounding is optional in motors as it is in generators and, for this reason, no attempt has been made to differentiate between them. In general, there is no appreciable difference between them.

9. Summary of Motor Characteristics. Figure 9–10 shows a comparison of the torque characteristics of the shunt, series, and compound motors for the same full-load torque. Figure 10–10 shows a comparison of the speed curves for the same full-load speed.

10. Speed Regulation. "The speed regulation of a constant speed direct current motor is the change in speed when the load is reduced gradually from rated value to zero, with constant applied voltage and field rheostat setting expressed as a per cent of speed at rated load." * D-c motors (with the exception of the series motor) are considered constant speed motors. The speed regulation seldom exceeds 15 per cent in the compound motors and 8 per cent in the shunt motor. The percentage speed regulation may be written in equation form as

$$\text{Percentage speed regulation} = \frac{N_{NL} - N_{FL}}{N_{FL}} \times 100$$

Example g. It was found, by test, that the speed of a shunt motor varied from 1275 rpm at full load to 1340 rpm at no load. What is the percentage speed regulation?

$$\text{Percentage speed regulation} = 100 \times \frac{1340 - 1275}{1275}$$

$$= 100 \times \tfrac{65}{1275} = 5.1 \text{ per cent}$$

11. Requirements for Motor Starting. The expression

$$V_T = K\phi N + I_a R_a'$$

is the voltage relationship in the armature circuit of the d-c generator. The value, R_a', is the resistance of the armature circuit and includes, in addition to the armature resistance, the series field, interpoles, and external resistances if they exist in the circuit.

When the speed is zero, the counterelectromotive force is zero and the armature current is limited only by the armature circuit resistance. The armature circuit resistance is relatively very small, and if full line voltage is impressed an excessive current results. In order to prevent damage to the machine or system at starting, an external resistance is connected in the armature circuit to limit the current to a safe value. As the machine develops speed, the counterelectromotive force builds up and the external resistance in the armature circuit is reduced to zero. The shunt-field winding of a motor is designed for rated line voltage and should have rated voltage upon it. Resistance is connected in series with the shunt field of a motor for speed control (discussed in the next article), but it should always be removed at the time of motor starting so that the machine may develop maximum torque for a given armature current. If the field is weak, the motor may not develop enough torque, with permissible armature current, to start. The series resistor used in the armature circuit usually has a value which limits the current to a maximum value of 150 per cent rated current.

* Definitions of Electrical Terms—American Institute of Electrical Engineers.

The internal connections and operation of these motor starters are fully discussed in Chapter 13. Figure 11–10 shows the schematic circuit diagrams for starting d-c motors. The external resistance should always be connected in the circuit as indicated.

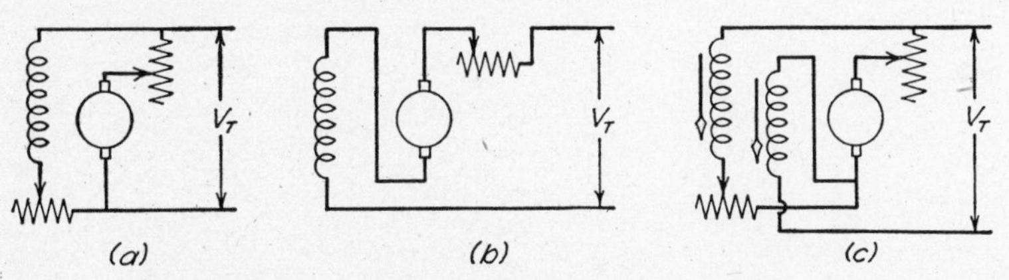

FIG. 11–10. Circuit diagrams for starting d-c motors: (*a*) shunt; (*b*) series; (*c*) compound.

Example h. The rated line current of a 230-volt shunt motor is 56 amp. If the shunt-field circuit resistance is 230 ohms and the armature circuit resistance is 0.15 ohm, what would be the line current, assuming that the motor, at standstill, is connected across rated voltage? How much external resistance must be connected in the armature circuit to limit the current at starting to 125 per cent full-load armature current?

$$I_f = \tfrac{230}{230} = 1 \text{ amp}$$

$$I_a = \frac{230}{0.15} = 1533 \text{ amp}$$

$$I_L = 1534 \text{ amp}$$

$$\text{Full-load } I_a = 56 - 1 = 55 \text{ amp}$$

$$125 \text{ per cent full-load } I_a = 68.75 \text{ amp}$$

$$\text{Total armature circuit resistance } \frac{230}{68.75} = 3.35 \text{ ohms}$$

$$\text{External resistance } 3.35 - 0.15 = 3.2 \text{ ohms}$$

Example i. A series motor is rated 100 amp, 500 volts, 600 rpm. If the series-field and armature resistances are 0.08 ohm and 0.06 ohm, respectively, what series resistance must be used at starting to limit the current to 125 amp?

$$\text{Total resistance} = \tfrac{500}{125} = 4 \text{ ohms}$$

$$\text{Series resistance } R = 4 - 0.14 = 3.86 \text{ ohms}$$

12. Speed Control. The speed of the d-c motor can be varied and controlled by varying the impressed voltage on the armature and the flux in the air gap. In order to vary these factors, the following methods are used:

a. Variation of the resistance of the armature circuit. This changes the voltage across the armature terminals.

b. Variation of the resistance of the shunt-field circuit. This changes the air-gap flux.

c. Variation of the reluctance of the magnetic circuit. This changes the air-gap flux.

d. Multivoltage control to change both the voltage across the armature terminals and the air-gap flux.

e. Ward-Leonard system of control.

f. Electronic motor control.

a. *Resistance in the Armature Circuit.* If resistance is inserted in the armature circuit of a motor, the voltage across the armature terminals is decreased and the speed decreases so that the counterelectromotive force can decrease. This method gives a poor speed regulation and poor efficiency.

Example j. A 230-volt shunt motor is operating at a full-load line current of 50 amp and a speed of 1200 rpm. The armature resistance is 0.15 ohm and the shunt-field resistance is 115 ohms. If a resistance of 2 ohms is connected in series with the armature and the armature current remains constant, determine the motor speed.

$$I_f = \tfrac{230}{115} = 2 \text{ amp}$$

$$I_a = 50 - 2 = 48 \text{ amp}$$

$$\frac{N}{1200} = \frac{230 - 48(0.15 + 2)}{230 - 48(0.15)} = \frac{126.8}{222.8}$$

$$N = 683 \text{ rpm}$$

Since the air-gap flux is constant, the speeds in the two instances are directly proportional to the counterelectromotive forces.

b. *Resistance in the Shunt-Field Circuit.* If a resistance is connected in series with the shunt field of a motor, the field current will be decreased and, for the same armature current, an increase in speed is necessary to generate the same counterelectromotive force. Care must be exercised in using this method of speed control, because commutation difficulties arise if the speed is very much above the rated speed of the motor.

A weakening of the main-field magnetomotive force results in a greater effect of armature reaction. The brushes must be shifted to a new position in order to remain at right angles to the main field. It is rather difficult to obtain good commutation if the motor speed is great, because the time for commutating a coil is greatly reduced and the voltage of self-induction is increased, both tending to give poorer commutation. Since the magnetic circuit of a motor is operated at a value of saturation above the bend (knee) in the curve, a given percentage change in the shunt-field current does not give the same percentage of variation in air-gap flux and motor speed. In most of the examples, however, a straight line relationship between field magnetomotive force and air-gap flux is assumed in order to simplify the calculations.

Example k. A 230-volt shunt motor is operating at a full-load armature current of 50 amp and a speed of 1250 rpm. The armature resistance is 0.15 ohm and the shunt-field circuit resistance is 115 ohms. If the shunt-field circuit resistance is increased to 150 ohms and the armature current is constant, determine the new speed. Assume the air-gap flux to vary directly with the shunt-field current and neglect the effects of armature reaction.

Since the countervoltage is constant, the speed will vary inversely as the air-gap flux and shunt-field current.

$$I_{f115} = \tfrac{230}{115} = 2 \text{ amp}$$

$$I_{f150} = \tfrac{230}{150} = 1.53 \text{ amp}$$

$$\phi_{1250} \text{ varies as } I_{f115} \qquad \phi_N \text{ varies as } I_{f150}$$

$$\frac{N}{1250} = \frac{2}{1.53} \qquad N = \frac{1250 \times 2}{1.53} = 1634 \text{ rpm}$$

c. Changing the Reluctance of the Magnetic Circuit. If the reluctance of the magnetic circuit of a motor is increased, the air-gap flux is decreased while the field current remains constant. The speed of the motor will increase, as it did under part *b*, to keep the counterelectromotive force at the proper value. Motors (Stow Motors) using this principle are in operation. The cores of the field can be moved in and out of the machine yoke and, in this way, the air gap can be varied. As a result, the reluctance of the magnetic circuit is varied.

Another type of motor (Lincoln Motor) operates according to a modification of this same principle. Instead of moving the field cores, the armature assemblage is moved along its shaft. As the armature is moved out of the main field, the effective length of the armature conductor cutting flux is reduced and the motor speed increases to maintain the correct value of counterelectromotive force.

Since the additional mechanism necessary for a change in magnetic circuit reluctance is somewhat complicated, motors using this principle have not been used widely. A change in the shunt-field circuit resistance serves the same purpose and is easier to handle.

d. Multivoltage Control. This method of speed control requires a source of several voltages. By a choice of voltages for the shunt-field circuit and the armature circuit, the combined results of parts *a* and *b* can be obtained. This, however, is an expensive method because it requires a special voltage supply. For the multivoltage supply, indicated by the circuit diagram of Fig. 12–10, the field current voltage or armature current voltage can be any one of the voltages A, B, C, or D. By this method of voltage control, a range of motor speeds above and below normal can be obtained.

e. Ward-Leonard System of Control. This system is quite similar to the one discussed under *d.* Figure 13–10 shows a schematic circuit diagram of the system. A motor M_1 drives a d-c generator G, the field of which is separately excited from the source for motor M_1. The generator armature output is fed directly into the motor armature M_2. The field of motor M_2 also comes from the same source as that used for the generator field.

FIG. 12–10. Schematic circuit diagram of a multivoltage source.

By controlling the generator voltage the armature current of the motor M_2 can be controlled. Also the field current can be varied through a fairly large range. Because of these two variables the speed of motor M_2 can be varied over a wide range. The chief disadvantage is the added equipment (motor-generator set) necessary and the accompanying low

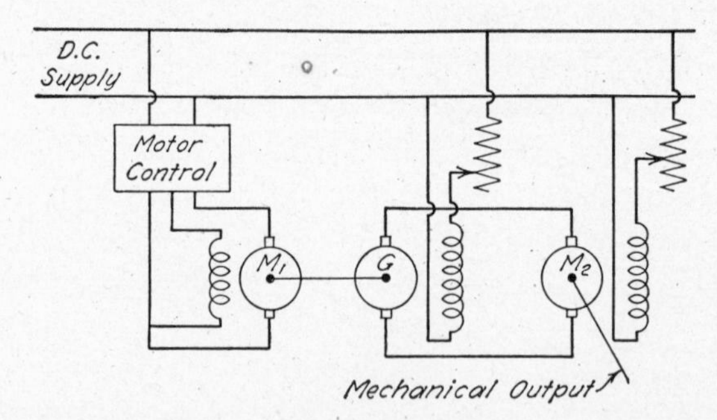

FIG. 13–10. Schematic circuit diagram of the Ward-Leonard system for motor speed control.

overall efficiency. This system is used in controlling large rolling mill motors.

f. Electronic Control. The development of electronic controls has been rather rapid during the past few years. Many schemes have been developed for motors of a small rating and complete information can be obtained from the manufacturers. During the next few years many new ideas of electronic controls certainly will be developed.

13. Comparison of Methods of Speed Control.

a. Resistance in Armature Circuit.

1. For speeds from below normal to normal speed with a reasonably constant load.
2. Changes in load produce large fluctuations in speed.
3. Appreciable loss of energy in series resistor.
4. Simple to operate and to construct.

b. Resistance in Shunt-Field Circuit.

1. For speeds above normal motor speed.
2. Speed not seriously affected by changes in load.
3. Comparatively small loss of energy.
4. Simple to operate and inexpensive to construct.
5. Poor commutation if the speed is varied over a wide range.

c. Changing Reluctance of the Magnetic Circuit.

1. For speeds above normal motor speed.
2. Speed not seriously affected by changes in load.
3. Comparatively small loss of energy.
4. Special design and costly construction.

d. Multivoltage Control.

1. For speeds from below normal to above normal motor speed.
2. Speed affected according to both parts *a* and *b* by changes in load.
3. Loss of energy not very great in the motor.
4. Very costly to construct.

e. Ward-Leonard System of Control.

1. For speeds from zero to above normal speed.
2. Speed affected according to both *a* and *b* by changes in load.
3. Loss of energy not very great in the motor. (The loss in the complete unit is comparatively large.)
4. Complete unit very costly. (The unit is more flexible than the system discussed in *d*.)

f. Electronic Control.

1. For speed from zero to above normal speed.
2. Speed usually affected by changes in load.
3. Loss of energy in the electronic equipment important when small units are controlled. (As the control of large units is developed, the equipment loss will be less important.)
4. Electronic equipment now costly. (The unit cost will probably decrease as this method is developed.)

PROBLEMS

1–10. A shunt motor is operating under the following conditions: $V_T = 250$ volts, $I_a = 200$ amp, $I_f = 10$ amp, and speed = 1200 rpm. The conditions are changed to the following: $V_T = 251$ volts, $I_a = 230$ amp, $I_f = 9$ amp, and speed = 1225 rpm. Compare the developed torques and power outputs for the two conditions. Assume a straight line saturation curve.

2–10. A d-c shunt motor takes 12 amp from a 250-volt source and is running at 1200 rpm. The shunt-field circuit resistance is 125 ohms, and the armature resistance is 0.2 ohm. Mechanical load is added to the motor until the speed has decreased to 1185 rpm. The resultant current increase has increased armature reaction so that the air-gap flux is now only 98 per cent of its original value. Determine the motor line current.

3–10. A long shunt, 220-volt, d-c compound motor has a no-load speed of 1200 rpm and a full-load speed of 1000 rpm. $R_a = 0.12$ ohm, $R_s = 0.08$ ohm, and $R_f = 110$ ohms. The line current is 7.3 amp at no load and 52 amp at full load. (*a*) What is the resultant air-gap flux at full load in terms of no-load condition? (*b*) What starting box resistance is required to give full-load torque at start?

4–10. A d-c motor runs at 1800 rpm and develops a torque of 80 lb-ft when the armature current is 100 amp with normal field excitation. Find (*a*) the speed and (*b*) the torque, when the armature current is 20 amp, if the counterelectromotive force is increased by 4 per cent by the reduction in armature current and if the flux is increased 10 per cent by increasing the field current.

5–10. A d-c motor has an armature resistance of 0.2 ohm. With 220 volts impressed on the armature terminals, the motor speed is 1050 rpm and rated torque is developed with normal excitation and rated armature current of 50 amp. At what speed will the motor operate if the torque is 40 per cent of rated torque when the armature current is 25 amp?

6–10. At no load, a shunt motor has the following constants: $V_T = 220$ volts, $I_a = 4$ amp, $I_f = 1.0$ amp, $R_a = 0.2$ ohm, and the speed = 1096 rpm. A 1-ohm resistance is placed in the line in series with the motor and the motor is loaded until the line current is 50 amp. Neglecting armature reaction and assuming a straight line magnetization curve, compute the motor speed.

7–10. A shunt motor operates at 900 rpm and develops a torque of 82 lb-ft when the armature current is 50 amp. The terminal voltage is 220 volts and the armature resistance is 0.2 ohm. (*a*) What is the horsepower developed by the motor? (*b*) What will be the speed and torque of the motor when the armature current is 25 amp if the air-gap flux is increased 4 per cent because of the decrease in armature current?

8–10. The following data are available for a motor when it is connected long shunt compound: $V_T = 240$ volts; I_a (full load) = 50 amp; $R_a = 0.2$ ohm; $R_s = 0.02$ ohm; no-load speed = 1200 rpm; series-field mmf is 20 per cent of the shunt-field mmf at full-load, straight line magnetization curve; I_aR_a is negligible at no·load; series-field mmf is negligible at no load; and armature reaction is negligible at all loads. Compare the speed, torque, and power of the motor operating as a shunt motor at full-load armature current with the corresponding values as a compound motor.

9–10. A series motor develops a torque of 35 lb-ft at 900 rpm for a line current of 10 amp and 500 volts. The series-field resistance is 0.15 ohm and the armature resistance is 0.35 ohm. Find the armature current and speed when the motor develops a torque of 70 lb-ft. Assume a straight line magnetization curve.

10–10. A shunt motor requires 6 amp line current at 225 volts when running at a no-load speed of 1120 rpm. The field circuit resistance is 225 ohms and the armature resistance is 0.2 ohm. What auxiliary resistance is required to cause the motor to run at 950 rpm and develop maximum torque for an input current of 51 amp? (Neglect the effects of armature reaction.)

11–10. The full-load speed of a 10-hp shunt motor is 1200 rpm when the line voltage is 220 volts and the line current is 42.2 amp. The field circuit resistance is 100 ohms and the armature resistance is 0.2 ohm. At no load the voltage is 235 volts because of line voltage regulation and the line current is 7.35 amp. What will be the no-load speed if armature reaction effects are negligible and a straight line saturation curve is assumed?

12–10. In a series motor where the series-field flux is proportional to the current, determine the ratio of currents when the power requirement of the motor is reduced from 100 per cent to 50 per cent. For this load change the motor speed increases 30 per cent.

13–10. The armature resistance of a 230-volt, d-c motor is 0.127 ohm, the series field resistance is 0.0546 ohm, and the shunt-field circuit resistance is 230 ohms. When operated under load as a shunt motor (series-field disconnected) the speed is 1115 rpm for a rated line current of 56 amp. When connected long shunt compound, the series field increases the air-gap flux by 10 per cent for rated line current. What is the effect of the addition of the series field on (*a*) the full-load speed and (*b*) power developed in the armature?

14–10. A 230-volt, d-c shunt motor requires 5.25 amp and runs at 1150 rpm at no load. The armature resistance is 0.25 ohm and the shunt-field resistance is 184 ohms. At full load, the motor current is 57.25 amp and the speed is 1120 rpm. What is the magnitude of the resultant air-gap flux at full load in terms of no-load conditions?

15–10. A 10-hp, d-c shunt motor with a nameplate rating of 220 volts and 41 amp can be purchased at a low price. Under test it runs at 1200 rpm with rated voltage impressed and loaded to rated input. The armature resistance is 0.15 ohm and the field circuit resistance is 220 ohms. If this motor is operated on a 110-volt d-c system, calculate (*a*) the speed and (*b*) the output horsepower for rated current input. Assume that the saturation curve is a straight line and that the stray power loss varies directly with speed and air-gap flux. (Neglect armature reaction.)

CHAPTER 11

EFFICIENCY AND LOSSES

1. Classification of Losses. A part of the power input to a piece of electrical equipment is not available as output, but appears as a heat loss. The design of electrical apparatus is based upon the ability of the equipment to dissipate this loss without excessive temperature rise, and the nameplate rating includes a permissible operating temperature for the equipment.

The efficiency of electrical equipment is defined as the ratio of power output to power input. The higher this ratio, the higher the efficiency of the machine. Most electrical equipment has a good efficiency (above 80 per cent), but the designing engineer is constantly striving to decrease the losses and, in this way, increase the efficiency.

Recent developments, including the hydrogen-cooled alternator and large mercury-arc rectifiers, are an indication of the constant effort in this direction. Transformers with efficiencies of 99.5 per cent and generators with efficiencies above 97 per cent are very common today.

The losses which occur in the electrical machines are made up of copper loss, iron loss, and friction loss. The copper loss, caused by the current flowing in the conductors, is usually referred to as the I^2R loss. The iron loss is the hysteresis and eddy current power loss in the iron part of the magnetic circuit in which the flux is varied. The stray power loss consists of the bearing, friction, and windage loss. In many instances, the iron loss of a machine is included as a part of the stray power loss and, in this way, the machine losses are grouped as copper and stray power losses.

The determination of the losses depends upon the kind of machine and, for this reason, this discussion considers the three classes of machines: (1) d-c machines, (2) alternators and synchronous motors, and (3) induction motors and transformers. The various losses and the method of determining them will be discussed for each class of machine. The procedure discussed can be used for testing nearly any piece of electrical power equipment.

The tests suggested give values which, for most conditions, will produce reasonably accurate results. The amount of power required for each test is only a part of that required in the actual load test and, if, by these test values, the efficiency of the machine can be predicted, the procedure is worthy of consideration. After the machine has been installed, an accurate determination of its efficiency can be made under actual load conditions.

The various losses for each classification are listed thus:

1. D-c machine losses
   A. Copper losses (I^2R)
      - Shunt-field circuit copper loss
      - Armature copper loss
      - Series winding copper loss
      - Brush and brush contact electrical loss (This loss is usually included in the armature loss.)

   B. Stray power loss (including iron loss)
      - Bearing friction and windage
      - Brush friction loss
      - Forced ventilation loss
      - Hysteresis loss
      - Eddy current loss
2. Alternators and synchronous motor losses
   A. Copper losses (I^2R)
      - D-c field-circuit copper loss
      - Armature copper loss
      - Brush and brush contact electrical loss

   B. Stray power loss (including iron loss)
      - Bearing friction and windage
      - Brush friction loss
      - Forced ventilation loss
      - Hysteresis loss
      - Eddy current loss
3. Induction motor and transformer losses
   A. Copper losses (I^2R)

Induction Motor	*Transformer*
Stator copper loss	Primary and secondary copper loss
Rotor copper loss	
Brush and brush contact electrical loss	

   B. Stray power loss (including iron loss)

Induction Motor	*Transformer*
Bearing friction and windage	Hysteresis loss
Brush friction loss	Eddy current loss (These two losses are combined and called the core loss. No friction and windage loss.)
Forced ventilation loss	
Hysteresis loss	
Eddy current loss	

2. D-C Machine Losses. The losses in a d-c generator or motor consist of the shunt-field loss, armature and series-field loss, and stray power loss.

a. Shunt-Field Loss. It has been established that no power is required to maintain the magnetic field, but that power is required for the ohmic resistance of the field windings. This loss is an I^2R loss and appears as heat. The field loss may be determined from the following:

$$P = I_f^2 R_f = V_f I_f = \frac{V_f^2}{R_f}$$

where I_f is the shunt-field circuit current, V_f is the voltage of the source for the shunt-field circuit, and R_f is the resistance of the shunt-field circuit (shunt-field winding and control rheostat).

Figure 1–11 shows the circuit diagram for measuring the shunt-field current and resistance. The readings of the ammeter and voltmeter

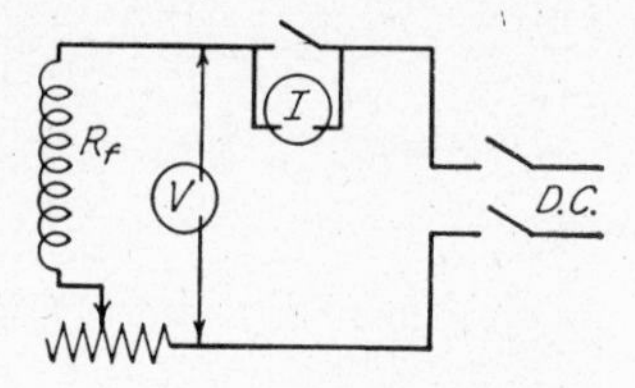

FIG. 1–11. Circuit diagram for the measurement of shunt-field circuit resistance.

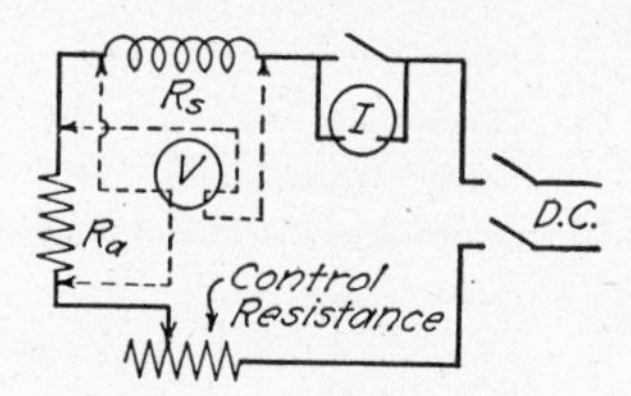

FIG. 2–11. Circuit diagram for the measurement of armature and series-field resistance.

should be taken and, if the meter losses are important, the meter readings should be corrected for these losses. The machine should be operated for a reasonable length of time, before the data are taken, to permit the resistance of the circuit to reach a value corresponding to operating temperature of the machine.

Since the line voltage remains fairly constant, the shunt-field loss is reasonably constant.

b. Armature and Series-Field Losses. The current through the armature and series field varies over a considerable range, with the result that the armature and series-field copper losses vary over a wide range. The resistances of the armature circuit R_a and of the series field R_s are determined in the same manner as that of the shunt field. However, since these resistances are low in value, rated machine voltage cannot be used unless a current-limiting resistance is used to control the current. Figure 2–11 shows the circuit diagram for determining the value of these resistances. The value of R_a includes the resistance of the armature winding, the brush, and brush contact. The resistance should be measured after the machine has been operated long enough for it to have reached the normal operating temperature.

c. Stray Power Losses. The losses just discussed are called copper losses and can be determined from experimental data. All the remaining losses of the d-c machine are usually considered in one division and are called the stray power losses. The losses which comprise the stray power losses are defined below.

1. Eddy current and hysteresis losses, which exist in the armature core, are caused by the reversals of magnetism in the iron as it rotates in the magnetic field. While this core is rotating in the magnetic field, a voltage is induced in the iron laminations. This induced voltage causes circulating currents in the iron, and these currents, with the resistance of the path, produce I^2R losses in the iron. These eddy currents, being proportional to the induced voltage in the iron, are dependent upon both armature speed and the flux. It follows, then, that the eddy current loss (I^2R) varies as the square of the speed and flux.

The hysteresis loss (Chapter 2) is the energy loss in a cycle of magnetization, determined by the hysteresis loop. The loss in ergs (Steinmetz' expression) is

$$P = nfVB_m^{1.6}$$

This loss, in a given machine, varies directly with the frequency (f), which depends upon speed, and the 1.6 power of the maximum flux density (B_m). (*Note:* The hysteresis loss may be expressed in watts by using the proper conversion factor to change ergs into watts.)

2. Friction losses in bearings and in brush contact are affected by speed and, for most practical considerations, are assumed to vary directly as speed.

3. Air friction or windage loss varies as some function of the speed. It is reasonable to assume this loss to vary as the third power of the speed.

It is practically impossible to separate these individual losses with any degree of accuracy, but the total stray power loss can be determined by experimental tests. If the machine is operated at constant speed with constant field, the stray power loss is approximately constant regardless of the machine output. Therefore, the stray power loss of a shunt machine is practically constant no matter what the load may be, and it varies only a small amount in compound machines, this variation being caused by a change in flux as well as speed conditions. The stray power loss varies greatly with load in a series machine, since there is a large change in both the flux and speed conditions.

Since the stray power loss is a function of the two variables, flux and speed, it is impossible to express the relationship for all conditions as a single curve. However, it is possible to determine the stray power loss for two conditions: (1) constant flux and variable speed and (2) constant speed and variable flux. In most instances, a comparison of generated voltages in a machine is considered a good indication of the effects of both flux and speed, because generated voltage depends upon these two. The various component parts of stray power are different functions of field excitation and speed, but it is sufficiently accurate to assume, for small variations of field excitation or speed, that the stray power loss is directly proportional to the electromotive force induced in the armature. This may be expressed as

$$\frac{(\text{S.P.})_1}{(\text{S.P.})_2} = \frac{E_{g1}}{E_{g2}}$$

To determine the stray power loss in a d-c machine it is only necessary to operate the machine as a motor at no load, duplicating the flux and speed conditions for any load. Figure 3–11 shows the circuit diagram of connections for operating the machine under the desired generated voltage and speed conditions. Since the machine is operated at no load, all the power input to the machine is loss and, if the various copper losses (I^2R) are subtracted from the input, the remainder is the stray power loss. (*Note:* R_x is the external resistance in the armature circuit, necessary to reproduce the proper speed and generated voltage for a machine under load.)

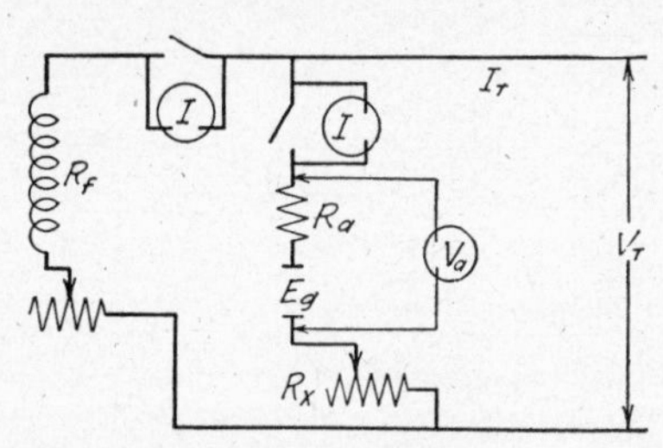

FIG. 3–11. Circuit diagram of connections for stray power measurement.

$$V_T I_T - I_f^2 R_f - I_a^2 R_a - I_a^2 R_x = \text{stray power loss}$$

The stray power can be determined, also, from the armature input minus the armature I^2R loss:

$$V_a I_a - I_a^2 R_a = \text{stray power loss}$$

Example a. The input current to a 220-volt, long shunt compound motor at no load is 6 amp. The shunt-field circuit resistance is 220 ohms; the armature resistance is 0.10 ohm; and the series-field resistance is 0.08 ohm. What is the stray power loss?

$$\text{Motor input} = 6 \times 220 = 1320 \text{ watts}$$

Shunt-field current is 1 amp. Shunt-field loss = 1 × 220 = 220 watts. Armature current is 5 amp. Armature and series-field loss:

$$(5)^2 \times 0.18 = 25 \times 0.18 = 4.5 \text{ watts}$$

$$\text{Stray power loss} = 1320 - (220 + 4.5) = 1095.5 \text{ watts}$$

If the operating conditions for a d-c machine can be determined, it is possible to predict the machine efficiency. This involves the following determinations: (1) shunt-field circuit resistance; (2) armature circuit and series-field resistance; and (3) the stray power loss, both at no-load and at various load speeds.

The predicted performance of a machine is not absolutely correct because it is very difficult to determine the true magnetic circuit conditions and the effects of armature reaction. However, the predictions from the no-load test data will be within 1 per cent of the true value of the efficiency. The rating of a machine is the output and, depending upon the class of machine, is expressed in horsepower or watts. The efficiency of a machine is

$$\text{Percentage efficiency} = 100 \times \frac{\text{output (watts)}}{\text{input (watts)}}$$

$$= 100 \times \frac{\text{(input} - \text{losses)(watts)}}{\text{input (watts)}}$$

$$= 100 \times \frac{\text{output (watts)}}{\text{(output} + \text{losses)(watts)}}$$

Example b. Assume the input rating of the motor in Example *a* to be 56 amp at 220 volts with a no-load speed of 1000 rpm. If the stray power loss varies as the counterelectromotive force and the effects of armature reaction are considered negligible, determine the efficiency at rated input.

$$\text{Full-load speed} = \text{no-load speed} \times \frac{E_g \text{ at full load}}{E_g \text{ at no load}}$$

$$\text{At no load, } E_g = 220 - 5(0.1 + 0.08) = 219.1 \text{ volts}$$

$$\text{At full load, } E_g = 220 - 55(0.1 + 0.08) = 210.1 \text{ volts}$$

$$\text{Full-load speed} = 1000 \times \frac{210.1}{219.1} = 960 \text{ rpm}$$

$$\text{Stray power loss at full load} = 1095.5 \times \frac{210.1}{219.1} = 1050 \text{ watts}$$

$$\text{Shunt-field loss} = 1 \times 220 = 220 \text{ watts}$$

$$\text{Armature loss} = (55)^2 \times 0.1 = 302.5 \text{ watts}$$

$$\text{Series-field loss} = (55)^2 \times 0.08 = 242 \text{ watts}$$

$$\text{Percentage efficiency} = 100 \times \left[\frac{(56 \times 220) - (220 + 302.5 + 242 + 1050)}{56 \times 220}\right]$$

$$= 100 \times \frac{12{,}320 - 1814.5}{12{,}320}$$

$$= 100 \times \frac{10{,}505.5}{12{,}320}$$

$$\text{Percentage efficiency} = 85.3 \text{ per cent}$$

The efficiency of a d-c machine increases with increase in load until approximately full load is reached. In most machines, the point of maximum efficiency occurs at 95 to 100 per cent of rating. Figure 4–11 shows the characteristic efficiency curve and division of losses in a shunt machine.

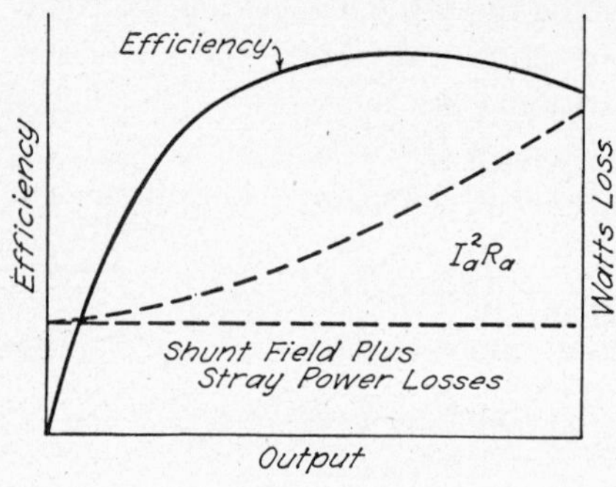

FIG. 4–11. Division of losses and efficiency curve of a shunt machine.

The efficiency of a small machine can be determined from actual load test. The efficiency of the large machines must be calculated after the losses have been measured. The actual load test on the large machine is made after the machine is installed in service.

3. Alternator and Synchronous Motor Losses. The losses in an a-c generator or synchronous motor consist of the following: d-c field copper loss, armature winding copper loss, and stray power loss. As for d-c machines, it is difficult to measure the input and output of a large a-c machine and, as a result, it is necessary to make certain tests at no load to determine the various losses. Once the losses have been determined, it is possible to calculate the efficiency.

The d-c field copper loss may be determined from the field voltage and current. If the actual ohmic resistance of the circuit is desired, it can be determined experimentally by using the circuit given in Fig. 1–11. In order to maintain constant terminal voltage as the load changes, the field excitation is varied by changing the field rheostat and, as a result, the field loss is not constant for all loads.

The armature copper loss in alternators and synchronous motors is not so easily determined as it is in the d-c machines. Since the current in the armature conductors is alternating, the armature loss will include the hysteresis and eddy current losses in the surrounding iron because of the magnetic fields produced by this current. The value of the resistance, which, when considered with the armature current, gives the total loss (caused by that current) in the copper conductor and surrounding iron, is called the effective resistance * and is greater than the ohmic resistance.

The most common method used to measure the effective resistance of an alternator or synchronous motor is to drive the machine with a d-c motor for which the losses are known. The power input to the machine, with the armature short-circuited and sufficient field excitation to give rated armature current, is measured and, then, with the armature open-circuited and no field excitation, the input is again measured. Both readings are taken at synchronous speed. The field excitation for full-load armature current is very small compared to normal field excitation and the effects of its magnetomotive force are negligible. The difference between the input to the machine in the two instances is the total armature loss. The effective resistance can be found from the following expression:

$$R_{\text{eff.}} = \frac{P_a}{nI_p^2}$$

where P_a is armature loss, n is the number of phases, and I_p is the phase current. It is difficult to determine, sometimes, whether the machine windings are star- or delta-connected. This, obviously, will make no difference in the total armature losses but, if the effective resistance per phase is stated, whether the winding is assumed to be star- or delta-connected must be stated also. The ratio of phase resistances in the two connections (Chapter 7) is

$$\frac{R_\Delta}{R_y} = 3$$

The power input to the machine with all circuits open is the loss caused by bearing friction and windage. Therefore, if the machine is operated as a synchronous motor at no load, the core loss can be determined by subtracting the friction, windage, armature, and field losses from the total input. The core loss, which will depend upon field excitation, should be determined for the operating range of field current.

From the previous tests, information relative to armature I^2R loss, friction and windage loss, and core loss has been determined.

* Effective resistance is the resistance to a periodic current. It is measured as the quotient of the average rate of transforming electrical energy into heat during a cycle, divided by the square of the effective current. (05.20.160) Electrical Definitions by American Institute of Electrical Engineers.

For an alternator the percentage efficiency is

$$\frac{nV_pI_p \cos\theta}{nV_pI_p \cos\theta + nI_p^2R_{\text{eff.}} + V_fI_f + \text{S.P.}} \times 100$$

and for a synchronous motor the percentage efficiency is

$$\frac{nV_pI_p \cos\theta - nI_p^2R_{\text{eff.}} - V_fI_f - \text{S.P.}}{nV_pI_p \cos\theta} \times 100$$

where $nI_p^2R_{\text{eff.}}$ is the armature loss, V_fI_f is the field loss, S.P. is the stray power loss which includes friction, windage, and core loss, and V_p and I_p are rated phase values of voltage and current.

Example c. A 220-volt, 25-amp, 60-cycle, 1200-rpm, 3-phase, star-connected alternator has an effective resistance of 0.12 ohm per phase. The stray power loss (friction, windage, and core loss) is 900 watts at full-load 80 per cent lagging power factor. The d-c field requires 3.5 amp at 110 volts. What is the alternator efficiency at full-load 80 per cent lagging power factor?

$$\text{Output} = 220 \times 25 \times \sqrt{3} \times 0.8 = 7630 \text{ watts}$$

Losses:

$$\text{Armature} = (25)^2 \times 0.12 \times 3 = 225 \text{ watts}$$

$$\text{Field loss} = 110 \times 3.5 = 385 \text{ watts}$$

$$\text{Stray power loss} = 900 \text{ watts}$$

$$\text{Input} = 9140 \text{ watts}$$

$$\text{Efficiency} = \tfrac{7630}{9140} \times 100 = 83.6 \text{ per cent}$$

4. Transformer and Induction Motor Losses. It has been shown in Chapter 8 that the induction motor is fundamentally a transformer in which the secondary is short-circuited and mounted on a shaft so that it can revolve and supply mechanical, instead of electrical, output. Therefore, with the exception of the mechanical losses (friction and windage), which do not exist in the transformer, the same losses occur in both the transformer and the induction motor. These are (1) copper and (2) iron losses (eddy current and hysteresis).

a. Transformer Loss Measurement. Since the copper loss is a winding loss (I^2R), the resistance of the windings should be known. This means that the equivalent resistance, referred to either primary or secondary, should be known. Then, the total copper loss can be determined for any value of load current. The equivalent resistance is determined as follows.

1. Short-circuit the transformer secondary and impress upon the primary an alternating voltage sufficient to give approximately full-load current in both windings. This voltage probably will be from 5 to 10 per cent of rated voltage for the winding.

Care must be exercised in protecting the transformer from excessive voltage during the short-circuit test.

2. Measure the power input, current, and voltage; and, from these values, the equivalent resistance, reactance, and impedance referred to the input side can be determined.

$$R_{op} = \frac{P}{I_p^2}$$

Figure 5–11 shows the circuit diagram for making this measurement. The iron loss for this test is negligible, since the flux density is low. The flux density is low because the impressed voltage for this test is only 5 to 10 per cent of rated voltage. This test was discussed in Chapter 4.

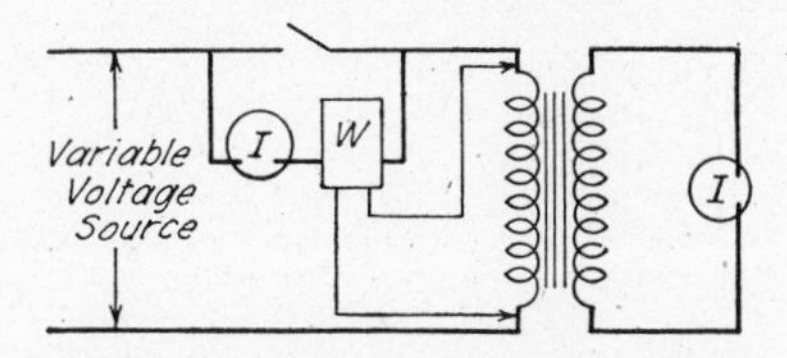

FIG. 5–11. Circuit diagram for the determination of the equivalent resistance of a transformer.

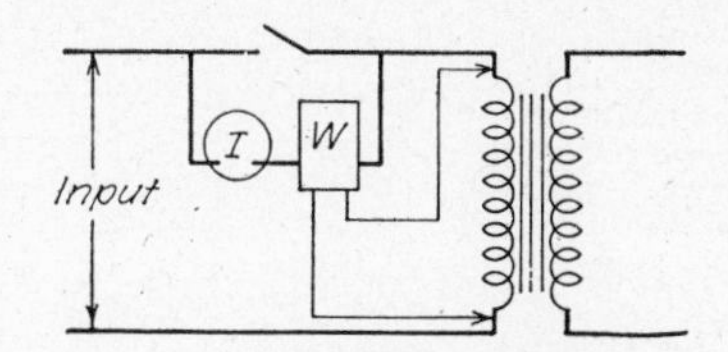

FIG. 6–11. Circuit diagram for the measurement of the core loss in a transformer.

The other transformer loss is the core loss, and, since the maximum flux density in the iron core is practically constant for all transformer loads, the no-load determination of the iron loss is sufficiently accurate for most purposes. Figure 6–11 shows the circuit diagram for measuring the iron loss. The input at no load to the circuit indicated includes the core loss and a small I^2R loss in the primary winding. This I^2R loss from such a small value of current compared to rated current is generally neglected and the entire input (corrected for meter losses) is considered the iron or core loss of the transformer.

After the core loss and equivalent resistance have been determined, calculate the transformer efficiency at any percentage rated output. This is shown in the following example.

Example d. A 5-kva, 2200/220-volt transformer has a resistance of 1 per cent and a core loss of 50 watts. Determine the transformer efficiency at full-load unity power factor and half-load 80 per cent power factor.

The solution will be based on the output side, which, in this example, is the 220-volt side.

$$\text{Full-load current} = \tfrac{5000}{220} = 22.7 \text{ amp}$$

$$\text{Full-load } I^2R \text{ loss} = 5000 \times 0.01 = 50 \text{ watts}$$

$$R_{os} = \frac{50}{(22.7)^2} = 0.097 \text{ ohm}$$

Efficiency at full-load unity power factor:

$$\text{Output} = 5000 \text{ watts}$$

$$I^2R \text{ loss} = 50 \text{ watts}$$

$$\text{Core loss} = 50 \text{ watts}$$

$$\text{Efficiency} = 100 \times \frac{5000}{5000 + 50 + 50} = 98.04 \text{ per cent}$$

and efficiency at half-load 80 per cent power factor:

$$\text{Output} = 5000 \times 0.5 \times 0.8 = 2000 \text{ watts}$$

$$I^2R \text{ loss} = (11.35)^2 \times 0.097 = 12.5 \text{ watts}$$

$$\text{Core loss} = 50 \text{ watts}$$

$$\text{Efficiency} = 100 \times \frac{2000}{2000 + 12.5 + 50}$$

$$= 100 \times \frac{2000}{2062.5} = 97 \text{ per cent}$$

b. Transformer. Transformers supplying power to residence lighting circuits and small power distribution circuits are practically idle during the major part of a day. Since the transformer is connected to the power source at all times, the core loss exists for the entire 24 hours, whereas the copper losses occur only during the load periods. Because transformers do not supply a constant load at all times, it is good practice to determine the all-day efficiency. This is determined from the ratio of output kilowatt-hours to input kilowatt-hours per day, and this means that the hourly load on the transformer must be known.

Example e. Determine the all-day efficiency for the transformer of Example *d* if it is loaded as follows.

(1) No-load	8 hr
(2) 50 per cent kva (80 per cent power factor)	4 hr
(3) 50 per cent kva (100 per cent power factor)	4 hr
(4) Full-load (100 per cent power factor)	8 hr

$$\text{Core loss} = 50 \text{ watts}$$

$$\text{Full-load secondary current} = 22.7 \text{ amp}$$

$$R_{os} = 0.097 \text{ ohm}$$

$$\text{Total energy output} = (2500 \times 0.8 \times 4) + (2500 \times 4) + (5000 \times 8)$$
$$= 8000 + 10{,}000 + 40{,}000$$
$$\text{Total energy output} = 58{,}000 \text{ whr}$$
$$\text{Total energy loss} = [(50 \times 24)] + [(11.35)^2 \times 0.097 \times 4]$$
$$+ [(11.35)^2 \times 0.097 \times 4] + [(22.7)^2 \times 0.097 \times 8]$$
$$\text{Total energy loss} = 1200 + 50 + 50 + 400 = 1700 \text{ whr}$$
$$\text{All-day efficiency} = \frac{58{,}000}{58{,}000 + 1700} \times 100 = 97.2 \text{ per cent}$$

c. *Induction Motor Loss Measurement.* If the induction motor is considered as a transformer, the same two tests that are made on the transformer will aid in determining the induction motor efficiency. An analysis of these two tests (no-load for core loss and blocked rotor for copper loss) as applied to the induction motor can be made as follows.

1. The equivalent resistance per phase can be found by using the short-circuit test. The rotor is blocked and sufficient voltage is applied to the stator winding to give full-load input current. The flux density is low and the equivalent resistance per phase can be calculated.

$$R_o \text{ per phase} = \frac{\text{total power}}{n \times (I \text{ per phase})^2}$$

where n is the number of phases.

2. The power input to the induction motor at no load includes a small copper loss (I^2R), core loss, and friction and windage loss. When correction is made for the small copper loss, the remainder is the stray power loss (iron loss, friction, and windage loss). This loss is substantially constant, since the change in speed from no load to full load is about 5 per cent (or less) and the iron loss is nearly constant.

From these two tests, it is possible to obtain data to determine the induction motor efficiency with a high degree of accuracy. In Chapter 8, the discussion on the circle diagram includes the motor efficiency as one of the values which can be determined. This method is used in most induction motor analyses, because it gives many other characteristics in addition to the motor efficiency.

In the American Standards for Rotating Electrical Machinery (approved by the American Standards Association on January 6, 1936, and sponsored by the Electrical Standards Committee of the American Engineering and Industrial Standards) can be found the following recommendations for induction machinery.

Paragraph 5.099 Friction, and Windage, and Core Losses.

(*a*) The sum of the friction and windage and core loss shall be determined by measuring the watts input at no-load, and normal voltage and frequency and subtracting therefrom the no-load I^2R loss.

(*b*) The friction and windage losses shall be included according to rules given under paragraph 3.189. (3.189 Friction and Windage. The friction and windage loss, including brush friction, is the power required to drive the unexcited machine at normal speed with its brushes in contact.)

Paragraph 5.100 Stator and Rotor I^2R Loss.

(*a*) Induction Generators and Motors—The stator I^2R loss shall be the square of the stator current at rated voltage, multiplied by the armature resistance as measured with direct current and corrected to 75° C. For large machines, when load test may not be practicable, the stator current shall be determined by calculation from no-load and locked test data, using such equivalent circuit or modified circle diagram methods as have been found to agree with load test data on similar machines.

(*b*) Polyphase Induction Machine Rotor—The I^2R loss in the rotor of a polyphase induction machine shall be determined from the slip, measured at full-load temperature rise, whenever the input and slip are accurately determinable, using the following equations:

For a Motor:

Rotor I^2R loss $= s$ (Measured input $-$ stator I^2R loss $-$ core loss)
where the slip, s, is expressed as a decimal.

For a Generator:

Rotor I^2R loss $= s$ (Measured output $+$ stator I^2R loss $+$ core loss)
where the slip, s, is expressed as a decimal.

In slip ring motors, in which the slip cannot be directly determined by loading, due to large size or for other reasons, the rotor I^2R loss shall be determined by direct resistance measurement. The rotor full-load current is calculated by the following equation, in which the slip s may be estimated or obtained from calculations.

$$\text{Current per ring} = \frac{\text{Watts Output}}{\text{Secondary ring voltage at standstill} \times \sqrt{3} \times (1 - s) \times 0.98}$$

This equation applies to three-phase rotors. For rotors wound for two-phase, use 2 instead of $\sqrt{3}$.

5. Ratings. The rating of a piece of electrical equipment is a statement, by the manufacturer, of the conditions under which the equipment can be operated without damage. The limiting conditions include speed, temperature rise, current, and voltage. The operating limits, as given on the nameplate attached to the piece of equipment, hold for continuous duty, unless otherwise stated. Machines which are designed for intermittent duty can be given a rating which is greater than the one for continuous duty. Though all the factors determining the limiting conditions are important, the current capacity is the most important. The size of conductor used, the type of ventilation, and temperature rise all depend either directly or indirectly upon the permissible current.

The nameplate of the piece of electrical equipment should carry ample information concerning it. It should give all operating limits for continuous duty or, if the equipment is designed for intermittent duty, the nameplate data should include that fact.

The following information, to be given on the nameplate, has been recommended as a minimum by the American Standards Association.

For Direct-Current Machines—

1. Output in horsepower for motors or kilowatts for generators.
2. Kind of rating (continuous or otherwise).
3. Temperature rise at rated load.
4. Revolutions per minute at rated load.
5. Voltage.
6. Amperes at rated load.
7. Shunt, series, or compound.

For Alternators and Synchronous Motors—

1. Output in proper units.
2. Voltage rating.
3. Kind of rating.
4. Revolutions per minute.
5. Amperes at full load.
6. Frequency.
7. Temperature rise.
8. Number of phases.
9. Power factor.
10. Exciter voltage.
11. Exciter current in amperes at rating.

For Induction Motors—

1. Horsepower output.
2. Kind of rating.
3. Temperature rise at full load.
4. Revolutions per minute at full load.
5. Frequency.
6. Number of phases.
7. Voltage.
8. Amperes at rated load.
9. Wound rotors:
   (*a*) Secondary voltage (open circuit voltage at standstill).
   (*b*) Secondary current at full-load.

For Transformers—

1. Rated output in kva available at the secondary terminals at rated voltage and frequency.
2. Temperature rise.
3. Kind of rating.
4. Type of winding connections.

PROBLEMS

1–11. A d-c motor armature has 100 watts hysteresis loss when rotating at 1200 rpm and the flux per pole is 10^6 lines. The eddy current loss in the armature is 75 watts for the same conditions. Find the losses in the armature if the speed is increased to 1500 rpm and the flux per pole is reduced to 900,000 lines.

2–11. A 3000-kva, 2300-volt, 3-phase, 60-cycle, wye-connected alternator has a field circuit resistance of 1 ohm and an armature resistance of 0.03 ohm from line to neutral. The field current for full-load unity power factor is 200 amp and for full-load 80 per cent power-factor lag is 250 amp. Friction, windage, and core loss amount to 60 kw and are considered constant for all loading. Determine the full-load efficiency at unity and 80 per cent lag power factors.

3–11. Power is supplied over a 3-phase, 3-wire system to a load of 1000 kw at 6900 volts and 80 per cent power-factor lag. The impedance per conductor is $0.9 + j7.2$ ohms. It is desired to improve the system power factor to unity by using a synchronous condenser. If the losses in the condenser and its direct-connected exciter are 100 kw, determine the system efficiency for the two conditions. Assume the load voltage constant.

4–11. A 15-hp, 440-volt series motor has 550 watts core loss, 1000 watts friction and winding loss, and 450 watts copper loss for full load at 700 rpm. Determine the motor efficiency for an input current of 15 amp, assuming that the friction and windage loss varies directly with speed and that the core loss varies as the square of the speed and air-gap flux. $R_a = 0.3$ ohm and $R_s = 0.2$ ohm. Assume a straight line magnetization curve.

5–11. Determine the full-load efficiency of a 25-kw, 250-volt, d-c shunt generator if the machine, operating as a motor at no load, takes 9 amp from a 250-volt source, and the field current is 4 amp. The armature resistance is 0.2 ohm. (Neglect the effect on stray power losses caused by a change in voltage.)

6–11. A 12.5-kw, long shunt overcompound generator delivers full load at a rated terminal voltage of 250 volts and rated speed of 900 rpm. The armature resistance, including brush contact and commutating field, is 0.4 ohm; the shunt-field circuit resistance is 125 ohms; and the series-field resistance is 0.02 ohm. The mechanical losses are 400 watts at rated speed and the iron losses are 200 watts at full load. Determine the efficiency (*a*) at full load and (*b*) at half-rated current output. The terminal voltage at half-rated current output is 230 volts and the speed is 950 rpm. Assume that the mechanical losses vary directly with speed and the iron losses vary as the square of the generated voltage.

7–11. A 10-kva, 2300/230-volt distribution transformer has 2 per cent resistance, 4 per cent reactance, and a core loss of 1.5 per cent. Determine the all-day efficiency for the following loading schedule.

Full-load unity power factor for 4 hr
Full-load 0.8 lag power factor for 4 hr
50 per cent load unity power factor for 6 hr
No load for 10 hr

8–11. What must be the driving torque of a prime mover driving a 400-kw, 600-volt, 750-rpm shunt generator at full load. Armature resistance is 0.028 ohm, the field circuit resistance is 52 ohms, and the stray power loss is 10.5 kw at full load and rated speed.

9–11. The full-load efficiency of a 15-hp, 4-pole, 60-cycle, 220-volt, 3-phase induction motor is 83 per cent. The power input to the motor at no load is 1100 watts. If the copper loss is divided equally between the stator and rotor, what is the motor speed at full load? Base the solution on the circle diagram.

10–11. Three 50-kva, 2300/230-volt transformers are connected in delta to supply a plant with power. Each transformer has the following constants: resistance of 1 per cent, core loss of 1 per cent, reactance of 6 per cent. The 3-phase loading on the bank is as follows.

30 kva at 0.8 power-factor lag for 4 hr
150 kva at 0.9 power-factor lag for 14 hr
60 kva at 0.7 power-factor lag for 2 hr
No load for 4 hr

What is the all-day efficiency of this bank?

11–11. The full-load efficiency of a 10-kva, 2300/230-volt, 60-cycle transformer at unity power factor is 98 per cent. Determine the transformer efficiency at 50 per cent kva rating, 80 per cent power factor. The core loss is 100 watts.

12–11. A 25-hp, 230-volt series motor is operating at full-load output at 675 rpm. The armature resistance is 0.10 ohm, the series-field resistance is 0.115 ohm, and the stray power loss is 2200 watts. Find the full-load efficiency.

13–11. A 15-hp, 230-volt, d-c shunt motor is 85 per cent efficient at full load. The shunt-field circuit resistance is 287 ohms, the armature circuit resistance is 0.15 ohm, and the iron loss is 500 watts. Determine the friction and windage losses of the motor.

14–11. A 5000-kva, 2300-volt, 3-phase, 60-cycle, wye-connected alternator has an armature resistance per phase of 0.02 ohm and a synchronous reactance per phase of 0.2 ohm. The loss due to friction and windage is 15 kw and the iron loss is 55 kw. What is the alternator efficiency at full load, 0.8 power-factor lag? The alternator excitation for this load is 110 amp at 250 volts.

15–11. The armature of a 25-hp, 220-volt, 1000-rpm shunt motor has a resistance of 0.1 ohm and a shunt-field circuit resistance of 100 ohms. The stray power loss at full load is 2000 watts. Determine the motor input and efficiency at full load.

CHAPTER 12

PARALLEL OPERATION OF GENERATORS

The necessity for larger generating units came with the increase in demand for electrical energy. The apparent procedure would be to build the unit large enough to supply the load. For a time this could be followed but, since the surface of the unit increases as a square law and the volume as a cube law, there are limiting conditions which produce a balance between radiation of losses and the creation of such losses. Even with forced ventilation and heat-resisting insulation, there are physical limits to the size of units which can be economically constructed for operating at a safe temperature.

In addition to physical limitations, it is desirable to operate a unit at high efficiency. This would be impossible if a single unit supplied a load which varied from hour to hour. There are also the economic and continuous service factors that must be considered, both of which point to the advisability of groups of smaller units instead of one large unit. As the networks develop, and as different factors of economic generation are considered, it becomes necessary to operate units in parallel on a system, each unit supplying its share of the load and dividing load changes in the proper proportion.

The principle of operating equipment in parallel is not new to the field of engineering, other branches of engineering having obtained effective results by arranging equipment so that the additive results were absorbed by a common system. The parallel operation of generators is merely the expansion of these principles to the electrical field.

1. Fundamental Principles in Parallel Operation of Generators. Basically, two generators must be so connected that they deliver energy to the external system without delivering energy to each other. If this fundamental principle is satisfied, machines will operate successfully in parallel. This principle is general and applies to both d-c and a-c systems.

This general statement may be expanded by analysis, and the principal conditions that must be fulfilled are

1. The frequency of the two machines must be the same.
2. The wave form of the two machines must be similar.

3. Similar terminals must be connected together (those which are positive or negative at the same time).
4. The machines must have equal terminal voltages at every instant. This terminal voltage will be the voltage of the system.
5. The voltages of the two machines must be opposite at every instant, so that the resultant voltage between the units at every instant will be zero, though they both have the same external voltage.
6. To satisfy the above five conditions, the machines must be in synchronism.
7. The machines, including prime movers, must have similar load characteristics if the load is to be divided proportionally between them, with a changing demand from the system.
8. If the machines have different ratings, the energy supplied by the driving unit must be regulated by either the electrical or mechanical characteristics of the equipment. This regulation may be by manual or by automatic control.

The foregoing principles may be viewed under two types of analysis: the theoretical (above) and the actual operation of the equipment. The latter may be listed under the following heads.

1. Connecting and removing generating equipment from the system with the least disturbance.
2. Dividing the load between generators and transferring load from one machine to the other.
3. Adjusting for minimum circulating current (zero desired) between the two machines.
4. What effect on the generator operation may be expected from the type of prime mover used?

These theoretical and physical considerations will be discussed at the same time.

2. Synchronism—Assuming that Voltage Conditions in the Machines Are Correct. In order to simplify the analysis, the problem of parallel operation will be considered under such conditions that only one variable exists at a time. In actual operation, all conditions may vary and the operation of machines in parallel necessitates the adjustment of several of the factors at one time.

Figure 1–12 shows (*a*) two batteries in parallel and (*b*) two generators in parallel. In each diagram there is a lamp connected in the lead between the two sources. The generators may be either d-c or a-c machines, and, for simplicity, the external system does not carry a load.

Consider two batteries with equal internal potentials which, if properly connected, will have voltages equal and opposite. The resultant voltage will be zero (Kirchhoff's Law for the closed circuit), or

$$\overline{V}_{AB} + \overline{V}_{DC} = 0 \quad \text{or} \quad V_{AB} + V_{DC} = 0$$

If a lamp (which should always be rated at double the system voltage) is placed as shown in Fig. 1–12*a*, there will be no resultant voltage to cause a current to flow and, therefore, the lamp will not light. The lamp may be replaced by a voltmeter, which, being more sensitive as an indicator, will indicate zero voltage.

This same analysis may be used in the d-c generator, for it too has a definite polarity and, if constant and equal voltage conditions are present, the lamp will not light if the machines are connected so that the positive and negative polarity terminals of each machine are connected to the same common system leads, respectively.

By this analysis, in d-c systems, whether composed of batteries or generators, if the connections are correct and the voltages are correct,

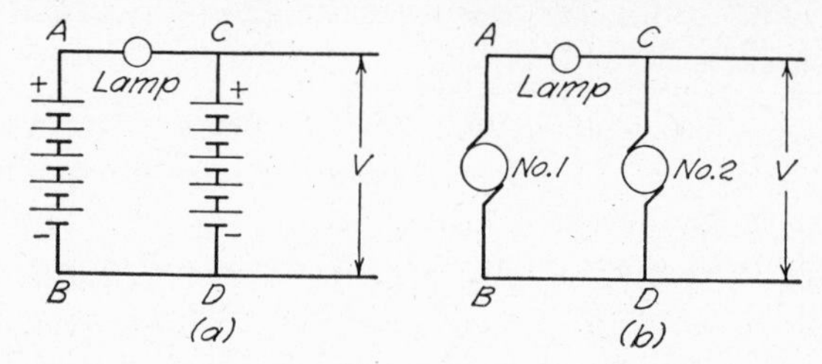

FIG. 1–12. (*a*) Two batteries in parallel without an external load. (*b*) Two generators in parallel without an external load.

there is no problem of synchronism, in the usual definition of the word. The term is generally not used in describing the connection of this type equipment.

Example a. Determine the current flow when two batteries are connected with positive terminals together if one battery has a resistance of 0.2 ohm and a voltage of 10 volts, on open circuit, whereas the second battery has a resistance of 0.5 ohm and a voltage of 9.5 volts, on open circuit.

By Kirchhoff's Law,

$$10 - 0.2I - 0.5I - 9.5 = 0$$

$$0.5 - 0.7I = 0$$

$$I = \frac{0.5}{0.7} = 0.714 \text{ amp}$$

Example b. The induced voltages of two d-c generators are 110 and 112 volts respectively. These machines are to be placed in parallel and a voltmeter is placed across the paralleling switch. What will be the reading across the switch (*a*) when the machines have like polarities connected? (*b*) when they have unlike polarities connected?

(*a*) $$112 - 110 = 2 \text{ volts}$$

(*b*) $$112 + 110 = 222 \text{ volts}$$

With the alternator, not only must the conditions encountered in the d-c system be met but the machines must also be correctly time-phased. If two alternators are identical and on the same shaft, the coils of the two machines must bear the same physical position with respect to the north and south poles at every instant before the alternators can be successfully paralleled. If the alternators are connected to two independent prime movers for parallel operation, the above still holds true, that is, if the alternators are situated near each other. If the machines are situated at considerable distances, there will be an angular displacement between them

Figure 2–12 will aid in clarifying this principle. In the battery and the d-c machine, the voltages are equal and opposite in the closed in-

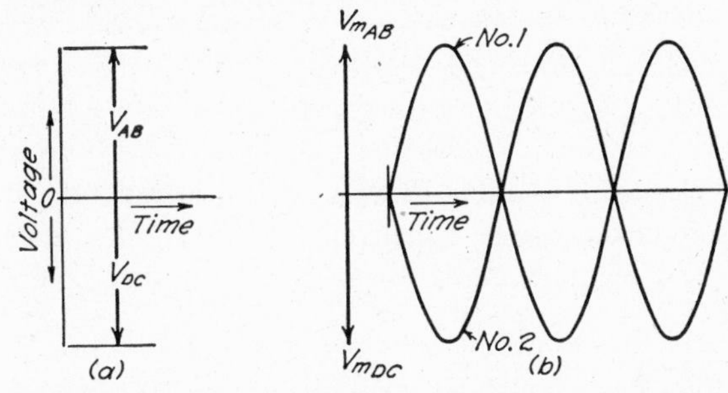

FIG. 2–12. (*a*) Two d-c voltages of machines or batteries in parallel without resultant voltage and circulating current. (*b*) Two alternators with sinusoidal voltage waves, in parallel without a resultant voltage or circulating current.

ternal circuit and Fig. 2–12*a* shows the plot of these voltages with time. This may, or may not, be true if the two machines are alternators. However, it is true if the machines are so operated that conditions shown in Fig. 2–12*b* are fulfilled. Here, the two machines, producing sine waves, are so time-phased that the instantaneous voltages are always equal and opposite and, for that reason, the resultant voltage is zero. When this resultant is zero, the lamp connected between the machines will be dark.

The difference between the d-c and a-c machines is that, in the d-c machine, there will be only one voltage which is the same at every instant, so that, when the machines are connected, the voltages either add or oppose. This leads to two possible values of voltage, whereas, in the a-c machine, regardless of equal voltage characteristics, an infinite number of voltages may result when two machines are connected.

In practice, it would not be possible to adjust the machines to meet the conditions of Fig. 2–12*b* for more than a short period of time, since the physical machines would drift apart and the closest approach would be a beat frequency between the two machines, which would be of a period depending upon the frequency of the two machines.

Example c. Two alternators with sine wave voltages of 110 and 115 volts, respectively, are placed in parallel with a lamp between them and are not in synchronism. If the above are effective voltages, what will be the maximum voltage across the synchronizing lamps?

$$\text{Maximum voltage No. 1} = 110 \times 1.414 = 155.54 \text{ volts}$$

$$\text{Maximum voltage No. 2} = 115 \times 1.414 = 162.61 \text{ volts}$$

$$\text{Maximum voltage across the lamps} = 318.15 \text{ volts}$$

3. Synchronizing A-C Generators. Since the alternators must be properly timed, it is necessary to take special precautions in placing an alternator, as the incoming machine, on the line with running equipment. Figure 3–12*a* shows the conditions when the machines are out of step by an angle α and the resultant wave of voltage which causes the lamp to light, in this way indicating that it is not safe to connect the machines together. If there is no voltage between points, it is safe to connect these points, because no current will flow; but, where there is a voltage, it is well to know more concerning the system before a connection is made.

Figures 3–12*b* and 3–12*c* show the voltage waves of two alternators and the resultant beat voltage. If two machines are so operated that the frequencies of the units are different, the machines will produce a beat frequency passing, as shown in Fig. 3–12*c*, from zero resultant voltage through a maximum back to zero, and repeating this as often per interval of time as the beat occurs. If two machine frequencies are very close together, this beat may be very slow and the lamp voltage will slowly increase, then decrease to zero. The dark interval of the lamp may be made comparatively long (8 to 10 seconds is possible). The dark period is the proper time for closing the switch. Once two beating machines have been connected together, under proper conditions they will remain in step because of the action of the circulating current, which will be discussed later in the operating characteristics of parallel machines.

The foregoing discussion has been limited to the single-phase machine. When the machine is of the polyphase type, the connections for polarity must be correct for each phase and, since it is possible to connect one line correctly, leaving the other two incorrect, it is necessary to determine the phase sequence of a system before making connections. After the polarity has been properly established, it will remain correct for future operation.

In practice, machines may be synchronized with either a bank of lamps or a synchroscope. The synchroscope may have lamps attached to indicate relative operation of the line and the incoming machine for emergency use when the synchroscope is not functioning.

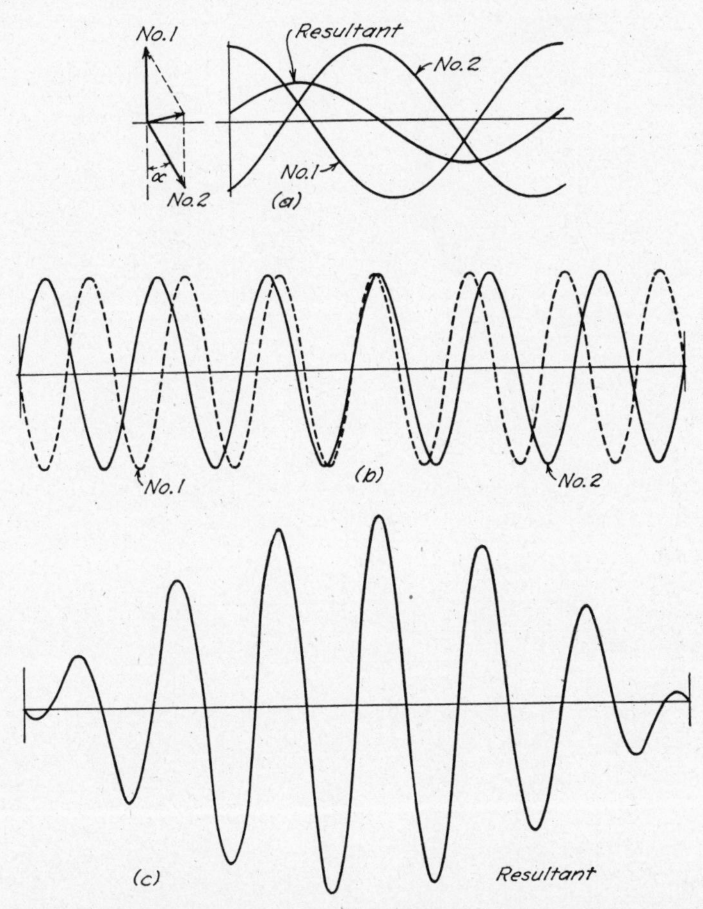

FIG. 3–12. Two voltages of alternators in parallel which have equal frequency when not in phase: (*a*) the voltage waves of two machines that have different frequencies; (*c*) the resultant beat frequency waves of the two machines in (*b*).

Figure 4–12 shows a view and circuit diagram of a synchroscope and the circuit diagram for the equipment; Fig. 5–12 shows diagrams for all-dark and two-bright-one-dark methods of synchronizing three-phase alternators with lamps. This latter system has the advantage of permitting a contrast visual determination of the point at which the voltage across one lamp is exactly zero, since at that point the two others will be equally bright. It also gives an indication of which is fast, the incoming or running machine. The three-dark system, though it does not give as accurate an indication of the zero point, does indicate whether

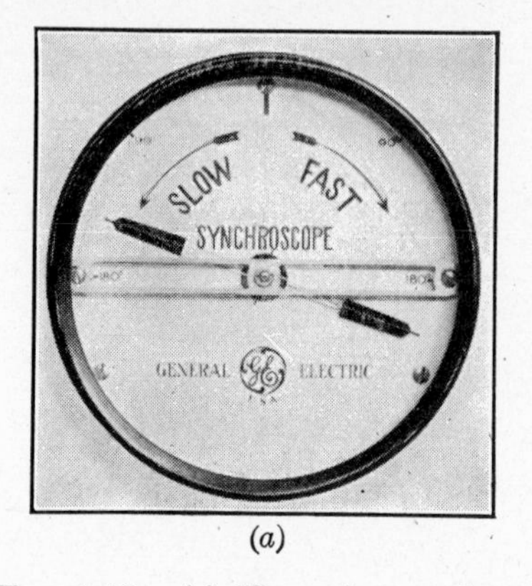

(a)

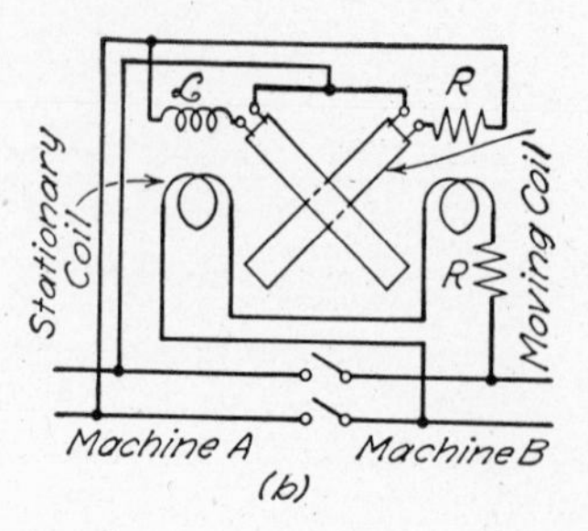

(b)

FIG. 4–12. (a) View of a synchroscope. (b) Diagram of connections for the synchroscope.

the machines are in proper phase sequence. If they are in proper sequence, all the lamps grow bright and dim together; if not, they "rotate," or grow bright and dim in sequence.

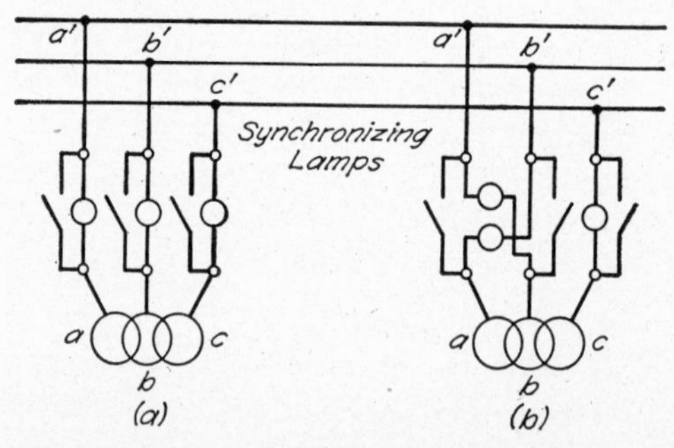

FIG. 5–12. The use of synchronizing lights in paralleling a-c machines: (a) synchronizing with lamps dark; (b) synchronizing with lamps two-bright-one-dark.

Example d. If the line frequency of a system is 60 cycles and the frequency of the incoming machine is 59.5 cycles, what will be the time in seconds between one bright period and the next on the synchronizing lamps?

$$60 - 59.5 = 0.5 \text{ times per second, lamp bright every 2 sec.}$$

4. Effect of Wave Form and Induced Voltage on the Operation of Generators in Parallel. In the operation of d-c machines, the problem of wave form does not exist, but the necessity to limit the circulating current by control of the generated voltage is ever present. In the previous discussion on the characteristics of motors and generators, it was shown that the establishing of motor or generator conditions depended upon the relative magnitude of line and generated voltage. If the line voltage is the greater, the machine is a motor; if the generated voltage is the greater, the machine is a generator. In regenerative braking with railway motors, this fact is utilized by the motor changing to a generator on down grades.

Figure 6–12 shows the condition of parallel operation of two d-c machines in which machine 1 is excited so that the induced voltage is

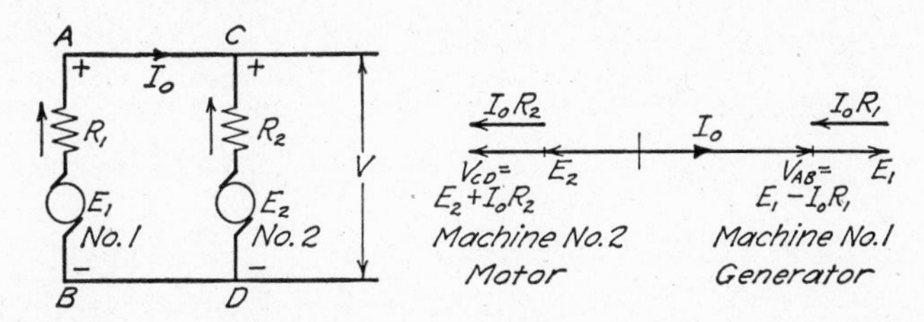

FIG. 6–12. Two d-c machines in parallel with equal induced voltages.

high enough to cause machine 2 to operate as a motor. A study of the figure and the equivalent voltage diagram will show that the current flows with the "voltage sense" in machine 1 and flows opposite to the "voltage sense" in machine 2, with the voltage drop equalizing the terminal voltages by adding to the generated voltage for one machine and subtracting for the other. The machines have been considered without external load in order to simplify the problem. The external load adds an increment of current to the condition existing between the two machines. There is a circulating current between them which tends to affect the induced voltage so as to give a common terminal voltage. The same discussion will apply to two batteries in parallel and even to the condition existing between two coils on the same armature having unequal voltages, where the circulating current may become so severe that it is necessary to connect coils together with "equalizing connections" to reduce internal heating.

In parallel operation of a-c machines, it is necessary to consider the wave form as well as the generated voltage of the machines. If two machines are in perfect synchronism, having equal maximum generated voltage and are properly time-phased, a variable residual voltage will exist whenever the machine wave forms are not the same. Figure 7–12*a* shows the characteristic wave forms of two machines, one with a flat-top, the other with a peak-top wave form with a resultant (shown by the heavy line) which would cause the synchronizing lamps to burn continuously, resulting in a circulating current if the switch is closed. These wave forms are extreme, being a combination of the most severe types possible, but the same effect exists to a lesser degree with any difference of wave form.

If the machines are assumed to be of the same wave form and in proper operating synchronism, it is still possible to have the indicating

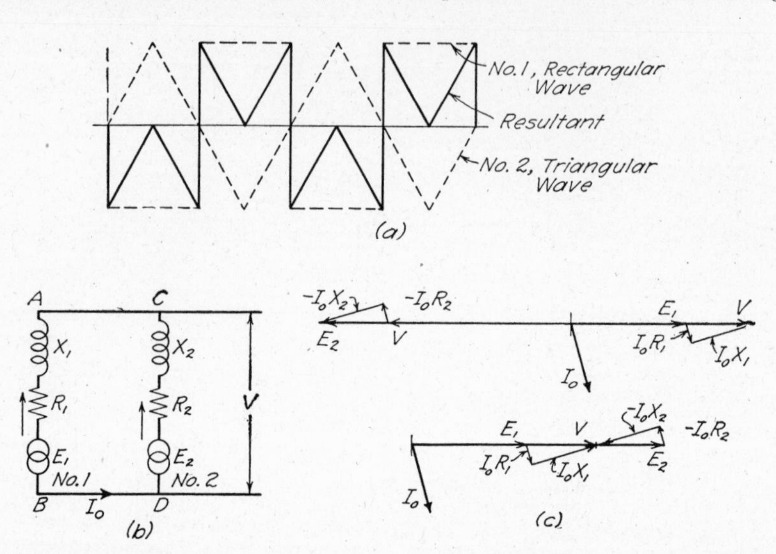

Fig. 7–12. (a) The resultant voltage wave when two machines in synchronism do not have the same wave form. (b) Two alternators in parallel with equal terminal voltages and a circulating current. (c) Vector diagram for the machines in (b).

lamp light, because the induced electromotive force of one machine is more than that of the other. If at this time the switch is closed, there will be a circulating current which attempts to establish voltage equilibrium in the system, but the power exchange may be very small. This analysis is shown in Figs. 7–12b and 7–12c; the first is a physical diagram, the latter a vector diagram. In machine 1, the current flow causes the impedance voltage component of the machine to lower the terminal voltage; in machine 2, the reverse is true, since the applied voltage overcomes the induced electromotive force and the impedance voltage component.

In both the d-c and the a-c systems, the effect of the circulating current is to restore a state of equilibrium. The current flows in such a manner as to cause generator action in one machine and motor action in the other, and the impedance produces voltage components that will equalize the terminal voltages of the two machines. This is a transient reaction, for the prime mover alone can control the energy delivered by the generator. Figure 8–12*a* shows the effect of circulating current in d-c machines and Fig. 8–12*b* shows the effect in a-c machines, when the excitation is different; Fig. 8–12*c* shows the effect when the a-c machines tend to separate because one machine either increases or decreases its speed momentarily. A study of the fundamental considerations will show that the two systems, direct and alternating, may be explained by similar analysis. Specific attention should be given Fig. 8–12*c*, because

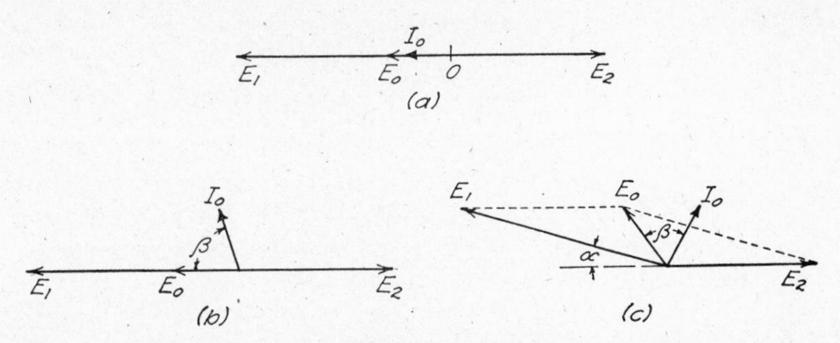

FIG. 8–12. (*a*) Diagram of the resultant circulating current and voltage when two d-c machines are in parallel. (*b*) When two alternators are in parallel and in synchronism. (*c*) When machine 1 drops back. In all the diagrams the excitation of the two machines is different.

a component of this circulating current will restore the machines to their normal synchronous operation. The machine that tends to speed up will become a generator with the energy projection of current in phase with the induced voltage, but the other machine becomes a motor with the energy projection of current negative with respect to the induced voltage. The generator action in one machine slows it down, but the motor action in the other speeds it up and equilibrium is restored in the connected system.

Example e. Two separately excited 7.5-kw, 125-volt shunt generators are placed in parallel. Determine the circulating current, when the two machines are placed in parallel, if the induced voltage of one is 115 volts and the induced voltage of the other is 118 volts. The armature resistance of each generator armature is 0.12 ohm.

$$E = 118 - 115 = 3 \text{ volts}$$

$$R = 0.12 + 0.12 = 0.24 \text{ ohm}$$

$$I = \frac{3}{0.24} = 12.5 \text{ amp}$$

Example f. Two single-phase alternators are in parallel and operating in synchronism. One machine has a sine wave effective voltage of 100 volts, the second has a square flat-top wave form of 100 volts effective. What is the maximum instantaneous circulating current between the two machines, if the synchronous impedance of each machine is 3.68 ohms?

$$\text{Maximum voltage of machine 1} = 100 \times 1.414 = 141.4 \text{ volts}$$

$$\text{Maximum voltage of machine 2} = 100 \text{ volts}$$

$$\text{Resultant maximum instantaneous voltage} = 100 \text{ volts}$$

$$\text{Maximum instantaneous current} = \frac{100}{2 \times 3.68} = 13.6 \text{ amp}$$

Example g. Two single-phase alternators, each having a synchronous reactance of 3.678 ohms and an effective resistance of 0.0554 ohm, are connected in parallel when the induced voltages are 6650 and 6550 volts, respectively, and in exact synchronism. Determine the circulating current and its power factor with respect to the terminal voltage.

$$\text{Resultant voltage} = 6650 - 6550 = 100 \text{ volts}$$

$$\text{Impedance of the system} = 2\sqrt{3.678^2 + 0.0554^2} = 7.3568 \text{ ohms}$$

$$\text{Circulating current} = \frac{100}{7.3568} = 13.59 \text{ amp}$$

$$\text{Power factor} = \frac{0.1108}{7.3568} = 0.015 \text{ lagging}$$

5. D-C Generators in Parallel with External Loading. The foregoing discussion was confined to the machines when they were not delivering external power. The object of parallel operation is to deliver energy to externally applied load, and the necessity for such methods of operation has its foundation in the inability to build and operate individual machines in single units to deliver these blocks of energy with economy. Interest lies in the successful delivery of energy to external loads without circulating current between the parallel machines.

In the d-c system, two types of machines are operated in parallel, shunt, and compound generators. The former is of academic interest only, inasmuch as modern d-c generators are wound compound to eliminate excessive regulation. In some older installations, however, shunt generators may still be found operating in parallel.

6. D-C Shunt-Wound Machines in Parallel. The shunt generator has a drooping voltage characteristic; that is, increasing load causes the voltage to decrease. Such machines, when operating in parallel, are stable because, if there is a momentary tendency for one machine to increase its load, the added current causes the voltage to drop and the generator must drop a portion of the load, since the IR component of the armature and the weakening of the field resulting from armature

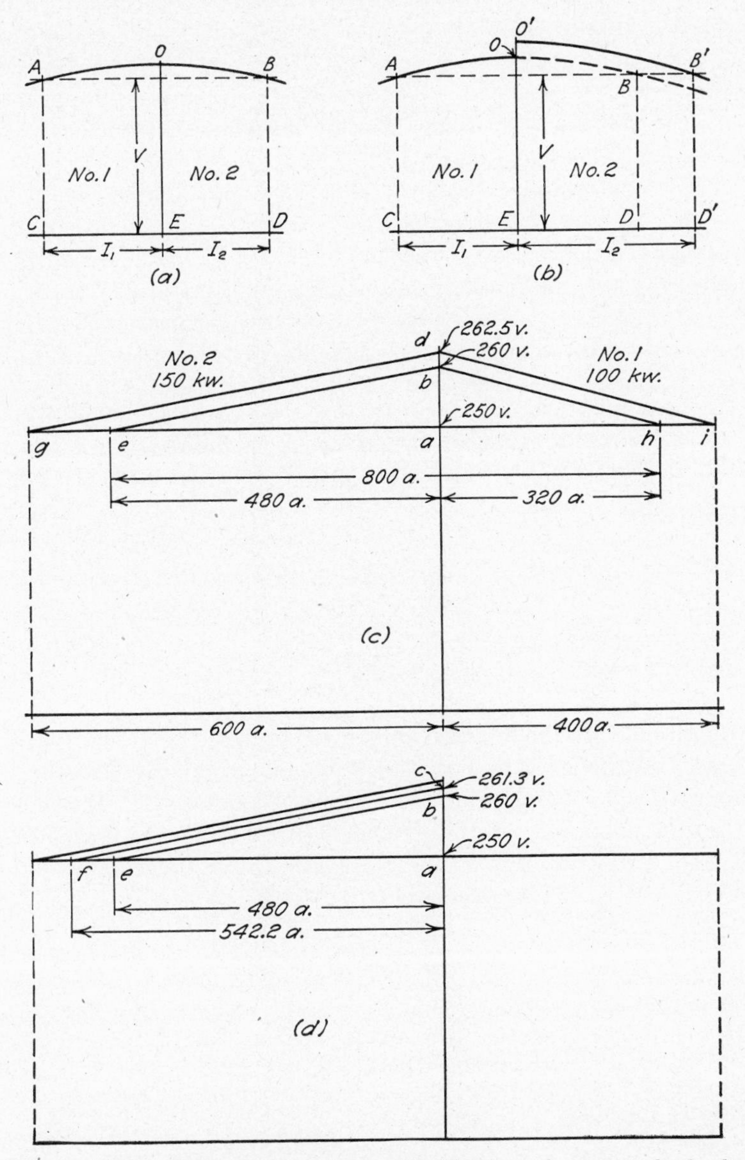

FIG. 9–12. (a) Two shunt generators in parallel which have the same no-load voltage. (b) Two shunt generators in parallel where no-load voltages are not equal.

reaction combine to lower the terminal voltage. A lowering of the induced voltage below the terminal voltage will cause the machine to operate as a motor, for it is necessary to have an induced voltage that exceeds the line voltage to continue operation as a generator.

This lowering of the voltage leads to the control of power delivery from a machine. A change of excitation will change the induced electromotive force and cause the generator either to take additional load or drop load. Figures 9–12*a* and 9–12*b* show machines operating in parallel at a common terminal voltage (V). In Fig. 9–12*a*, the two machines have the same no-load voltage, whereas in Fig. 9–12*b* machine 2 has a higher no-load terminal voltage than machine 1, if the machines are operated separately.

When the two machines divide the load, as shown in Fig. 9–12*a*, the external characteristic (this characteristic assumes constant speed) of the machine is the determining factor in the division of load. The currents CE and DE will depend upon the relative regulation of the two machines and, for automatic division of load on machines of equal capacity, their regulation should be the same. If the machines have unequal ratings (voltage versus kilowatts or current), the above statement is still true but the machine with the lower capacity will have an external characteristic that, to the same scale, is much steeper. If, for any reason, it is desirable to shift the characteristic curve of one machine, this is accomplished by increasing or lowering the excitation. Excitation change does not appreciably change the slope of the curve but merely changes its position. In Fig. 9–12*b*, the characteristic curve changes from OB to a new position $O'B'$ by adjusting the field rheostat. In this new position, with the terminal voltage held constant, the machine load increases in machine 2 from ED to ED' and, correspondingly, the machine is capable of furnishing the additional increment of current DD' to the external system. If the external load and terminal voltage remain constant, the load is reapportioned between the two machines (that is, machine 1 drops and 2 takes load).

Example h. Two 250-volt, d-c shunt generators of 5 per cent regulation each operate in parallel and deliver 200 kw to the external circuit. One machine is rated at 100 kw, the other at 150 kw, and the line voltage is 250 volts. How much load does each machine deliver to the system? Assume that the characteristics of the two machines are straight lines and that they have the same no-load voltage.

Refer to Fig. 9–12*c*.

Machine 1: $$I_1 = \frac{100 \times 1000}{250} = 400 \text{ amp } (ai)$$

Machine 2: $$I_2 = \frac{150 \times 1000}{250} = 600 \text{ amp } (ag)$$

Load: $$I = \frac{200 \times 1000}{250} = 800 \text{ amp } (eh)$$

At 5 per cent regulation: $ad = 12.5$ volts

$$\frac{ag}{ae} = \frac{ad}{ab} \qquad \frac{600}{ae} = \frac{12.5}{ab}$$

$$\frac{ai}{ah} = \frac{ad}{ab} \qquad \frac{400}{ah} = \frac{12.5}{ab}$$

$$ae + ah = 800 \text{ amp}$$

Solving the three equations,

$$ae = 480 \text{ amp, Machine 2}$$

$$ah = 320 \text{ amp, Machine 1}$$

$$ab = 10 \text{ volts}$$

No-load voltage: $250 + 10 = 260$ volts

where the rated voltage at 200 kw is 250 volts.

$$\frac{250 \times 320}{1000} = 80 \text{ kw, load on Machine 1}$$

$$\frac{250 \times 480}{1000} = 120 \text{ kw, load on Machine 2}$$

Example i. How much more load will the 150-kw generator in Example *h* be able to furnish if the terminal voltage remains the same and the no-load voltage of the 150-kw machine is increased 0.5 per cent? (Fig. 9–12*d*.)

Machine 2, no-load voltage 260 volts

0.5 per cent increase, 1.3 volts

$$ac = 11.3 \text{ volts}$$

$$\frac{af}{ae} = \frac{ac}{ab} \qquad \frac{af}{480} = \frac{11.3}{10}$$

$$af = 542.2 \text{ amp}$$

$$\frac{250 \times 542.2}{1000} = 135.6 \text{ kw, load}$$

Machine 2 could take an increase of $135.6 - 120 = 15.6$ kw, which the system could demand in excess of the connected load.

7. D-C Compound-Wound Generators in Parallel. In the compound machine there will be different operating conditions for the three different types of regulation. The undercompound machine will function as does the shunt generator. In flat-compound machines, operating in parallel, one may tend to absorb the whole load for a time, but even though the principle is the same as that of the shunt generator after the terminal voltage begins to droop, it is better to "equalize." Flat-compound generators in parallel should have an equalizer bus-bar, as the overcompound machines have, to divide load according to their capacities.

When the machines have overcompound characteristics, normal connections would create an unstable system for, if one machine were able to increase its load for even the shortest interval of time, the increase in load would cause the induced voltage to increase and this, in turn, would immediately require more load current to increase the internal voltage drop (Fig. 10–12*a*). One machine would drop all its load and the second would increase its load until it was not only taking all the line load, but was also driving the other unit as a motor. However, the

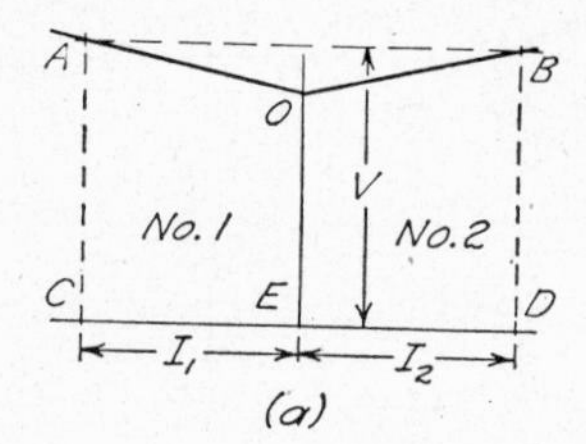

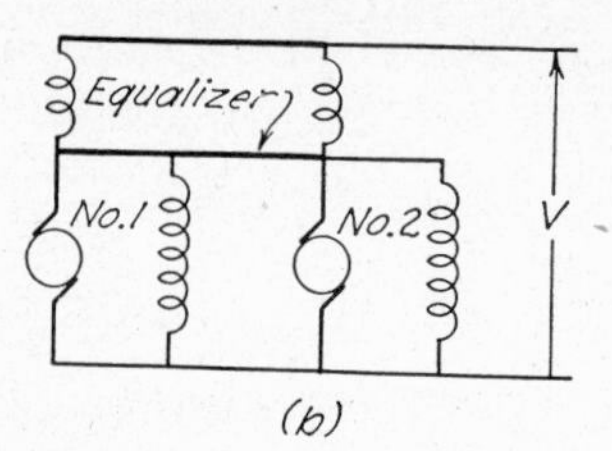

Fig. 10–12. (*a*) Characteristic of two over-compound generators in parallel with the same no-load voltage without the equalizer. (*b*) Circuit diagram of two compound machines showing the equalizer.

two machines in parallel, though they have characteristics which would cause unstable operation, may be stabilized by the use of an equalizer.

The division of the load between overcompound machines cannot be determined by the methods used for determining the division of loads for the shunt generators. The stability of the machines and the adjustment for characteristics, which are not the same, is brought about through the effect of series-field adjustment and equalizer. The equalizer bus-bar called "equalizer" introduces series ampere turns changes as shown for overcompound generators in Chapter 9. Because of the influence of the series ampere turns on the machine characteristics, the more steeply rising characteristic will take the larger load, a condition which does not follow those outlined for the parallel shunt generators.

Since the series fields are connected in parallel the characteristics of the two machines are influenced by both series fields and the incoming current will divide, between these fields, in inverse proportion to the resistances. The division of the load is dependent upon equalizer current, the connection of which, with respect to the fields and armatures of the machines, is shown in Fig. 10–12*b*. Though division of the load between the two machines may be controlled by an adjustment of the series fields it is not sufficient to place a diverter on one of the fields, for such a device would be in parallel with the other fields as well and would affect all machines in parallel. It is necessary to add the proper increment of resistance in series with the field and, in this way, control the change of field flux with load. This adjustment of series-field resistance should be in inverse proportion to the generator rating.

To shift the load from one machine to another it is not only necessary to adjust the shunt-field rheostats but also to divide the load according to the ratings at all loadings, without constant attendance. Series-field adjustment is necessary.

Example j. Two compound generators are operated in parallel. If generator A has a series-field resistance of 0.0015 ohm and is adjusted to take 30 per cent of the line load while generator B with a series field resistance of 0.001 ohm takes the remainder of the load, determine the current flow in the two series fields and the equalizer when the load is 230 kw at 230 volts.

$$I = \frac{230{,}000}{230} = 1000 \text{ amp}$$

$$I_A + I_B = 1000 \text{ amp}$$

$$\frac{I_A}{I_B} = \frac{0.001}{0.0015}$$

$$I_A = 400 \text{ amp, series-field current}$$

$$I_B = 600 \text{ amp, series-field current}$$

$$I_A = 0.3 \times 1000 = 300 \text{ amp, machine } A \text{ armature}$$

$$I_B = 1000 - 300 = 700 \text{ amp, machine } B \text{ armature}$$

$$I_E = 400 - 300 = 100 \text{ amp in the equalizer after adjustment}$$

8. Parallel Operation of Alternators. If two machines of similar characteristics and equal excitation are placed in parallel and properly adjusted, the external load is divided as shown in Fig. 11–12*a*, with each machine taking the same amount of load and the power factor of a lagging load causing the load current to lag behind the terminal voltage by an angle θ. If the characteristics of the two machines with their prime movers are the same, each machine will take an equal share of the load, as additional load is applied to the system. The voltage may be kept constant during this operation if the machines are equipped with voltage regulators, and the speed and frequency will decrease as load is added unless the governor is adjusted.

When it becomes necessary to shift the load from one machine to the other, more power must be supplied to the shaft of the machine which is to take more load. The shift cannot be made by a change of excitation, as in the d-c machine. The effect of a change of excitation is shown in Fig. 11–12*b*, where machine 1 has had its excitation increased. The current and power-factor values of the two machines will change but each will deliver the same amount of power to the system as before. The change of excitation causes a circulating current to flow between the two machines, which increases the copper losses and causes an unnecessary heating of the windings. The current of the underexcited machine leads more and the overexcited machine lags more than previously if the terminal voltage is the same.

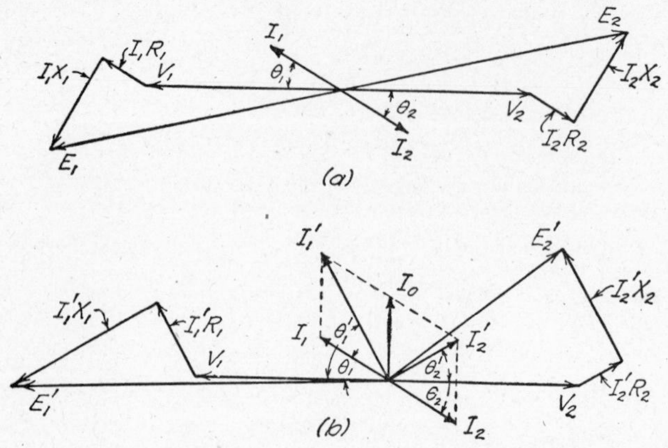

FIG. 11–12. (a) Vector diagram of two alternators in parallel with no circulating current and the system load divided equally between the two machines. (b) Vector diagram of two alternators in parallel with unequal induced voltages and circulating current and with the system load divided equally between the two machines.

Example k. Two single-phase alternators rated at 100 kva, 2300 volts, and with 4 per cent resistance and 40 per cent reactance are operated in parallel. The total load is 150 kva at unity power factor, and machine 1 takes 25 amp at 0.8 power factor lagging. What will be the current and power factor of machine 2 and what will be the induced voltage of each of the machines?

$$\text{Rating of machines} = \frac{100 \times 1000}{2300} = 43.48 \text{ amp}$$

$$R = \frac{0.04 \times 2300}{43.48} = 2.116 \text{ ohms}$$

$$X = \frac{0.40 \times 2300}{43.48} = 21.16 \text{ ohms}$$

I_t as a reference,

$$\bar{I}_t = 65.217 + j0 = \frac{150 \times 1000}{2300} = 65.22 \text{ amp}$$

$$\bar{I}_1 = 20 - j15 = 25 \text{ amp}$$

$$\bar{I}_2 = \bar{I}_t - \bar{I}_1 = 45.22 + j15 = 47.64 \text{ amp}$$

$$\cos\theta_2 = \frac{45.22}{47.64} = 0.9491 \qquad \sin\theta_2 = \frac{15}{47.64} = 0.3149$$

Power factor 94.9 per cent leading

I_1 as a reference,

$$\bar{E}_{g1} = 2300(0.8 + j0.6) + (25 + j0) \times (2.116 + j21.16)$$

$$= 1893 + j1909$$

$$E_{g1} = 2688 \text{ volts}$$

I_2 as a reference,

$$\bar{E}_{g2} = 2300(0.9491 - j0.3149) + (47.64 + j0)(2.116 + j21.16)$$

$$= 2283 + j284$$

$$E_{g2} = 2300 \text{ volts}$$

9. A-C Generator Load Controlled by the Prime Mover. Since the alternators have the same relative speed and the prime movers cannot change their output without a change of speed or an opening of the steam valve, it follows that there is nothing that can be done to the alternators that will cause them either to take or drop load. A change of system load will influence the speed (or frequency) of the system and the terminal voltage, but this is not desirable and every effort is directed to keeping these two values (frequency and voltage) constant by the installation of very elaborate regulating devices or by constant attendance by skilled operators.

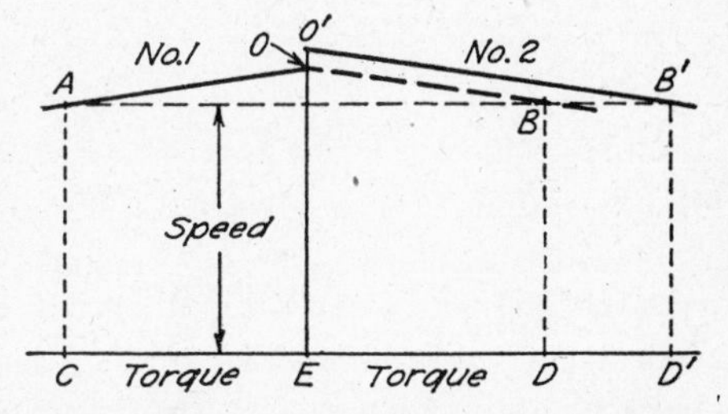

FIG. 12–12. Speed-torque characteristics for two prime movers driving two alternators. The speed-torque curve of machine 2 has been raised to cause it to take more load.

The only way to enable an alternator to increase its load is to supply more energy to the shaft at the same speed. For stable parallel operation, it is necessary to have turbines or other prime movers with drooping (speed versus load) characteristics. If more power is to be delivered at a given speed, it is necessary to shift the prime-mover characteristic in a manner similar to the shift of the characteristic curve of the d-c generator, that is, raise it very close to parallel to its original position. Figure 12–12 shows the effect of raising a prime-mover characteristic. This adjustment must be accomplished at the governor of the prime mover in order to admit more steam or water at the same speed; this means that the tension of the governor spring must be increased. As was shown before, a change of excitation compensating for the change in impedance drop will not affect the load distribution, but will change the power factor of the machines. In Fig. 12–12, the adjustment of the governor permits machine 2 to take an additional increment of torque DD' which, in this case, would have to be an added load on the system, since machine 1 does not change.

If several alternators are operated in parallel, the prime mover with the flattest characteristic will increase its load rapidly and those with the drooping characteristics will increase their load slowly. As the load decreases the reverse is true. When machines of different capacities are operated in parallel, the speed characteristics of the prime movers should be such that the slopes are proportioned on a percentage of the full-load capacity of the alternator. If machines are to operate in a stable manner, it is necessary that the speed regulation be 2 or 3 per cent, because a smaller regulation tends to cause unstable operation for changes of load.

The control of an individual prime mover is accomplished by a motor which operates on the spring tension of the governor and may be operated by remote control from the switchboard. Whenever the installation is confined to a small space and under the control of a single operator, the adjustment of the system frequency is accomplished by a simultaneous adjustment of all the units. The adjustment of only one machine to correct the system frequency would disturb the load distribution between the machines. If the voltage needs adjustment, the changing of the excitation of one machine would do little to relieve the situation; however, this would produce a very undesirable circulating current. A simultaneous adjustment of the excitation of the alternators would adjust any induced voltage discrepancies.

When frequency and voltage must be adjusted on large networks, the corrections are assigned to a "peak load" plant. These adjustments necessarily cause the plant to change load frequently, and frequent load changing is unsatisfactory for continuous operation. These plants, through the power dispatcher, are permitted to shift their loads when a load unbalance between the plants requires an adjustment for efficient operation. In this type of operation, much reliance must be placed upon cooperative effort in controlling the system and in reading the instruments at the control boards.

10. Automatic Synchronizing. Because it may be necessary to synchronize alternators or synchronous motors with the system many times a day, it becomes important that some form of automatic synchronizer be used. In some instances, particularly in substations where converters are used in railway practice, the unit must be connected and removed from the line as the voltage at a point decreases or increases.

Magnetic devices were first developed for performing this task. These required adjustment and there was always present the unreliable factor of friction and a time lag that could not be depended upon to remain constant.

Since the electronic tube is essentially an electrical relay without friction and practically zero time lag, it has been applied to equipment where speed of operation and sensitivity of control are required. The thermionic automatic synchronizer, because there are no springs or sensitive balanced moving parts and because it remains calibrated indefinitely, makes an ideal device for controlling synchronizing.

Figure 13–12 shows the circuit diagram of one type of automatic synchronizer. The synchronizer is connected through transformers 4 and 5 to the machine and to the line to be synchronized. The secondaries of these transformers cause a frequency beat across the rectifiers 6 and 7, which deliver a pulsating d-c voltage since the condensers 8 and 9 have smoothed the a-c components. The output varies between zero and maximum once per second for each cycle of frequency difference between the two systems.

Relay *A* is the lock-out relay and tube 3 (UX 112A) is connected in series with the coil of this relay, which is operated from a 250-volt d-c source. Tube 3 has a constant negative bias, which may be varied by means of potentiometer 10 plus a bias equal to the voltage across rectifier 7. This will be a maximum when the phase displacement is 180°. As the bias on tube 3 is reduced, there comes a time when relay *A* will close, and the phase angle closing position may be controlled by potentiometer 10.

Relay *B* will operate at an advance phase angle position, depending upon the bias on tube 2, the amount being proportional to the instantaneous frequency difference. The voltage drop across resistance 13 gives a positive bias to tube 2 and a constant negative bias is supplied by potentiometer 14. Rectifier 7 supplies a varying negative bias. Potentiometer 14 is so adjusted that, at zero phase displacement, relay *B* will operate.

When the frequency difference is zero, the voltage across condenser 12 equals the output of rectifier 6. If the frequency difference is changing from 180° to zero, correspondingly, the voltage across 6 and 12 will decrease; but across 12 it will be higher than across 6, depending upon the frequency difference of the line and the machine. The discharge from condenser 12 will produce a voltage drop across 13 which is proportional to the frequency difference, and this will give the desired positive bias to tube 2. The foregoing constitutes the synchronizing control.

In addition to the major control unit, several relays are necessary. Relay C is a master relay and makes the synchronizer operative. Relay D interposes a time delay to permit condenser 12 to charge properly,

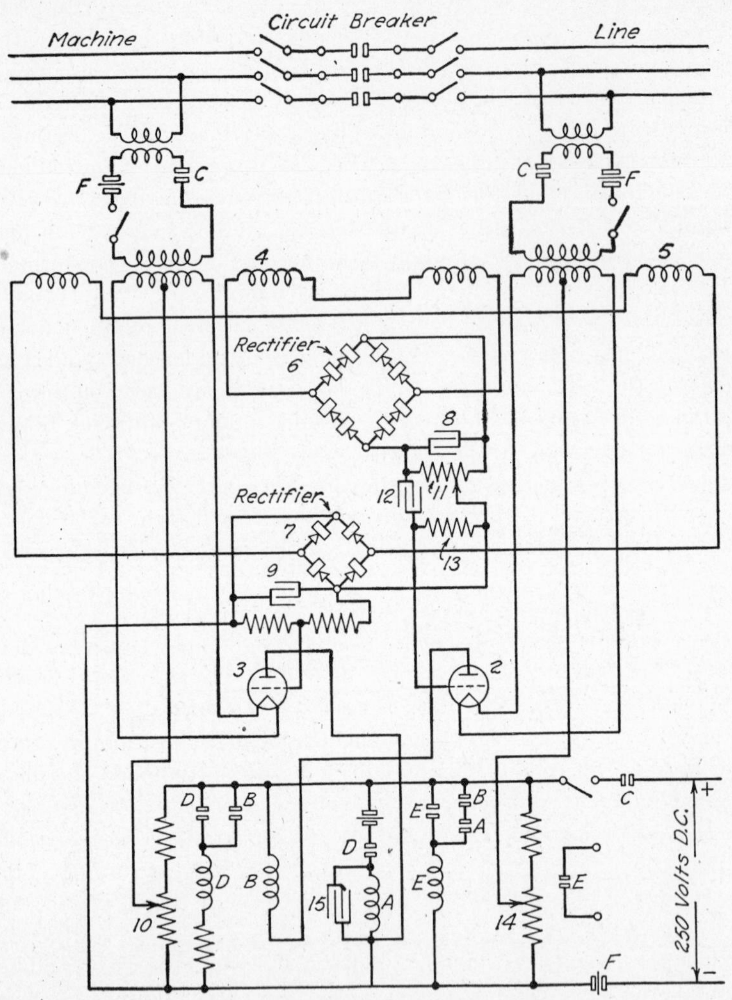

FIG. 13–12. Elementary wiring diagram of an automatic synchronizer. (Courtesy of Westinghouse Electric Corp.)

and this relay is closed by contacts on relay B, which operates at the phase displacement angle. Relays A and B are interlocked so that both must be connected and the connections must be in the proper sequence before relay E will close the circuit breaker. Condenser 15 holds relay A long enough for relay E to close. Since both relay A and relay B must close before the circuit breaker will close, a tube failure will make the device inoperative, and the circuit breaker will not close at an improper phase displacement angle. Relay F disconnects the synchronizer when the operating cycle is complete and the line and generator are in parallel. The automatic synchronizer may be used to synchronize two generators, a generator and a system, or two systems.

PROBLEMS

1–12. Three batteries are connected in parallel and connected to a 10-ohm external resistance. The internal voltages of the batteries are 31.5, 30, and 31 volts with resistances of 0.01, 0.02, and 0.03 ohms respectively. What will be (*a*) the current for each battery, (*b*) the terminal voltage, and (*c*) the total current?

2–12. The bus-bar frequency at a generating plant is 60 cycles and a generator to be paralleled with the bus is operating at 60.2 cycles. If the incoming generator is connected to the bus through a lamp, what will be the time interval between brightness periods, assuming that both wave forms are sinusoidal?

3–12. Two d-c shunt generators, with straight line current characteristics, are operating at full load:

	Kw	Voltage	Regulation
Machine 1	100	250	8 per cent
Machine 2	150	250	What?

The load is reduced until the terminal voltage has reached 260 volts, at which time the load on the two machines is the same. Determine the regulation of machine 2.

4–12. Two d-c shunt generators are paralleled at no load, and have the following ratings:

	Kw	Volts	Regulation
Machine 1	100	250	10 per cent
Machine 2	50	250	10 per cent

The machines are loaded to 100 kw with an external load. Determine (*a*) the load on each machine, (*b*) the system voltage.

5–12. Two d-c shunt generators with ratings of 100 kw, 230 volts, with the regulation of Machine 1 at 4 per cent and that of Machine 2 at 5 per cent, have a load of 100 kw divided between them. Assuming a straight line kilowatt characteristic and the no-load voltages of Machine 1 at 240 volts and of Machine 2 at 235 volts, determine (*a*) the division of the load between the two machines and (*b*) the terminal voltage; assuming a straight line current characteristic with each machine taking one half of the load determine (*c*) the no-load terminal voltage when disconnected from the system.

6–12. Two undercompound d-c generators are placed in parallel.

	Kw	Volts	Regulation
Machine 1	100	250	4 per cent
Machine 2	125	250	5 per cent

The load current is 500 amp, and the external generator characteristics are assumed to be straight line. Determine (*a*) the current taken by each machine, (*b*) the system voltage.

7–12. Two short shunt cumulative-compound generators are placed in parallel.

	Kw	Armature	Shunt Field	Series Field
Machine 1	100	0.1 ohm	50 ohms	0.05 ohm
Machine 2	75	0.13 ohm	50 ohms	0.10 ohm

Adjust the series fields of the machines so that they will divide the load proportionally from no load to full load.

8–12. Two 500-kva, 2300-volt, 1-phase, 60-cycle alternators each having an armature resistance of 2 per cent and synchronous reactances of 10 per cent. Machine *A* swings to a position 20° ahead of the 180° position of Machine *B*. Determine the circulation current.

9–12. Two 100-volt, 1-phase generators are placed in parallel without an external load. The armature resistance of each is 0.1 ohm and the synchronous reactance 1 ohm. If one machine falls back 15° what will be the circulating current furnishing the restoring torque?

10–12. Two alternators are placed in parallel without an external load. The synchronous reactance of each is 0.25 ohm and the resistance is neglected. The induced voltage in Machine 1 is 100 volts and that in Machine 2 is 110 volts. If Machine 2 falls back 10°, determine (*a*) the circulating current, (*b*) the power factor for I_2, and (*c*) draw the vector diagram, indicating the various vectors.

11–12. Two 220-volt, 3-phase, 25-cycle, wye-connected alternators are connected in parallel with Machine 1 overexcited 17.32 per cent and Machine 2 underexcited 17.32 per cent. If each machine has a reactance of 1.1 ohms and the resistance is neglected, determine (*a*) the magnitude and direction of the power transfer, (*b*) the current flow in each machine, with power factor, and (*c*) the terminal voltage of the machines.

12–12. Two 1000-kva, 2300-volt, 3-phase, 25-cycle alternators are operated in parallel. When in parallel the machines are at full load, which is reduced to a total load of 1200 kw at unity power factor. The frequency remains constant and there is no change on the setting of the governor of the prime mover of Machine 2. What is the load on Machine 1 after the change?

13–12. Two alternators are operating at no load, Machine 1 at 62 cycles and Machine 2 at 63 cycles. When paralleled the common frequency is 59 cycles with the load on Machine 1 1500 kw, and that on Machine 2 2000 kw. With a change in load so that Machine 1 carries 1000 kw, determine (*a*) the load on Machine 2 and (*b*) the operating frequency. If the governor is adjusted as above and the load is disconnected without separating the machine, what will be the load on each machine because of the circulating current?

14–12. Two alternators, 10 kva, 100-volt, 1-phase, and 60-cycles, are connected to a unity power-factor load. If Machine *A* has a load of 4000 watts and 80 per cent lagging power factor, determine (*a*) the current for Machine *B*, (*b*) the power factor for Machine *B*.

15–12. Two alternators rated at 2500 kva, 2300-volts, 3-phase, 60-cycles, wye-connected are in parallel and carry a load of 4000 kw at 80 per cent lagging power factor. Machine 1 carries 1800 kw at 90 per cent lagging power factor. Determine (*a*) the output of Machine 2, and (*b*) its power factor.

CHAPTER 13

ELECTRICAL APPLICATIONS AND RATES

Electrical machines for power development and utilization are of prime importance, but heating and welding are consuming more electrical energy each year in electrical applications. The machine, as discussed up to this point, has been studied as a unit separate from numerous pieces of auxiliary equipment needed for its control and operation. Manufacturers of electrical equipment have large divisions of their plants devoted to control and starting equipment.

The application of motors often depends primarily upon the voltage and the kind of electricity available as well as the special service required from the driving units. The selection of equipment of the proper size may be determined by a calculation of the mechanical requirements and the use of judgment and experience in applying the results.

MOTOR APPLICATIONS

1. Selection of Voltages and Kind of Electricity. Since alternating current is becoming the type of electricity delivered by the power companies in most districts, the kind of electricity obtainable is fixed. In electrical installations, it is necessary to start planning from the energy source available. In the past, whenever equipment was to be located in the business district or the manufacturing section of a city, direct current was available if it was desired. In localities so far from a power center that cost prohibits the extension of lines from the general power distribution system, there is a choice of either d-c or a-c installation. Often the choice is made by considering the duty the plant will require from its motors and the size of the distribution system. Wherever only alternating current is available, any direct current that is necessary may be obtained by using motor-generator sets, synchronous converters, or rectifiers which show promise of replacing other means.

Voltages must be selected by considering the size of equipment and the service requirements of the customer. In the event that a separate circuit installation is not used for lighting, it is better to limit the lighting circuits to 110 or 115 volts, which, on a three-wire system, would limit motor circuits to 220 or 230 volts on d-c or single-phase a-c circuits. It is possible to operate a lighting system at 220 volts, giving, by means of a three-wire distribution, 440 volts for motor service. These proportions must be adhered to if direct current is being used from isolated plants. The usual power supply in d-c current districts is limited to three-wire, 110–220 volt systems, with 600–700 volts direct current available from street car service lines. The standard voltages of d-c motors are 115, 230, or 550 volts. The voltages of a-c systems are easily changed by the use of transformers; therefore, any voltage may be obtained from the power source. In a-c systems, lighting is usually taken from 110-volt or three-wire, 110–220-volt distribution circuits, whereas motors are either 110, 220, 440, 550, or 2200 volts. The voltage selected should depend upon the nature and mechanical requirements of the circuit installed. Motors under 100 horsepower should not be operated at 2200 volts, because the windings must be made of very fine wire and the motor is so small that there is not sufficient room for proper insulation. A 110-volt distribution system is not satisfactory for motors larger than 10 horsepower (a 5-horsepower limit is better) because of excessive line current and voltage drop that would result.

The frequency is usually fixed in any community but there are some requirements that determine the frequency. Lighting does not work satisfactorily on frequencies lower than 40 cycles, and 25 cycles gives a very undesirable flicker. For some industrial purposes, a power supply having lower frequencies is desirable but the limitations of speed range must be studied in connection with frequency. At present, 60 cycles appears to be the accepted standard, and systems of this frequency are capable of supplying both lighting and motor service within reasonable economic requirements and operating efficiency. When high frequencies are desired for induction furnaces, high frequency heating and certain shop tools, such as high speed drills and riveters, these are obtained by the use of motor-generator sets and electronic devices located in the individual plants.

2. Effect of Voltage and Frequency Variations. Electrical equipment seldom functions properly if either frequency or voltage varies 10 per cent or more from the rated value. Since, at present, frequencies are very accurately controlled, the only danger lies in not purchasing equipment of the proper frequency rating or in faulty operation of isolated plants. Voltage control does not depend only upon the power source, because a faulty wiring installation may reduce the voltage on the equipment through excessive line drop. One of the common signs of low voltage, as well as overload, is undue heating of motors. With the use of three-phase four-wire distribution circuits, 120 volts for lighting and three-phase, 208 volts for motor service are available. In this type of distribution it is satisfactory to operate a 220-volt motor on 208 volts, since the performance and the efficiency will not be materially changed, although the safe rating is reduced.

3. The Demands of the Service upon the Motor. The service requirements of the motor determine the design of motor. Motors may be grouped into three classes: those for continuous duty (general-service motors), short-time duty motors, and enclosed motors which may be for either continuous or intermittent use. The intermittent-duty motor will carry about twice the load of the continuous-duty motor, and the enclosed motor will carry about half the load of an open motor of the same electrical construction. Special designs must be used wherever motors are to be operated in highly explosive atmospheres or in very damp places. Motor speed requirements are also used for classification. There are constant speed, variable speed, or adjustable speed types.

4. Selection of Motor for Performance. The requirements for motor selection depend upon the torque and speed performance. Although speed regulation is of prime interest, torque at starting may limit the service of the motor. The amount of current required to obtain the required torque (as previously stated), however, may be controlled by the voltage. Regardless of the voltage used, the "light flicker," resulting from voltage reduction caused by motor starting current, is an objectionable feature which should be reduced to a minimum. The problem of "light flicker" is very important in high grade office buildings, and serious flicker conditions will not be tolerated. The performance characteristics of the common types of motors are listed in Table I–13, and in Table II–13 are listed specific motor applications.

The induction motor is probably the most reliable and satisfactory motor for general purpose use. It is a motor which, within reasonable limits, may have almost any desired starting torque without a great sacrifice in efficiency or performance. The speed is practically constant, and the two desirable features, reliability of operation and low first cost, are bringing this motor into universal use for almost every application. Though speed control, of a kind, can be applied to the induction motor through a loss in resistances (where speed control is a necessity), its efficiency cannot compete with that of the more costly d-c motors.

5. The Size of Motor Required. When the size of the load can be determined by a direct calculation (as in elevators and hoists), the size of motor may be determined accurately. When the cutting of material enters into the problem, only empirical formulas depending upon the experience developed in practice will give an answer to the problem,

TABLE I–13

MOTOR PERFORMANCE

Direct Current	Characteristic	Alternating Current
SPEED PERFORMANCE		
D-c motor with Ward Leonard control	Constant	Synchronous motor
Shunt Differential compound	Approximately constant	Induction (all types)
Cumulative compound	Semi-constant	High resistance rotor induction
Series	Varying speed	Series
Shunt motor with field control Ward Leonard control	Constant speed with speed adjustment	Pole-changing or counter E.M.F. Squirrel-cage induction
Cumulative compound motor field control	Semi-constant speed with speed adjustment	Rotor resistance control, wound-rotor induction
RATIO OF STARTING TO RUNNING TORQUE		
Differential compound	Low	Squirrel-cage induction (high reactance) Single-phase (split-phase)
Shunt Cumulative compound	Medium	Squirrel-cage induction (high resistance) Synchronous
Series	High	(Wound rotor induction external resistance) Single-phase (comm. types)
RATIO OF STARTING TO RUNNING CURRENT		
Series Cumulative compound	Large	Single-phase (split-phase) Single-phase (repulsion) Synchronous (induction motor start)
Differential compound	Medium	Induction polyphase (high reactance) Induction (high resistance)
Shunt	Small	Induction (wound rotor)

TABLE II–13

Motor Application

Types of Motors and Loads	Speed				Blower (Large)	Blower (Pressure)	Compressors	Conveyors	Cranes	Crushers	Extractors	Elevator (Freight)	Elevator (Passenger)	Generators	Fan (Disc)	Fan (Small)	Hoist (Bucket)	Hoist (Mine)	Kilns	Line Shaft	Machine Tools	Pumps (Centrifugal)	Pumps (Reciprocating)	Punches	Shaper	Shears	Stokers	Traction	Woodworking
	Very Constant	Constant	Adjustable	Variable																									
Steady Load					×	×		×			×			×	×	×				×	×	×							×
Medium Shock Load						×	×	×	×		×	×	×				×	×	×				×				×	×	
Heavy Shock Load							×	×	×	×								×					×	×	×	×			
Direct Current: Shunt		×	×		×	×	×							×	×	×				×	×	×	×						×
Compound (Cum.)			×	×		×	×	×		×	×	×	×					×	×		×	×	×	×	×	×	×		×
Compound (Diff.)	×																												
Series			×	×				×	×			×			×		×	×										×	
Alternating Current: Induction 3-Phase		×			×	×					×		×	×	×	×				×	×	×							×
High R				×	×		×	×	×		×	×					×	×											
High X		×			For line starting—3-phase induction motor application																								
Double (R and X)		×				×		×													×		×						
Slip-ring			×	×		×	×		×			×	×					×				×	×						×
Multispeed		×	×		×						×										×	×	×						
Brush-shifting			×	×			×	×											×			×							
Synchronous	×													×															
Series 1 or 3-Phase			×	×					×			×					×											×	

since there is no theoretical base for the calculations. The movement of materials by conveyors involves some modification of theoretical calculations, because the friction cannot be accurately determined. Wherever the motor size is determined by actual test installations using calibrated motors, results have proved very satisfactory. There should be a 10 or 15 per cent allowance over the theoretical size of motor re-

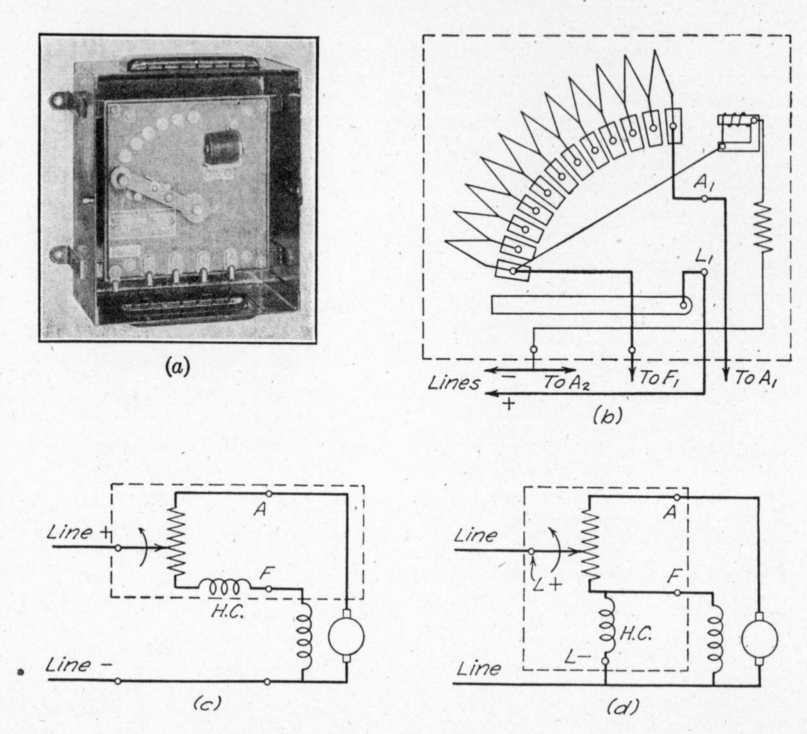

FIG. 1–13. (*a*) Photograph of a four-point starting box. (*b*) Wiring diagram for a four-point box. (*c*) Circuit diagram for a three-point box. (*d*) Circuit diagram for a four-point box. (Courtesy of General Electric Co.)

quired for variation in voltages and increased friction, when oiling is neglected. The power required to drive cranes and pumps may be calculated by their mechanical formulas but the size for other equipment should be determined from empirical formulas.*

6. Starting and Control Equipment for the D-C Motor. D-c motors are usually started through either a three-point or a four-point starting box. Figure 1–13 shows a starting box and circuit diagrams for the

* Harold W. Brown, in Chapter 22 of *Electrical Equipment*, gives several tables of motor horsepowers for various applications.

three-point and four-point starting box. These boxes are equipped with a holding coil, which also acts as a low voltage release. When the voltage falls below a predetermined value, the handle is returned to the starting position and the circuit is opened.

The three-point and four-point boxes differ only in the position of the holding coil in the circuit. In the three-point box, the holding coil is in series with the motor field and any weakening of the field for speed control weakens the holding coil which acts as a release if the field current is decreased too much, even when the lines are under normal voltage. In the four-point box, the holding coil is connected across the

(a)

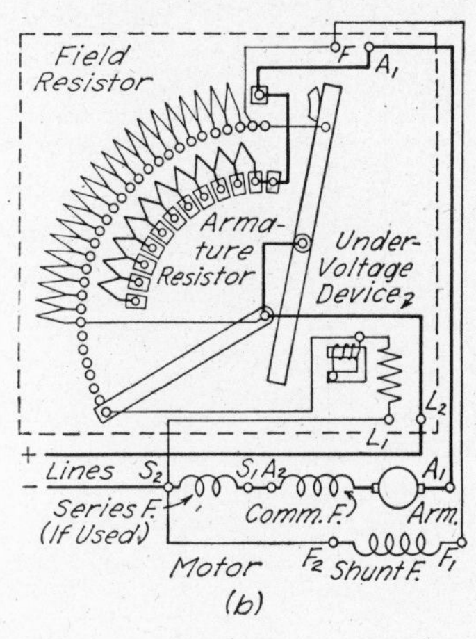

(b)

FIG. 2–13. (a) Photograph of a hand-operated compound starter. (b) Circuit diagram of a compound starter. (Courtesy of General Electric Co.)

line in series with a high resistance and the field may be weakened for speed control without weakening the magnetic field of the holding coil. Figure 2–13 shows a starting box used for a speed control as well as a starting device. These compound starters have the essential parts of a starting box and, also, a variable resistance in series with the field circuit that may be varied to control the machine speed. This variable resistance is controlled by an auxiliary handle which moves forward with the starting handle and may be returned independently, while the starting handle is held in position by the holding coil.

For heavy-duty installations and for places where the equipment is started frequently, a more rugged starter, known as the drum switch, has been developed. Figure 3–13 shows a drum switch and a circuit diagram for switches of this type. These switches are used in cranes, street cars, and for motor-driven machine tools. The resistors used with these motors are usually of such capacity that the switch may be left at any intermediate position without causing the resistance to overheat.

Since the rate at which resistance may be safely removed from the armature circuit of a machine is limited, it is not unusual to remove this hazard (excessive rate of removing resistance) from the hands of the

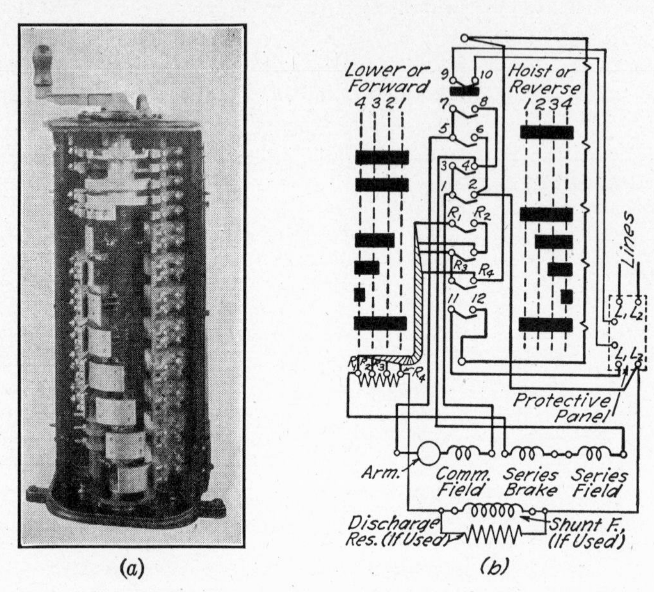

Fig. 3–13. (*a*) Photograph of a drum or cam switch. (*b*) Wiring diagram of a drum switch. (Courtesy of General Electric Co.)

operator by use of automatic controls. Figure 4–13 shows one of these controls and the circuit diagram with a curve showing the decrease of the current before the next contact can close. The closing of the first contact, which closes the circuit through a series resistance, holds out the other contacts until the current falls to a predetermined value, when the other contacts can close in proper sequence and cut out all resistance. This sequence is complete when full-load voltage has been applied to the machine and all the resistance has been removed from the line.

Though numerous controls are on the market, all types may be listed under one or more of the above-described methods of starting or controlling the motor. External resistances may be introduced into the field and armature circuits for speed control. The introduction of the resistance may be accomplished by either automatic or manual operation, and it need not be located at the motor but may be at some distant place. By automatic means, a process of manufacture or the level of a fluid in a reservoir may turn the motor off or on, or control its speed as may be required.

(a)

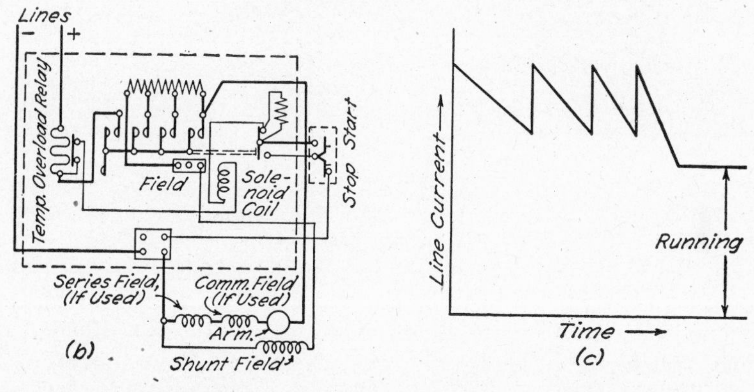

FIG. 4–13. (a) Photograph of a magnetic controller. (b) Circuit diagram of the automatic magnetic starter. (c) Curve of the current showing rise in current as resistances are cut out. (Courtesy of General Electric Co.)

7. Starting and Control Equipment for A-C Motors. Speed control is of little importance in a-c motors, except for the control of wound-rotor induction motors, which may be brought about by the use of a rheostat connected to the rotor slip rings. Any other form of speed control for an a-c motor is very costly and elaborate and, therefore, seldom used.

The "line starting" method of starting small a-c motors has been used for a long time and is becoming increasingly desirable for larger motors. By a suitable switch the motor is started by being connected directly to the line. If a large motor is used, this may be done only by agreement with the power company. Care must be taken so that there will be no objectionable flicker of lights and so that the distribution system will not be seriously disturbed by the large current drawn by a line starting

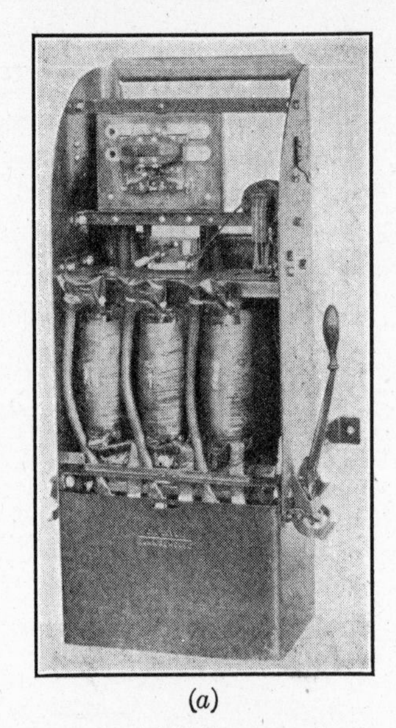

(a)

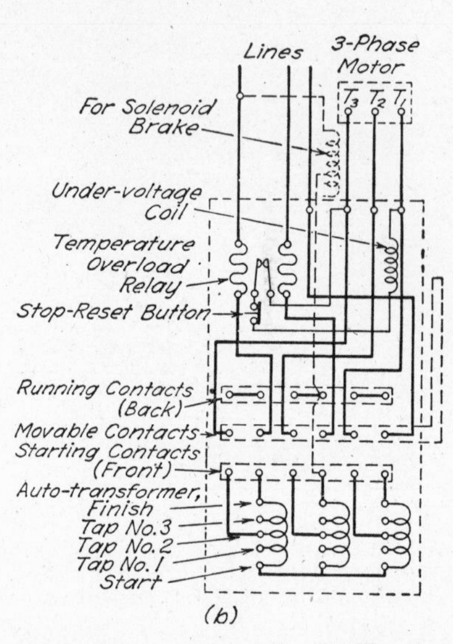

(b)

Fig. 5–13. (a) Photograph of a compensator, with cover removed. (b) The circuit diagram of a compensator. (Courtesy of General Electric Co.)

motor. Switches for these motors are equipped with overcurrent and low voltage releases for the protection of the system and the motor.

Figure 5–13 shows a compensator which is used to reduce the voltage for the starting of an induction motor. This starter uses tapped auto-transformers for voltage reduction at starting. Usually this device has two positions: one approximately half voltage for starting, the other for line connection. Moving the lever to the starting position connects the starting tap of the transformer directly to the motor. The handle returns to the off-position when a button marked "stop" is pressed. The compensator is equipped with an interlocking device so that the handle cannot be placed at full-line position until the motor is up to speed. It is also equipped with overload and undervoltage relays.

Induction motors may be started by introducing resistance or reactance in series with the line to reduce the voltage. The introduction of the reactance lowers the power factor and is not so desirable as the introduction of resistance. Figure 6–13 shows a photograph of a resistance starter and the circuit diagram.

(a) 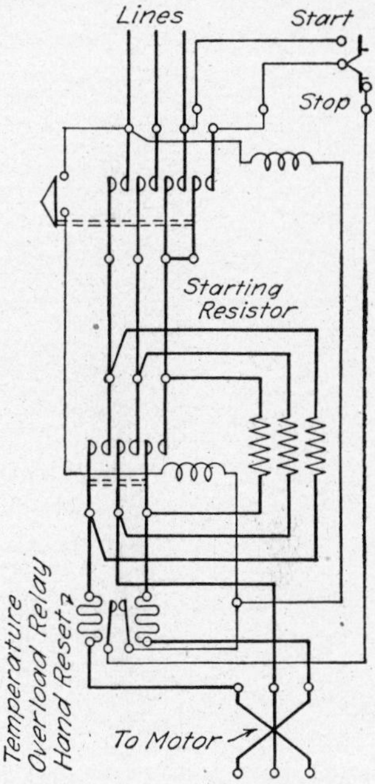 (b)

FIG. 6–13. (a) Photograph of resistance starter. (b) Circuit diagram of a resistance starter. (Courtesy of General Electric Co.)

By means of a tap-changing switch and a three-phase bank of transformers (or the windings of the motor may be used), it is possible to start a motor connected in star and to run it connected in delta. The

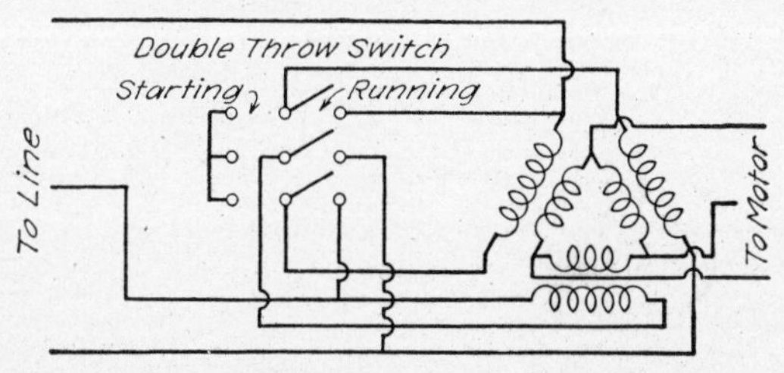

FIG. 7–13. Circuit diagram of star-delta method of starting induction motors (may be applied to motor windings).

starting voltage will be 58 per cent of full-line voltage. This method is definitely fixed in voltage relationships and cannot be adjusted with the torque required for starting, if the load conditions are unusually heavy.

Figure 7–13 shows a circuit diagram for switching the transformer bank from star-connected to delta-connected.

The synchronous motor needs no special treatment with regard to starting. The latest motors of this type, as well as synchronous converters, start using their damper (amortisseur) windings on the induc-

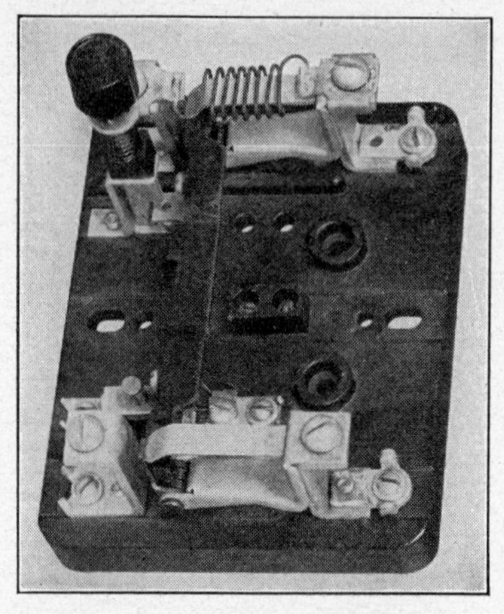

(a)

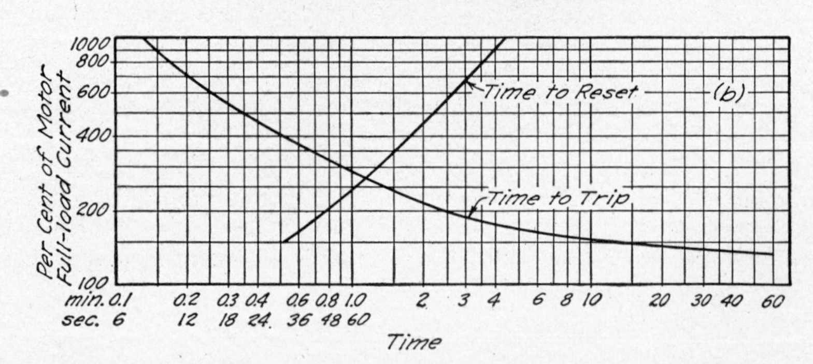

Fig. 8–13. (a) One type of thermal cutout. (b) Time-current curve for a thermal cutout.

tion motor principle, and the same starting devices are used in both synchronous and induction motors.

8. Thermal Cutouts. The thermal cutout is used in place of a running fuse. The characteristic curve of the thermal cutout differs markedly from that of a fuse. Figure 8–13 shows the time-current curve of a thermal cutout and a photograph of one type of cutout.

A motor may be equipped with a magnetic circuit breaker or fuse and low voltage release and still burn out because of a steady overload.

The circuit breaker is set and designed for circuit interruption in the event that an unusual demand is made on the system, and the low voltage release protects the motor when the voltage drops, but the motor is not protected at the critical point of load, that is, between full load and 25 per cent overload. The thermal cutout performs this function because it heats up with the motor and, if properly designed, will not again close the circuit at a temperature at which the motor will not be protected. It will not interfere with the starting of the motor because the short high current period does not heat the unit to a point at which the

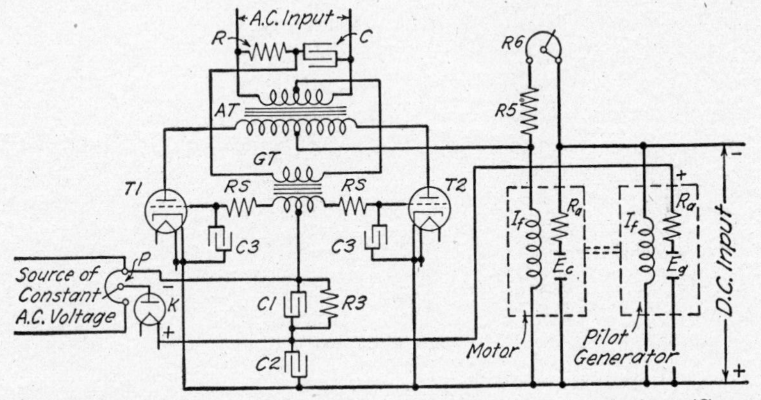

FIG. 9–13. Circuit diagram for an electronic motor-speed control device. (Courtesy of General Electric Co.)

circuit is opened. The thermal unit is surrounded by a heater, which heats a bi-metal strip or an alloy, which, in turn, restrains a tripping mechanism under spring tension. Either a high overload for a short period of time or a slight overload for a long period of time will move the bi-metal strip or melt the alloy and release the tripping mechanism. Some units are so arranged that the motor and the alloy cool at approximately the same rate and, in this way, do not allow the motor to be connected until it has cooled to a safe temperature. These units satisfactorily replace the old method of installation, using starting and running fuses for motor starting, where line starting was used. The time delay permits starting and the thermal unit protects against overloads.

9. Motor Speed Control by Electron Tubes. Where accurate speed control is desired, particularly where correlation between machines or sections of one machine is necessary, tubes of the vapor discharge type may be used in the motor-field circuit for speed control. Figure 9–13 shows the circuit for the control of speed through a grid control in the grid circuit of a discharge type of tube. This is only a type; variations in control are numerous. The introduction of electronic controls in industry has developed into a special field of *industrial electronics*.

The field of the motor is adjusted to give the maximum speed, and the discharge tube increases the current value of the field for control purposes. The feedback circuit to the grid of the discharge tube is controlled by a pilot generator mounted directly on the shaft of the motor.

A practically pure d-c voltage is introduced into the grid circuit of the control tube by a local circuit composed of the potentiometer P, the two-element tube K, the capacity C_1, and the resistance R_3. The condenser C_1 and the resistance R_3 circuit have a time constant, which is large compared to the frequency period of the supply source. In the grid circuit of the control tube the voltage from the pilot generator, across the filter condenser C_2, opposes that of the local d-c circuit. By transformer coupling, alternating current obtained from the bridge circuit composed of the transformer primary, R and C, is introduced into the grid control. This lags the applied anode voltage by 90°. An effective phase control may be obtained by varying the d-c difference voltage through small values. When this control is applied to the shunt motor, it may be expected that the speed regulation will be less than 2 per cent, for the grid circuit of the control tube regulates to produce a pilot generator voltage (through the motor speed) about the same as the potentiometer, regardless of the load or circuit characteristics.

Figure 9–13 shows the input from a d-c source. This source may be from thyratrons as well as any direct current supply. The driving power as well as the control when supplied by an a-c source becomes one type of variable speed a-c motor. Motors of this type are sold under the name of Thy-mo-trol or Mot-o-trol controlled motors.

10. The Amplidyne. The amplidyne is an externally driven d-c generator which, by the use of a short circuit and compensating winding, is capable, through a precise electrical balance, of controlling large power outputs through a very small signal release. This is electrical equipment which has the characteristics of grid control in an electronic device; therefore, its function for control purposes is that of an electronic control with power possibilities which are unlimited, as contrasted to the control tube.

Figure 10–13*a* shows a schematic diagram of the machine. It differs from the conventional d-c generator in that the size of the field coil has been reduced to a point where power has been reduced until it can be handled by precise control devices. The armature is short-circuited to give approximately full-load armature reaction field, which is under the control of the much reduced field excitation. A second set of brushes is added at the center of each armature loop flux, with the conventional brushes located as usual at the center of the excitation flux and forming a short circuit through a jumper. The armature produces full voltage through the auxiliary brushes. One of these auxiliary brushes is connected direct to the load and the other through a compensating winding. The load current flowing through the armature now adds to and subtracts from the short-circuit current. The compensating winding is to neutralize the tendency of the load current to set up its own armature flux in opposition to the control flux, thereby eliminating the control desired.

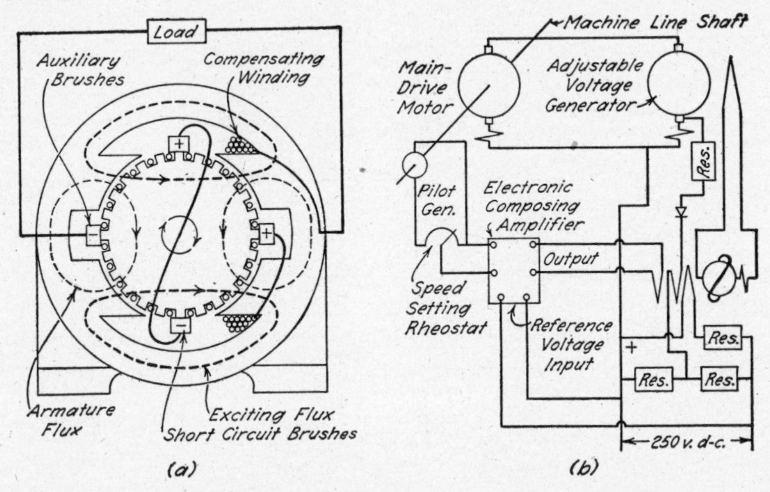

Fig. 10–13. (*a*) Amplidyne circuit. (*b*) Control circuit.

The operating cycle of the amplidyne is as follows. Assume that the exciting current is doubled; this will then double the short-circuit current, increasing the voltage between the auxiliary brushes to twice its previous value. The applied load operating under twice its previous voltage will double the load current. An excitation increase of a few watts will result in an output rise of a corresponding number of kilowatts. Besides the economy of combining the control and power supply in one machine the close coupling between the control and the load results in practically an instantaneous response.

The applications of this control are numerous; either the voltage or the current may be controlled, not only to value but also within predetermined limits. Speed and position in motion or rest can be regulated. In addition, successful application in power-factor control permits increasing the system capacity or regulating the voltage of the system. Figure 10–13*b* gives a schematic diagram for the speed control of a single-motor paper machine.

ELECTRICAL HEATING

11. Use and Advantages of Electrical Heating. In recent years, with the lowering of electrical rates, electrical heating has been used increasingly in both the manufacturing and domestic fields. With even lower rates, and an adjustment of the hours for using it, electrical heating will be able to compete, in some localities, with other forms of energy for heating ovens and furnaces.

Electricity is especially advantageous in special processes and for domestic use because it is not necessary to devote much time to controlling the operations. In manufacture, this form of heating utilizes very compact equipment.

The controlling of the temperature, when electrical heating is used, is very uniform and accurate and, if necessary, the control can be automatic. The maintenance cost of electrical furnaces is low as compared with other types, and these furnaces are simple to operate, are noiseless, and are advantageous from the health consideration, since they give off no fumes. Since the energy is delivered over wires, no fuel need be stored or handled. The conversion of energy from electrical to thermal form is 100 per cent since practically all the electrical energy is converted to heat. The use of electrical heating eliminates the necessity of preheating a mass of air, required by fuels, which adds nothing to the results.

12. Types of Electrical Heating. There are three types of equipment used for heating and furnace purposes. The resistance furnace consists of metal or carbon resistors which are in the heating compartment of the furnace. In some instances, the resistance of the material to be heated is utilized as a resistor, but this usually does not prove satisfactory. The resistance method of heating is most applicable to the oven and the submersion water heater, for in any service it is a system which may be easily and accurately controlled. The induction furnace group is divided into the low and high frequency types: the first, heating by transformer secondary action; the second, by circulating eddy currents in the material to be melted or heated and heating non-conducting material by dielectric loss. These furnaces are used for high temperatures and large capacities. The induction furnace can be easily controlled. The arc furnace is for very high temperatures and may have either a direct arc or an independent arc relative to the material.

13. Design of Electrical Furnaces. Electrical furnaces are simple to design but only by the method of trial and error, and seldom will the inexperienced designer obtain an efficient furnace. The results obtained from using design formulas, which are more or less empirical, depends upon the experience of the person using them. Some factors may be calculated very accurately but, when the question of leakage around the doors and through the steel structure of the furnace is subjected to mathematical treatment, the degree of accuracy by calculation is low.

The amount of energy needed to heat the mass under consideration is obtained directly from the specific heat, the weight, and the desired temperature change. The kilowatt hour is equivalent to 3412 Btu and the energy needed to heat a mass of material will be

$$\text{(Mass heating) kwhr} = \frac{\text{specific heat} \times \text{weight} \times (T_2 - T_1)}{3412}$$

where the temperature is in degrees Fahrenheit and the weight is in pounds.

When the heat is applied for drying, or moisture must be driven from the material, enough heat must be added to convert the water into steam. It requires 0.285 kilowatthour to evaporate 1 pound of water (from and at 212° F) besides the Btu required to bring the water to 212° F. The energy required for moisture vaporization is

$$\text{(Vaporization heat) kwhr} = \left[0.285 + \frac{(212^\circ - T_1)}{3412}\right] \times \text{pounds}$$

where the temperature is in degrees Fahrenheit. It must be recognized that the vapor must escape from the oven, that air will have to be admitted to the material, and that this air must be heated. To calculate the energy required for heating the air, use the expression for calculating the mass heat.

Even though the furnace is well insulated, loss by radiation may be considerable, depending upon the thickness of the side walls and the amount of material of high heat conduction characteristics used in building the oven or furnace. The calculation of these losses may be very inaccurate. Experience is the most important factor in using formulas for these computations. Designers have their own favorite expressions for heat radiated, but one that is frequently used is

$$\text{(Radiated heat) kwhr per hr} = [\text{inside area} \times (T_2 - T_1)]10^{-4}$$

where the temperature is in degrees Fahrenheit and the area is in square feet. When material is to be melted, an allowance must also be made for change of state.

14. Resistor Heating. The amount of temperature rise that may be obtained safely in ovens of this type depends upon the resistance units used. The normal maximum temperature is about 1100° C (2000° F).

The most common alloy for heater units is a nickel-chromium alloy (80% nickel, 20% chromium) which is good for temperatures up to 1100° C (2000° F). This material will allow power (from 8 to 20 watts per square inch) to be dissipated on the heater surface in ovens where the resistor is open and permits air circulation. When the heater is submerged in water, power equal to 50 watts per square inch may be dissipated. Nickel-chromium alloy, which melts at 1400° C (2550° F), has a very high specific resistance (620 ohms per circular mil-foot) with approximately a zero temperature coefficient and the ability to resist oxidation. The formation of the first coat of oxide is a protection against further oxidation.

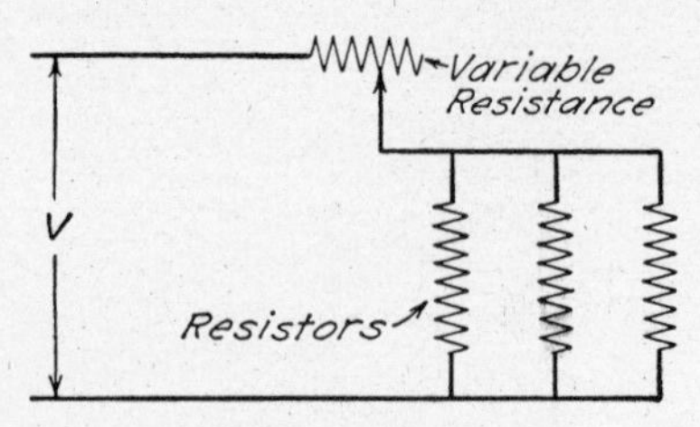

FIG. 11–13. Resistance furnace circuit diagram.

The resistance furnace (Fig. 11–13) may be constructed for higher temperatures if non-metallic resistors are used. These resistors may be silicon carbide, carbon, or graphite formed into rods or plates through which the current passes. The non-metallic resistor may be used for temperatures up to 1700° C (3000° F) and the watts per square inch may be increased to values as high as 80.

15. Induction Furnaces. Induction furnaces are divided into two types: those for low frequency, which depend upon transformer action, and the high frequency furnaces, which depend upon an oscillating system for operation. Figure 12–13*A* shows schematic diagrams of the low and high frequency induction furnaces respectively.

The commercial low frequency furnace (Fig. 12–13*Aa*) usually operates on the frequency available, but installations have been made for frequencies under 10 cycles. As shown in the diagram, the furnace operates as the secondary of a transformer with a single turn, while the primary is supplied from the power source. The heat is produced in the metal, or in the container if a non-conducting material is to be melted; it is caused by the circulation of current in the closed path. Since the transformer has a high leakage reactance, the power factor is necessarily low. The heavy currents which are circulating in the molten metal may cause what is termed pinch effect, because the magnetic forces cause the metal to separate, thereby opening the electric circuit and interrupting the current. This effect may be decreased by a reduction of the current which follows the lowering of the applied voltage. This is usually accomplished by the use of a tapped primary.

When lower frequencies are used, these furnaces may be built for very large capacities and work in regions above 1100° C (2000° F), limited, in many instances, only by the crucible. With a good graphite crucible, very high temperatures, up to 3350° C (6000° F), may be obtained. The heating is produced by the energy losses in the material which are caused by eddy currents. If the material is non-conducting, the temperature rise depends upon the heating of a conducting crucible.

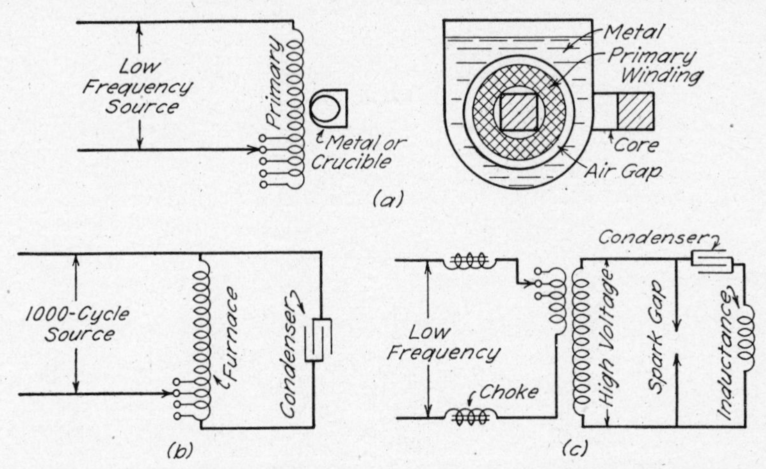

FIG. 12–13*A*. (*a*) Low frequency induction furnace. (*b*) Induction furnace for approximately 1000 cycles. (*c*) Induction furnace for high voltage and frequency in resonant circuit.

16. High Frequency Heating. In the preceding article the discussion has been confined to melting rather than to heating. Production methods of rapid and localized heating have been developed which permit placing the heat where it is wanted, at any intensity desired and under the most exacting controlled conditions. Figures 12–13*Ab* and 12–13*Ac* suggest principles for the higher frequency type of furnace. If the furnace is centered in the *inductance* the type is known as *induction heating;* if centered in the *condenser* the type is known as *dielectric heating.*

The principle is the same in either type of heating; however, the two types require different types of design and different ranges of frequency. For induction heating the material heated must be of an electrical conducting type, whereas dielectric heating is used for material which would be classified as insulating material.

For *induction heating* the generated voltage is usually obtained by rotating machines producing frequencies from 60 to 12,000 cycles, the lower frequencies being used for melting material. Electronic and spark-gap equipment supplies frequencies from 20,000 to 100,000 cycles where

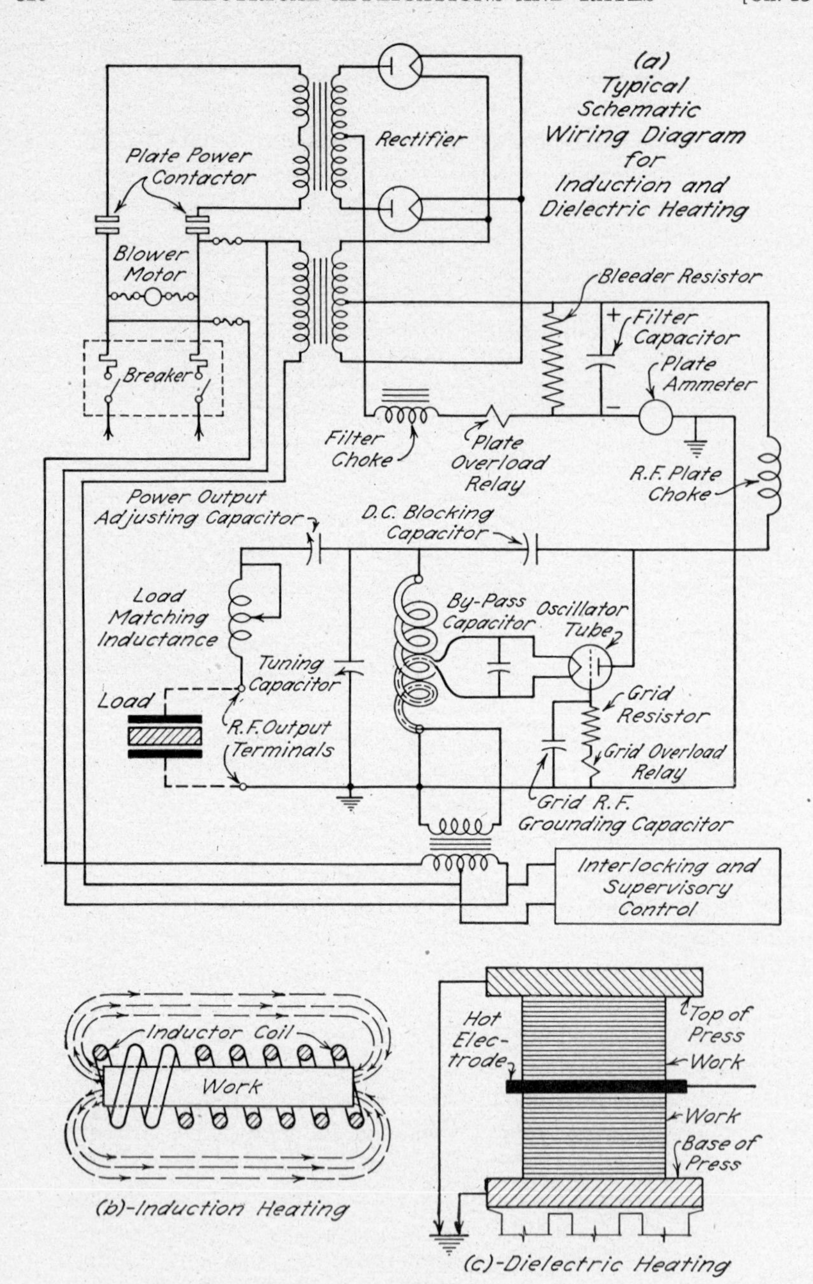

Fig. 12–13*B*. Induction and dielectric heating. (Courtesy of Westinghouse Electric Corp.)

heating is confined to the surface of the material. For the higher frequencies, 100,000 to 450,000 cycles, electronic oscillators are used. Voltages range from 200 to 1000 volts and current densities to 200,000 amperes per square inch. Power factor is relatively low—5 to 20 per cent. In heating processes, from melting metal to hardening very thin films, corresponding frequencies, from the lowest to the highest, are used. Induction heating is used for forging, brazing, and hardening as well as for melting metal. The deposition of films of coating metal is accomplished very satisfactorily by induction heating. The material to be treated is placed in one or more turns of the induction coil where the degree of heat penetration is controlled by the frequency of the system. Crankshafts and cylinders for engines are uniformly heat-treated by induction processes.

Dielectric heating, because it is used with insulating material, cannot depend upon conducting currents for heating but must obtain the heat from losses in the material. If the substance to be treated is placed between the plates of a condenser it becomes the dielectric and, since no insulator is perfect, the resultant heating is put to a useful purpose. Frequencies ranging from 2 to 100 megacycles are used to produce the required losses. To date this type of heating has been used for curing plastics and for drying synthetic binders, an important process in making plywood.

The advantage of heating internally is that time can be saved and a more uniform product can be produced. Figure 12–13*B* shows a typical schematic diagram for high frequency heating.

17. Arc Furnaces. These furnaces are excellent for high temperatures, because the material is brought into contact with the very high temperatures of the electric arc. The furnaces are divided into three general subdivisions: (1) the direct arc, where the material forms one of the electrodes; (2) the independent arc, where the arc takes place from electrode to electrode; and (3) the repel arc, which is a three-phase furnace of the independent type with the arc forced against the material by electromagnetic action.

Figure 13–13 shows the arrangement of the direct and independent arc principle. A three-phase system supplies balanced voltages and the system voltage remains balanced if the furnace (or furnaces) is properly arranged for balancing the load. The polyphase furnace (Fig. 13–13*c*) meets this requirement automatically, and single-phase furnaces should be so distributed that the normal plant operation will require approximately a balanced three-phase load.

The arc furnace normally uses carbon electrodes which reach densities of 50 amperes per square inch, whereas with special graphite electrodes in the smaller furnaces the current density can reach 250 amperes per square inch. These furnaces are for high temperatures from 1100° C to 1600° C (2000° F to 2900° F) and usually operate from the d-c or the a-c system available at the plant. Wherever high temperatures for large masses are desired and the electrodes would reach very large diameters, the size of the electrode is controlled by placing several electrodes in parallel and, in this way, decreasing the electrode size without increasing the current density of the electrode.

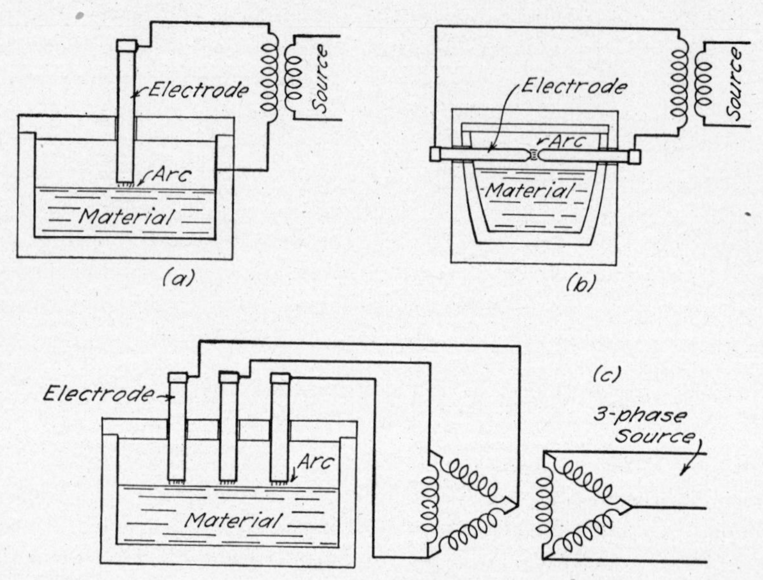

FIG. 13–13. (*a*) Direct arc furnace. (*b*) Independent arc furnace. (*c*) Three-phase direct arc furnace.

ELECTRICAL WELDING

18. The Uses and Advantages of Electrical Welding. Electrical welding, like electrical heating, has been used more generally since electrical power has been made cheap and convenient. The use of the various methods of welding in manufacturing has to a great extent eliminated riveting, screws, bolts, brazing, and soldering; also considerable bending of material to make surfaces available for fastening by other methods. Electrical welding is used for fabrication of buildings and frames of machines; for making the rotating parts of electrical generators and motors. In the manufacture of large machine parts, which were formerly cast, the time period of production has been reduced by welding. The structural members are properly cut and placed and the whole assemblage welded together, after which it may be machined in the normal manner. In the assemblage of small parts, spot welding has replaced practically all other forms of fastening. There are very few combinations of metal that cannot be spot-welded. In the manufacture of tubing and pipes, the fastening of seams can be cheaply and quickly done with automatic welding machines. In the repair of broken parts and the installation of all types of piping and structural members, the electrical welding methods cannot be surpassed in speed and efficiency.

The electrical weld may be used to gain strength alone or the objective may be merely tightness of joints or seams. Frequently, both strength and tightness are desired. If the weld is formed to hold some fluid, the requirement is tightness but, if pressure as well is present, then both strength and tightness are desirable. In the fabrication of building or bridge members, the prime interest lies in strength.

The advantages of welding over riveting are numerous: noise is eliminated, the joints will not slip, less material is used (thereby reducing the weight), the results are controllable, and the work is accomplished in less time; there is a saving on labor and, the welded joint, if not stronger and more durable than the riveted joint, is at least equal to it.

There are three general methods of welding, classified as spot welding, arc welding, and resistance welding. Arc welding may be divided into two classes, depending upon whether a metal or carbon rod is used as an electrode.

19. Spot Welding. Spot welding is used extensively for small parts welding in metal manufacturing plants. By this process, the pieces are held firmly together and electrodes are pressed against the material on opposite sides of the weld. The current flows through the area to be welded, heating it to a molten state and, if the current is removed and the piece allowed to cool under pressure, the parts will be found welded together in the area where the electrodes were placed. Many classes of metal or even dissimilar metals may be welded together. The field of materials that will weld together is so broad that it is simple to select some satisfactory combination. Material one-fourth inch thick is easily welded, and one-inch material has been welded by this process. If the material is very thin, the electrodes must be several times (3 to 5) the thickness of the material; but, if the material is thick, the electrode need be only one and one-half times as thick as the material for a satisfactory weld. The power consumed will depend upon the thickness of the metal and may range from a fraction of a kilowatt to 30 or 40 kilowatts. Though spot welding is used in fastening two or more pieces together, it can be used to fasten seams by welding at close intervals along the seam.

20. Arc Welding. Arc welding is divided into two classes, depending upon the type of electrode used. The use of a carbon electrode tends to embrittle the weld and a metallic electrode has the advantage that material may be placed directly from the electrode into the weld. In using d-c arc welding, the work is made positive with respect to the welding electrode.

Carbon arc welding is usually only applicable to iron and steel and is very satisfactory when material is to be cut or cleaned by taking out slag and cleaning out holes in castings. The carbon arc tends to cause considerable oxidation. The oxide enters the weld and causes the joint to be brittle. When the carbon arc is used, it is necessary to feed material into the weld from a metal rod or from a metal strip which is placed over the joint.

The use of the metallic arc eliminates this last factor, because the melting electrode, itself, fills the weld. In continuous machines, the electrode as it melts is fed into the weld automatically. Metallic arc welding is more universal than carbon arc welding and can be used to weld very large pieces of almost any thickness. As with the carbon arc, the best work is on iron and steel but many other metals may be welded by this process. A single arc of this type needs 25 volts (open circuit voltage of generator 55 to 90 volts) and a current depending upon the thickness of the material that is to be welded. A 200-ampere machine will meet the usual needs if only a single arc operates from a machine. The usual proportion of current is 500 amperes for each inch of thickness. Since the process is one of heating and melting the material, it is desirable to concentrate as much current as possible in small areas. An electrode whose diameter is approximately one-half the thickness of the material to be welded will give a satisfactory current density for good operation. The small welding rods ($\frac{1}{16}$ to $\frac{1}{8}$ in. in diameter) used on the ordinary plant job will carry from 50 to 100 amperes.

21. Resistance Welding. Though this is a rapid method of welding, the accumulation of impurities in the weld limits its strength. The weld is made by bringing the edges of the material into contact under pressure. The electrical current passing through the joint heats it until the metals flow together and the material, when cooled, becomes homogeneous in the joint. This may be considered a modified spot-welding process covering considerably more surface. This method of welding is widely used in bonding the rails together for car tracks.

22. Atomic Hydrogen Welding. This type of welding has been developed to create higher temperatures and to eliminate the troubles of oxidation. A stream of hydrogen is directed upon the electrodes, where it forms an intense blue flame in a reducing atmosphere and where the temperature will reach 4000° C (7200° F). The presence of an oxygen-free atmosphere removes the bad effects of oxidation. Therefore, with this equipment many metals may be welded which would be difficult to weld by any other means.

23. Welding Using Electron Tubes. The electron tube has been very successfully used in communication and electrical measurement devices; however, though this still remains its specific application, industrial control and power application of electronics are advancing rapidly.

The application of the electron tube to welding is one of its most successful uses in industrial practice. Figure 14–13 shows the circuit diagram for an electron tube controlled resistance line welder. The welding equipment may be divided into three parts: the power, control, and timing circuits. Because as a complete unit the welding equipment is difficult to explain, each individual circuit will be considered separately before the whole operation is analyzed.

In the power circuit if *TG* is open-circuited, tubes *T*1 and *T*2 are non-conducting; but when power passes through *TG* the tubes are conducting, because the a-c voltage of a large value in phase with the anode is superimposed upon the d-c bias. The anode output of the tubes through the series transformer controls the power flow to the welder transformer. When the tubes are non-conducting a small exciting current flows, but when the tubes are conducting the transformer presents a negligible reactance in the welder circuit. To make the vapor discharge tubes completely non-conducting a bias is applied to the grids from the full-wave rectifier tubes *T*7 and *T*8, having their output filtered by the circuit formed with *R*3 and *C*3. Resistor *R*7 limits the grid current when the grid is positive with respect to the cathode, whereas *C*2 increases the grid cathode capacity. Condenser *C*2 and the resistance (with a negative resistance-current characteristic) across the secondary of the series transformer assure that the tube will not lose control because of voltage surges from the welder.

If the control over the welder is to be satisfactory, it is necessary to draw minimum current and not heavy transients in the supply line; in addition, the d-c components must not saturate the transformer core. This requires accurate timing, and a timing device cannot be connected directly to the power tube. The control circuit uses the same principles used in the power tube circuit. There is, however, no transformer coupling, for the tubes *T*3 and *T*4 are directly in the a-c supply lead to *TG*. Tube *T*3 is a three-element tube, and *T*4 is a four-element tube because it can be positively controlled with a minimum amount of power. If the four-element tube is used the limiting resistance *R* may be high, and thereby reduce the load on the timing circuit. The characteristics of this type of tube change little with temperature. If timing could be introduced directly into the circuit of the grid of $T1$ and $T2$ without too large a power drain, the control circuit unit could be eliminated.

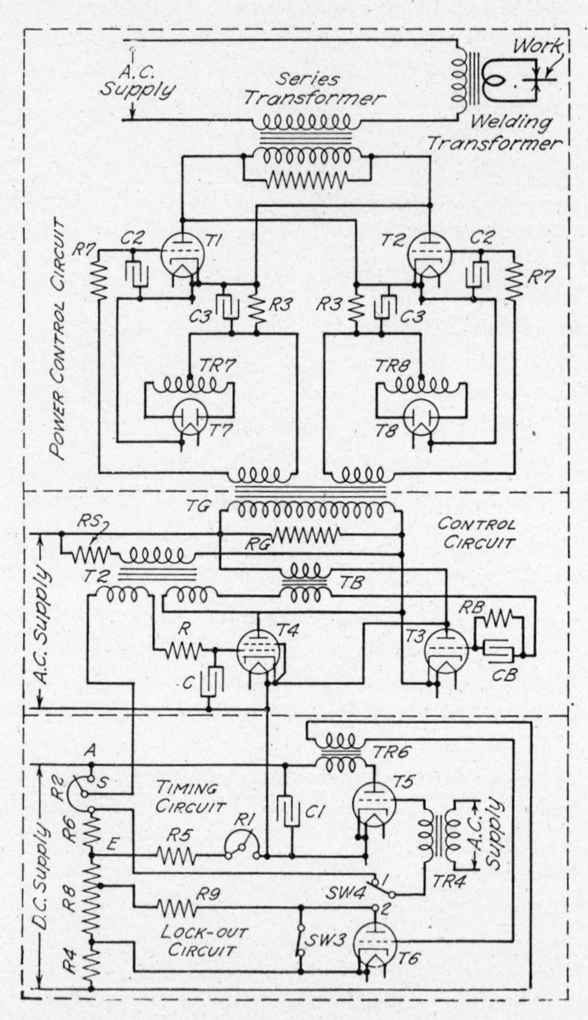

FIG. 14–13. Circuit diagram for an electronic controlled resistance type of line welder. (Courtesy of General Electric Co.)

The timing circuit includes $TR4$, $T5$, $R1$, $R5$, $R6$, $R2$, $C1$, and $TR6$, which acts as a limiting reactor to limit the peak value of the discharge current of $T5$ and as a part of the lockout circuit. The impulse circuit is classed as an inverter, used to perform the timing task for the welder.

The pulsating inverter is controlled by the peak a-c voltage; therefore it is exactly synchronized at an even number of half-cycles of the a-c power supply. The length of the welding cycle is determined by the length of time required to charge C_1, of the timing circuit, to a critical value, and the length of time the current flows depends upon the period of time the grid of $T4$ is positive during the cycle. The resistor setting of $R1$ determines the first and the value of $R2$ determines the second. These two form a very simple device for adjusting the welder operation.

The lockout circuit permits only one impulse to be made by the timing circuit. This converts the welder into a spot welder. The lockout circuit operates very rapidly; therefore the welder is adaptable for high speed spot welding.

These welders give synchronous timing control without any moving parts. Production may be increased, and the consistency of timing and current values permits the welding of materials which are very difficult to weld by any other process. By reducing transient current demand and light flicker, and using a simple accurate control, these welders constitute the outstanding industrial application of electronic tube control in the power field.

POWER RATES

24. Development of Electrical Rates. The cost of energy is susceptible to analysis and partial control. With the advent of electrical driving units, there followed a series of power rates which have slowly shifted the burden of cost to those consumers who, by improper operation and control, create the major portion of the excess generator, line, and transformer capacity. When electrical energy was sold on a basis of a fixed charge for a given connected load (flat rate), there was no problem of load control because plant efficiency did not enter into the study of economical operation. When utilities were expanding into the power field and wished to encourage industrial load, block rates were developed which in many installations made it possible to dispense with isolated plants of the steam-driven shaft or steam-driven generator type. Block rates are charged at a fixed amount up to a certain kilowatthour consumption; from this consumption to another fixed limit all energy used is charged for at a lower rate, and so on, with each higher energy consumption block having a lower rate. The block rate introduced overhead charges, for the first time, directly into the bill. Consumers using the most energy for factory load, which was an off-peak load with respect to the lighting load, enabled the utility to operate equipment at a higher efficiency because of the increased output, causing a saving which was given in part to the plants using the larger blocks of energy.

The overhead charge made necessary because of demands of the industrial plant for short periods of time, requiring the installation of larger generating units, transmission lines, and transformers, was added to the power bill in the form of a demand charge. In recent rate fixing, the item of power factor is considered, since low power factor has the same effect on the system economics as a high demand.

25. Billing. Table III–13 shows the division of electrical energy cost and the complex rates developed to place the cost of power plant operation directly upon the loads which bring about such costs instead of spreading the overhead over all industrial loads and domestic users.

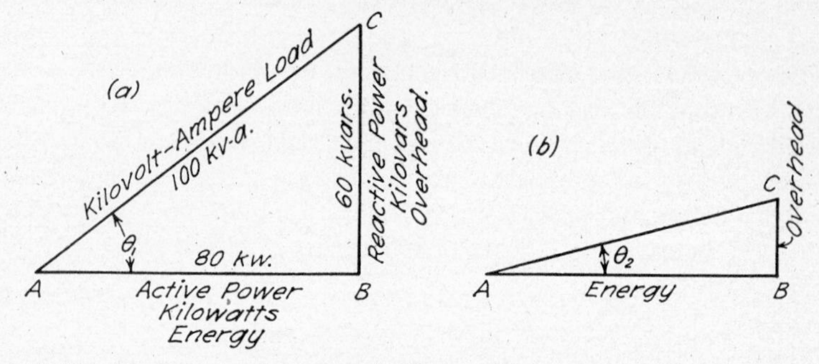

FIG. 15–13. Diagrams to show graphically the billing factors: (*a*) the original load showing the active and reactive power with the power-factor angle θ_1; (*b*) the relationship when the demand and the power-factor angle θ_2 have been reduced by plant study to reduce the billing.

The billing for a d-c load is relatively simple, because the rate depends upon the energy consumed and the demand of the plant; therefore, the discussion will deal, for the most part, with the a-c bill. The bills represent three distinct items: the first represents the direct charge for energy consumed; the second, the additional expense of supplying large periodic loads for short periods; and the third, poor power-factor characteristics of the connected load. The power factor item does not enter into the d-c billing.

Figure 15–13 shows the relationship between the various factors that go into billing. The base of the triangle represents the active power, which is the energy part of the load, and the altitude represents the reactive power, that part of the overhead which is the controlling factor in the power-factor billing of the load. It is the objective of the plant management to reduce this altitude to a minimum, the details of which are treated under power-factor correction. The demand changes the base of the triangle and, for good economical operation, it is necessary to decrease the altitude and keep the triangle proportionately small. The two diagrams in the figure indicate the possible correction of a load where the power factor improves and the demand has been reduced by a study of the plant requirements. The necessity of the charge for power factor is given by the numerical figures in Fig. 15–13. The load is composed of two components: 80 kilowatts of active power and 60 kilovolt-amperes of reactive power. This would be described as an 80-kilowatt load at 80 per cent power factor. The utility must purchase and operate a 100-kilovolt-ampere capacity unit with only 80 per cent of this capacity producing revenue, if the rates are based on energy consumed. The cost

TABLE III–13

The Power Bill

Energy	Overhead or Fixed Charges	
	Demand	Power Factor
Cost of energy.	Usually based on 15-min. demand of $1.00 to $3.00 per kilowatt.	Usually based on an operating power factor of 80 to 85%. Increases demand charges in inverse proportion. (Base power factor 80 to 85%.)
Some Correction Methods		
Operate motors at capacity. Proper voltage. Proper types of motors. Remove dead load. Remove defective equipment. Control system voltage drop.	Analysis of load. Analysis of operation. Schedule machines on intermittent operation. Relay control of maximum demand for the plant. Continuous supervision with records.	Remove all high inductive loads. Operate all induction motors at rated load. Use static condensers for power factor correction. Use synchronous motors for power factor correction.
Method of Billing		
(1) Flat rate. (2) Block rate. Product of the meter reading by the rates. Measured by watt-hour meter.	Fixed charge on 15- to 60-minute demand. Measured by a demand meter or a demand attachment on the watt-hour meter.	Power factor is computed from active and reactive watt-hour meter readings. Power factor = $\dfrac{\text{Active}}{\sqrt{\text{Active}^2 + \text{Reactive}^2}}$ Demand Billing Increase = $\dfrac{\text{Base Power Factor}}{\text{Power Factor}}$

of supplying reactive power to the utility which supplies the power justifies an additional charge.

The method set forth in Table III–13 is basic in nature; however, contracts may be written in which each of the items may be elaborated, and in some instances the demand and power factor may be completely neglected. To make the charges clear, a discussion of a typical bill with a demonstration example will be given.

Example a. The readings of the plant meters for the month show 16,500 kwhr active power, 16,150 kva reactive power, and a demand of 225 kw. The contract specifies an energy charge of 2 cents per kwhr, and a demand charge of $1.75 per kw, based on an 80 per cent power factor. The demand in kilowatts increased inversely by the power factor.

Energy cost:

$$16{,}500 \times 0.02 \qquad = \$330.00$$

Billing demand: Power factor:

$$\frac{16{,}500}{\sqrt{16{,}500^2 + 16{,}150^2}} \times 100 = 71.46$$

$$\frac{80}{71.46} = 1.119 \text{ demand factor}$$

Demand cost:

$$225 \times \$1.75 \times 1.119 \qquad = \$440.76$$

$$\text{Total bill} \qquad \$770.76$$

If a study of the plant made it possible to reduce the demand to 200 kw and the power factor was improved to 85 per cent, the demand cost would be reduced to $329.41, representing a saving of $111.35 per month, which would soon pay for the time and equipment needed to make the study.

26. Plant Survey with Recording Instruments. Since much of the equipment in the modern plant is driven by electric motors, it is possible to make a very complete plant analysis with recording electrical meters. Figures 16–13*a* and 16–13*b* show a recording wattmeter and a unit assembled on a portable table for the study of individual installations.

A complete plant record should be taken with a permanent meter installation.

Installation of recording electrical meters will aid in a study and control of such items as

1. Analysis of peak loads.
2. Control of manufacturing processes.
3. Study of production cycles.

4. Analysis of intermittent loads.
5. Elimination of defective equipment.
6. Control of maximum demands.

These are general items; many more detailed problems will suggest themselves to one trained in observing continuous records in plants using recording equipment.

(*a*) (*b*)

FIG. 16–13. (*a*) Recording wattmeter. (*b*) An assembled testing unit on a portable table. (Courtesy of Esterline–Angus Co.)

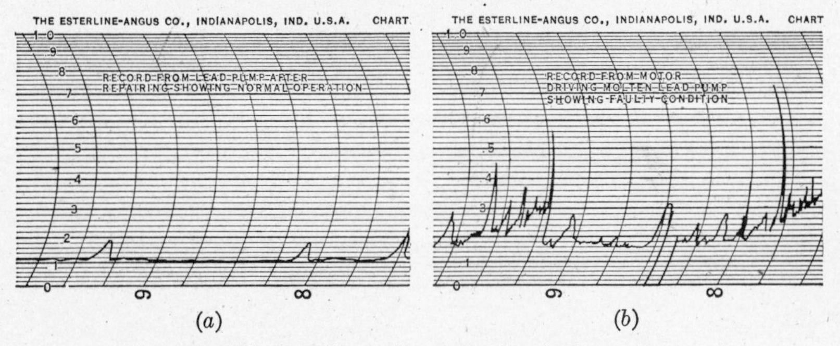

(*a*) (*b*)

FIG. 17–13. Charts from recording instrument.

Figures 17–13*a* and 17–13*b* show two records obtained by using recording instruments. Though the recording of electrical quantities has been stressed, many instruments that depend upon electrical principles for their operation measure speed, pressure, flow, and time, and these measurements may be used equally well for a study of plant economics and production control. The advantage of continuous records lies in their permanence and their detailed accuracy. The recording equipment may be operated by persons without technical training. The final analysis depends more upon native ability of the individual than upon developed technical skill.

PROBLEMS

The following rates are given for problem calculation and will be referred to in the problems according to title and class.

Commercial Service

A

1st	10 kwhr	\$1.00
		per kwhr
Next	140 kwhr	6.5¢
Next	150 kwhr	5.0¢
Next	300 kwhr	4.0¢
Excess	600 kwhr	2.5¢

B

		Per kwhr
1st block	30 hr use of demand	7¢
2nd block	30 hr use of demand	6¢
Excess	60 hr use of demand	3¢

Power Service

A

		Per kwhr
1st	100 kwhr	6.0¢
Next	200 kwhr	5.0¢
Next	300 kwhr	3.0¢
Over	600 kwhr	2.5¢
Excess	12,000 kwhr	1.5¢

B

		Per kwhr
1st block	400 kwhr	6.5¢
2nd block	600 kwhr	4.0¢
3rd block	4000 kwhr	3.0¢
Excess	5000 kwhr	2.0¢

C

Demand charge \$1.00 per kw for 1000 kw
\$0.75 per kw for additional

Power-factor charge—demand charge based on an 85 per cent power factor

1st block 50,000 kwhr	2.0¢ per kwhr
2nd block 500,000 kwhr	1.0¢ per kwhr
Excess kilowatthours	0.7¢ per kwhr

1–13. Under power service rate A, calculate the bill for the following energy consumption: (*a*) 100 kwhr, (*b*) 300 kwhr, (*c*) 600 kwhr, (*d*) 1200 kwhr, (*e*) 12,000 kwhr.

2–13. Under commercial service rate A, calculate the bill for the following energy consumption: (*a*) 10 kwhr, (*b*) 150 kwhr, (*c*) 300 kwhr, (*d*) 600 kwhr, (*e*) 1200 kwhr.

3–13. A submersion-type water heater is used to heat a tank. It has a resistance of 10 ohms and is operated from a 110-volt supply. In a well-insulated tank, where radiation and conduction losses can be neglected, how many gallons of water can be heated from 50° F to 150° F per hr?

4–13. How many kilowatthours are required to heat 1000 lb of zinc oxide from 60° F to 100° F if the specific heat is 0.114 calories per gram per degree centigrade (consider this the average for the range)? Under power service rate A, what would be the cost of heating 100 tons of this material?

5–13. Electricity is considered for drying lumber in a kiln. It is necessary to evaporate 200 gallons of water per hour and the lumber temperature must be raised from 70° F. Determine the power bill for a 30-day month with 24-hr operation; use power service rate A.

6–13. A drafting room requires twenty 300-watt lamps burning 200 hours per month. Determine the bill for a month under commercial service rate B.

7–13. A plant, with 100 hp installed, uses 10,000 kilowatthours per month and has an average 80 per cent lagging power factor. The demand is 70 kw. Determine the power bill under power service rate (*a*) C and (*b*) A.

8–13. The following are the power requirements per day for an industrial plant.

Light	Power
25 kw for 12 hr	1500 kw for 10 hr
15 kw for 6 hr	2000 kw for 8 hr
8 kw for 6 hr	500 kw for 2 hr

Consider the lighting load under commercial service rate A and the power under power service rate B. What will be (*a*) the bill for a 20-day month, (*b*) the average cost per kilowatthour?

9–13. The meter readings for the month at an industrial plant are: 170,000 kvar-hr, 175,000 kwhr, and a demand of 500 kw. Calculate the bill under power service rate C.

10–13. An installation of ten 300-watt lamps develops 60,000 lumens. The installation is to be replaced by 40-watt fluorescent lamps where each lamp delivers 2100 lumens. Under commercial service rate A determine the power requirements for comparative systems of lighting for a work month of 24 days of 8 hr each. An additional 12 watts is necessary for each two fluorescent lamps to cover the auxiliaries.

11–13. A 15-hp motor of 85 per cent efficiency is to be added to a monthly average bill of 800 kwhr under power service rate A. What will be the cost of operating the motor for an hour?

12–13. Determine the size of motor needed to pump 500 gallons per minute against a 200-ft head if the fluid is water. The pump has an efficiency of 70 per cent and the motor an efficiency of 85 per cent. Under power service rate B, determine the cost of pumping 1000 gallons with an average monthly load in excess of 5000 kwhr.

13–13. A 70 per cent efficient hoist, of 3-ton capacity, operates at an average of 80 ft per min. Determine the motor size for the installation.

14–13. A manufacturer is faced with two possible solutions in adding motor capacity to his plant:

A. A 94 per cent power-factor induction motor with a line requirement of 100 kw.

B. A synchronous motor arranged for correcting the plant power factor to 80 per cent lagging with the same requirements from the line.

The plant requires 2000 kva at 60 per cent lagging power factor. The average monthly requirement is 200,000 kwhr under power service rate C. Determine (*a*) the cost of each of the arrangements per month, with the demand fixed at 1000 kw, (*b*) the per cent of increase in the bill using the induction motor.

15–13. Under power service rate B a plant operates 20 days a month and 8 hr a day with an average consumption of 350 kw. The old installation has a 10 per cent voltage drop and an improved system is being considered which will reduce the voltage drop to 4 per cent. Compare the power bills under the two conditions.

CHAPTER 14

ELECTRICAL ILLUMINATION *

With the recognition of the importance of good lighting in the conservation of human nervous energy, illumination engineering, which is a division of the engineering profession, has become a factor of importance in increasing production in manufacturing. The design of electrical illumination is relatively simple now that such designing has been reduced to the "lumen or flux method." This method gives a maximum error of 15 to 20 per cent but, since there is this much variation between lamp sizes, it is sufficiently accurate for practical purposes. Considering its simplicity and speed, it proves to be a satisfactory engineering method.

The lumen method is based upon a determination of the required lumens on the working surface, depending upon the room size, the light absorption of the enclosing surfaces, and the equipment efficiency, giving the required lumens that must be emitted by the lamp. These calculations assume the work surface to be 30 inches above the floor and, if the working plane differs appreciably from this, corrections must be made to insure satisfactory results. In general, the method makes use of several predetermined constants, used in the following expression:

$$\text{Total lamp lumens per outlet} = \frac{E \times A}{MF \times UF \times \eta} \qquad (a\text{–}14)$$

where E = illumination
A = area per outlet
MF = maintenance factor
UF = utilization factor
η = equipment efficiency.

In preparing the tables of the predetermined constant, technical factors which influence the results have been considered. Some judgment must

* Tables and figures are taken from Transactions of the Illuminating Engineering Society, Bulletins of the Nela Park Engineering Department of the General Electric Company, and *The Magazine of Light.*

be used in applying the data given in the tables but, if they are used in conjunction with the principles given in the following articles, satisfactory results will be obtained.

1. Units of Light. Four units are of particular importance to the designer using the lumen method. These units are brightness, intensity, quantity of light, and illumination.

Brightness. The brightness of a surface, when viewed in any direction, is considered to be the ratio of the luminous intensity, or flux, expressed in candlepower, or lumens measured in that direction to the area of this surface projected on a plane perpendicular to the direction considered.

Brightness is measured in either candles per square inch or lumens per square foot. The latter unit is known as the foot-lambert (1 lumen per square foot). If the number of foot-lamberts is divided by 144π (452), the result is candles per square inch. The illumination in foot-candles multiplied by the reflection factor will give the foot-lamberts of brightness. Brightness limits the illumination from the lighting equipment that may be utilized, and no unit or surface should have a brightness in excess of 75 foot-lamberts if in the line of vision.

Intensity. Candlepower is luminous intensity expressed in candles. The International Candle, which is the unit of luminous intensity, is maintained by means of standard incandescent lamps in the national laboratories of the nations entering into the agreement of standardization.

Quantity. The lumen is the unit of luminous flux and takes account of the area over which the light is distributed. If a unit light source (candle) is in the center of an imaginary sphere of 1 foot radius, the total flux is 4π units. In this assumption, a steradian will cover 1 square foot on the surface of the sphere. The lumen is the amount of light emitted by a uniform source of one candle through a steradian. Incidentally, the surface of the sphere of 1 foot radius will be illuminated at 1 foot-candle. This fact leads to some interesting and useful relationships.

A. Total lumens = $4\pi \times$ mean spherical candle power.
B. Foot-candle = lumens per square foot (not foot-lambert).
C. Lumens = average foot-candles $\times$ square feet of area.

It is this last expression (C) that is of prime importance in the lumen method.

Illumination. The quantitative unit is the foot-candle. This unit is measured by a meter known as the foot-candle meter. This, however, is merely a makeshift, for the final measure of all illumination is the eye, since color enters into the final evaluation of the result. Illumination is the visible radiation falling on a surface. The foot-candle, until recent years when it became apparent through research that other factors are as important for adequate and comfortable seeing as is the illumination, has been used as a measure of lighting effectiveness. The lumen and the foot-candle are the most important of these units to the designer, and the foot-lambert must be considered when studying the comfort provided by the lighting installation.

The efficiency of the light source is measured in lumens emitted per watt. Wherever the color of the light is involved, there is a reasonable doubt in the interpretation of efficiency. It would be reasonable to reduce the whole subject of light to an energy base, which holds until applied to effective illumination. Up to the present time the only instrument for measuring this effectiveness is the human eye, and that varies with different individuals.

There are many more units of light and the subject of photometry is very extensive but, for the problem of illumination design, which is solved by the engineer, it is better to obtain the photometric information from tests made by laboratories equipped with properly trained personnel.

2. Factors Involved in Useful Illumination. Two factors must be considered in good illumination: the vision and light. One without the other is worthless and each can contribute to the problem of distinguishing quickly and accurately the details of the task without too large a demand upon the nervous energy of the human observer.

The size of the object determines the amount of light that will be needed, for the smaller the object the more light will be needed to see the details. The surroundings are also a factor in the amount of light needed, because a marked contrast with the background will set off the details of the task. Both the brightness and speed with which the object moves enter into the lighting requirements. All these factors determine the number of foot-candles needed to light the task properly. Foot-candle requirements have been increasing steadily as better equipment becomes available for producing and controlling the light source, making higher intensities safe and economical.

3. Foot-Candle Requirements. Table I–14 gives a table of foot-candles desirable for the various tasks in the office and shop of the industrial field. These data † are graded according to the different levels of the task instead of according to industries. It will be found that these recommendations are superior to those found in the normal installation.

† See Illuminating Engineering Society reports for shoe, textile, assembly and inspection, candy, and printing industries, American Recommended Practice of Industrial Lighting, March 17, 1942.

TABLE I–14

Industrial Illumination

Recommended Minimum Standards of Illumination for Industrial Interiors (These foot-candle values represent order of magnitude rather than exact levels of illumination.)

	Minimum Operating Foot-Candles (Measured on the Work)
Aisles, Stairways, Passageways	5
Assembly:	
Rough	10
Medium	20
Fine	B [1]
Extra fine	A [1]
Automobile Manufacturing:	
Assembly line	B [1]
Frame assembly	15
Body manufacturing	
Parts	20
Assembly	20
Finishing and inspecting	A [1]
Bakeries	20
Book Binding:	
Folding, assembling, pasting, etc.	10
Cutting, punching, and stitching	20
Embossing	20
Breweries:	
Brew house	5
Boiling, keg washing, and filling	10
Bottling	15
Candy Making:	
Box department	20
Chocolate department	
Husking, winnowing, fat extraction, crushing and refining, feeding	10
Bean cleaning and sorting, dipping, packing, wrapping	20
Milling	C [1]
Cream making	
Mixing, cooking, and molding	20
Gum drops and jellied forms	20
Hand decorating	C [1]
Hard candy	
Mixing, cooking, and molding	20
Die cutting and sorting	C [1]
Kiss making and wrapping	C [1]
Canning and Preserving	20
Chemical Works:	
Hand furnaces, boiling tanks, stationary driers, stationary and gravity crystallizers	5
Mechanical furnaces, generators and stills, mechanical driers, evaporators, filtration, mechanical crystallizers, bleaching	10
Tanks for cooking, extractors, percolators, nitrators, electrolytic cells	15
Clay Products and Cements:	
Grinding, filter presses, kiln rooms	5
Molding, pressing, cleaning, and trimming	10
Enameling	15
Color and glazing	20
Cleaning and Pressing Industry:	
Checking and sorting	20
Dry and wet cleaning and steaming	10
Inspection and spotting	A [1]
Pressing	
Machine	20
Hand	C [1]
Receiving and shipping	10
Repair and alteration	C [1]
Cloth Products:	
Cutting, inspecting, sewing	
Light goods	20
Dark goods	A [1]
Pressing, cloth treating (oilcloth, etc.)	
Light goods	10
Dark goods	20
Coal Tipples and Cleaning Plants:	
Breaking, screening, and cleaning	10
Picking	A [1]
Construction — Indoor:	
General	10
Dairy Products	20
Elevators—Freight and Passenger	10
Engraving	A [1]
Forge Shops and Welding	10
Foundries:	
Charging floor, tumbling, cleaning, pouring, and shaking out	5
Rough molding and core making	10
Fine molding and core making	20

[1] See reference footnote at end of table.

TABLE I–14 (*Continued*)

	Minimum Operating Foot-Candles
Garages—Automobile:	
Storage—live	10
Storage—dead	2
Repair department and washing	C [1]
Glass Works:	
Mix and furnace rooms, pressing and Lehr, glass blowing machines	10
Grinding, cutting glass to size, silvering	20
Fine grinding, polishing, beveling, etching, and decorating	C [1] D [1]
Inspection	B [1] D [1]
Glove Manufacturing:	
Light goods	
Pressing, knitting, sorting	10
Cutting, stitching, trimming and inspecting	20
Dark Goods	
Cutting, pressing, knitting, sorting	20
Stitching, trimming, and inspection	A [1]
Hangars—Aeroplane:	
Storage—live	10
Repair department	C [1]
Hat Manufacturing:	
Dyeing, stiffening, braiding, cleaning and refining	
Light	10
Dark	20
Forming, sizing, pouncing, flanging, finishing, and ironing	
Light	15
Dark	30
Sewing	
Light	20
Dark	A [1]
Ice Making—Engine and Compressor Room	10
Inspection:	
Rough	10
Medium	20
Fine	B [1]
Extra fine	A [1]
Jewelry and watch manufacturing	A [1]
Laundries	20
Leather Manufacturing [2]	
Leather Working [2]	
Locker Rooms	5
Machine Shops:	
Rough bench and machine work	10
Medium bench and machine work, ordinary automatic machines, rough grinding, medium buffing and polishing	20
Fine bench and machine work, fine automatic machines, medium grinding, fine buffing and polishing	B [1]
Extra fine bench and machine work, grinding	
Fine work	A [1]
Meat Packing:	
Slaughtering	10
Cleaning, cutting, cooking, grinding, canning, packing	20
Milling—Grain Foods:	
Cleaning, grinding, and rolling	10
Baking or roasting	20
Flour grading	30
Offices:	
Bookkeeping, typing, and accounting	30
Business machines—power driven (transcribing and tabulating)	
Calculators, key punch, bookkeeping	B [1]
Conference room	
General meetings	10
Office Activities—*See* Desk work	
Corridors and stairways	5
Desk work	
Intermittent reading and writing	20
Prolonged close work, computing, studying, designing, etc.	C [1]
Reading blueprints and plans	30
Drafting	
Prolonged close work—art drafting and designing in detail	C [1]
Rough drawing and sketching	30
Filing and index references	20
Lobby	10
Mail sorting	20
Reception rooms	10
Stenographic work	
Prolonged reading shorthand notes	C [1]
Vault	10
Packing and Boxing	10
Paint Mixing	10
Paint Shops:	
Dipping, simple spraying, firing	10
Rubbing, ordinary hand painting	

[1] See reference footnote at end of table.

[2] An I.E.S. research study of lighting in this industry is now in progress.

TABLE I–14 (*Continued*)

	Minimum Operating Foot-Candles		Minimum Operating Foot-Candles
and finishing; art, stencil, and special spraying	20	Punches, presses, shears, stamps, welders, spinning, medium bench work	20D [1]
Fine hand painting and finishing	B [1]	Tin plate inspection	B [1] D [1]
Extra fine hand painting and finishing (automobile bodies, piano cases, etc.)	A [1]	Shoe Manufacturing (Leather):	
Paper Box Manufacturing:		Cutting and stitching	
Light	10	Cutting tables	10
Dark	20	Marking, buttonholing, skiving, sorting, vamping, and counting	
Storage	5	Light materials	20
Paper Manufacturing:		Dark materials	C [1]
Beaters, grinding, calendering	10	Stitching	
Finishing, cutting, trimming, paper-making machines	20	Light materials	C [1]
Plating	10	Dark materials	B [1]
Polishing and Burnishing	15	Making and finishing	
Power Plants, Engine Room, Boilers:		Stitchers, nailers, sole layers, welt beaters and scarfers, trimmers, welters, lasters, edge setters, sluggers, randers, wheelers, treers, cleaning, spraying, buffing, polishing, embossing	
Boilers, coal and ash handling, storage battery rooms	5	Light materials	20
Auxiliary equipment, oil switches and transformers	10	Dark materials	C [1]
Engines, generators, blowers, compressors	15	Storage, packing, and shipping	10
Switchboards	C [1]	Shoe Manufacturing (Rubber):	
Printing Industries:		Washing, coating, mill run compounding	10
Type foundries		Varnishing, vulcanizing, calendering, upper and sole cutting	C [1]
Matrix making, dressing type	A [1]	Sole rolling, lining, making and finishing processes	C [1]
Font assembly—sorting	B [1]	Soap Manufacturing:	
Hand casting	C [1]	Kettle houses, cutting, soap chip and powder	10
Machine casting	20	Stamping, wrapping and packing, filling and packing soap powder	20
Printing plants:	C [1]	Steel and Iron Manufacturing:	
Presses	C [1]	Billet, blooming, sheet bar, skelp and slabbing mills	5
Imposing stones	A [1] D [1]	Boiler room, power house, foundry and furnace rooms	5
Proofreading	A [1]	Hot sheet and hot strip mills	10
Photography:		Cold strip, pipe, rail, rod, tube, universal plate and wire drawing	10
Dry plate and film	2000	Merchant and sheared plate mills	15
Wet plate	3000	Tin plate mills	
Printing on metal	2000	Hot strip rolling and tinning machine department	10
Electrotyping:		Cold strip rolling	15
Molding, finishing, leveling molds, routing, trimming	B [1]	Inspection	
Blocking, tinning	C [1]	Black plate	C [1]
Electroplating, washing, backing	20		
Photo engraving:			
Etching, staging	20		
Blocking	C [1]		
Routing, finishing, proofing	B [1]		
Tint laying	A [1]		
Receiving and Shipping	10		
Rubber Manufacturing and Products [2]			
Sheet Metal Works:			
Miscellaneous machines, ordinary bench work	15		

[1] See reference footnote at end of table.

[2] An I.E.S. research study of lighting in this industry is now in progress.

TABLE I–14 (*Continued*)

	Minimum Operating Foot-Candles		Minimum Operating Foot-Candles
Bloom and billet chipping	C [1]	Inspection	
Tin plate and other bright surfaces	B [1] D [1]	Grey goods (hand turning)	C [1]
Machine shops and maintenance department		Denims (rapidly moving)	A [1]
Repair shops		Automatic tying-in, weaving	B [1]
Rough bench and machine work	10	Drawing-in by hand	A [1]
Medium bench and machine work	20	Silk and Rayon Manufacturing:	
Fine work—buffing, polishing, etc.	B [1]	Soaking, fugitive tinting, and conditioning or setting of twist	10
Extra fine work	A [1]	Winding, twisting, rewinding, and coning, quilling, slashing	30
Blacksmith shop	10	Warping (silk or cotton system)	
Laboratories (chemical and physical)	15	On creel, on running ends, on reel, on beam, on warp at beaming	C [1]
Carpenter and pattern shop	20	Drawing-in	
Storage	2	On heddles	A [1]
Stone Crushing and Screening:		On reed	A [1]
Belt conveyor tubes, main line shafting spaces, chute rooms, inside of bins	5	Weaving	
Primary breaker room, auxiliary breakers under bins	5	On heddles and reeds	5
Screens	10	On warp back of harness	10
Storage Battery Manufacturing:		On woven cloth	30
Molding of grids	10	Woolen:	
Store and Stock Rooms:		Carding, picking, washing, combing	10
Rough bulky material	5	Twisting, dyeing	10
Medium or fine material requiring care	10	Drawing-in, warping	
Structural Steel Fabrication	10	Light goods	15
Sugar Grading	30	Dark goods	30
Testing:		Weaving	
Rough	10	Light goods	15
Fine	20	Dark goods	30
Extra fine instruments, scales, etc.	A [1]	Knitting machines	20
Textile Mills (Cotton):		Tobacco Products:	
Opening, mixing, picking, carding and drawing	10	Drying, stripping, general	10
Slubbing, roving, spinning	20	Grading and sorting	A [1]
Spooling, warping on comb	20	Toilets and Wash Rooms	5
Beaming, and slashing on comb		Upholstering—Automobile, Coach Furniture	20
Grey goods	20	Warehouse	5
Denims	B [1]	Woodworking:	
		Rough sawing and bench work	10
		Sizing, planing, rough sanding, medium machine and bench work, gluing, veneering, cooperage	20
		Fine bench and machine work, fine sanding and finishing	C [1]

[1] Lighting recommendations for the more difficult seeing tasks, as indicated by A, B, C, and D in the foregoing table, are given in the following:

Group A:

These seeing tasks involve (*a*) the discrimination of extremely fine detail under conditions of (*b*) extremely poor contrast (*c*) for long periods of time. To meet these requirements, illumination levels above 100 ft-c are recommended.

To provide illumination of this order a combination of at least 20 ft-c of general lighting plus specialized supplementary lighting is necessary. The design and installation of the combination systems must not only provide a sufficient amount of light but also must provide the proper direction of light,

Table II–14A gives the lumen output of the lamps generally used in industrial installation.

4. Distribution Curves. The candlepower distribution curve for a lamp or lighting unit gives the pictorial history of the manner in which light is emitted from the unit tested. This curve, with the associated photometric data, enables the designer to classify the unit into the

Direct, less than 10 per cent upward and more than 90 per cent downward.
Semi-direct, more than 10 per cent upward and more than 60 per cent downward.
General diffusing, 40 to 60 per cent upward and 60 to 40 per cent downward.
Semi-indirect, more than 60 per cent upward and more than 10 per cent downward.
Indirect, more than 90 per cent upward and less than 10 per cent downward.

The semi-direct and general diffusing classifications have only recently been used in this country, but they have been used for some time in English and European practice.

Utilization factor, one of the coefficients used in the lumen method of design, depends upon the characteristic shape of the distribution curve. Table VI–14 shows distribution curves with corresponding utilization

---

diffusion, eye protection, and in so far as possible must eliminate direct and reflected glare as well as objectionable shadows.

Group B:

This group of visual tasks involves (*a*) the discrimination of fine detail under conditions of (*b*) a fair degree of contrast (*c*) for long periods of time. Illumination levels from 50 to 100 ft-c are required.

To provide illumination of this order a combination of 10 to 20 ft-c of general lighting plus specialized supplementary lighting is necessary. The design and installation of the combination systems must not only provide a sufficient amount of light but also must provide the proper direction of light, diffusion, eye protection, and in so far as possible must eliminate direct and reflected glare as well as objectionable shadows.

Group C:

The seeing tasks in this group involve (*a*) the discrimination of moderately fine detail under conditions of (*b*) better-than-average contrast (*c*) for intermittent periods of time.

The level of illumination required is of the order of 30 to 50 ft-c and in some instances it may be provided from a general lighting system. Oftentimes, however, it will be found more economical and yet equally satisfactory to provide from 10 to 20 ft-c from the general system and the remainder from specialized supplementary lighting. The design and installation of the combination systems must not only provide a sufficient amount of light but also must provide the proper direction of light, diffusion, eye protection, and in so far as possible must eliminate direct and reflected glare as well as objectionable shadows.

Group D:

The seeing tasks of this group require the discrimination of fine detail by utilizing (*a*) the reflected image of a luminous area or (*b*) the transmitted light from a luminous area.

The essential requirements are (1) that the luminous area shall be large enough to cover the surface which is being inspected and (2) that the brightness be within the limits necessary to obtain comfortable contrast conditions. This involves the use of sources of large area and relatively low brightness in which the source brightness is the principal factor rather than the foot-candles produced at a given point.

In these areas many of the machines require one or more supplementary lighting units mounted on them in order effectively to direct light toward the working points.

factors for room size and color change. The classification of the equipment is shown by the markings on the left side of the tables.

These curves are drawn with candlepower as the absolute value relative to angular displacement, but this information is not necessary.

TABLE II–14A

Lumen Output of Multiple Lamps

July 1, 1945

110–115–120 Volt Standard Lighting Service Clear Lamps		110–115–120 Volt Standard Lighting Service Mazda Daylight Lamps		220–230–240–250 Volt Service Clear Lamps	
Size of lamp in watts	Lumen output	Size of lamp in watts	Lumen output	Size of lamp in watts	Lumen output
100	1,620	100	1,050	100	1,240
150	2,600	150	1,600	.....	......
200	3,650	200	2,350	200	2,950
300	5,650	300	3,650	300	4,850
500	9,850	500	6,400	500	8,800
750	14,900	...	.....	750	13,600
1,000	21,000	...	.....	1,000	19,100
1,500	33,500				

TABLE II–14B

High Pressure Mercury Vapor Lamps

General Lighting

Watts	Lumens at 100 hr	Rated Life hr
100	3,000	1,000
250	10,000	2,000
400	16,000	3,000
3,000	120,000	2,000

Sufficient information for normal designs is available when the lumens represented by the distribution, the shape of the distribution, and the relative brightness at the important angles are given.

5. Light Sources. The usual light source is the incandescent lamp. The values of lamp output (Table II–14) are changed so frequently that it is best to refer to the most recent publications of output to be positive of the correct values to use.

The low pressure mercury vapor lamp has been used extensively in industry because of its distributed light source. It removes shadow and, since the light is monochromatic, it brings out details. The high intensity mercury vapor lamp is being introduced very rapidly into industrial plants because of the high lumen output for the watts consumed. In addition to being monochromatic, these lamps require some time to come to full brilliancy, and any interruption lasting only a cycle will extinguish the lamp, which will again require its lighting time to pass before full illumination is available. This condition can be corrected partially by using a combined lighting system (Fig. 1–14) of mercury and incandescent lamps. The two kinds of light sources give some color correction but not a matching color.

The sodium lamp has been developed primarily for outdoor lighting. The efficiency of the lamp is very high but the color is objectionable. At some future time, however, it may find a place in some manufacturing establishments. Fluorescent lamps using mercury vapor for an exciting source and powdered phosphors, which become fluorescent, for making radiant ultra-violet energy available in the visible region have been used extensively during the war period. Time will have to determine if continued use is economical. These lamps show high efficiencies and make possible many colors of light. Light sources are changing so rapidly that catalogs of manufacturers and publications should be used in determining what is the most satisfactory light source available for the task.

6. Light Control. To control the light from the light sources of high intensity, represented by the modern incandescent and discharge lamps, various types of equipment have been developed. The direct unit redirects the light downward; the semi-direct, general diffusing, and semi-indirect send light both upward and downward; and the indirect unit sends light upward. In the semi-indirect and indirect the ceiling acts as a reflector. The two latter types are used for office work and drafting rooms; the direct light is used for illumination in shops and manufacturing processes. Direct equipment is efficient and easy to service, because it is not seriously affected by dirt produced in the shop, but the others have the advantage of good appearance and light control.

The equipment must remove the glare, both direct and indirect, for this is the most annoying by-product of artificial illumination. Direct glare is controlled by the use of diffusing glass which surrounds the light source or by the removal of the light source from the line of vision. If the source is at an angle of more than 18° to the line of vision, there is little annoyance. Indirect glare must be removed by changing the angle from which the light falls on the work or by reducing the specular

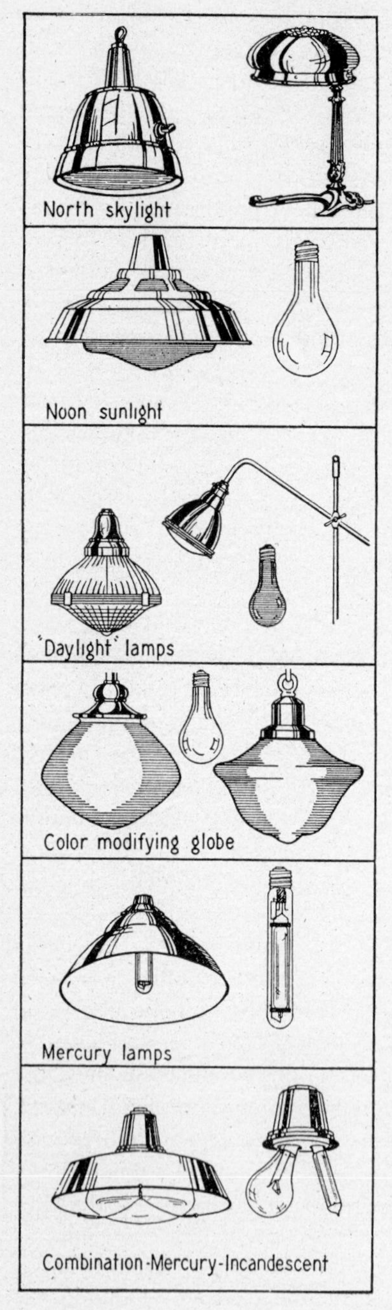

Equipment using accurately correcting filters to duplicate outdoor daylight. Color-matching units in stores and factories.

Approximates the color of direct sunlight at noon. Less exacting color discrimination in manufacturing process may be done under this lamp.

The daylight lamp emits a whiter light than the incandescent lamp. Some color correction and it mixes well with natural light indoors.

Very little color correction but these lights have a whiter appearance. It corrects the yellowish tone of the ordinary glassware.

Mercury lights have a decided bluish cast though the yellow and green lines predominate. Colors cannot be matched under these lights but there is a pronounced contrast between colors.

Where the incandescent and mercury lamp are used in combination, a synthetic white is obtained by additive rather than subtractive methods. Does not give accurate color discrimination but is useful in many processes.

FIG. 1–14. Equipment for light color control.

effect (reflected image) of the light source either by lowering the intensity or by increasing the diffusion.

Shadows may cause interference with the performance of a task. This is very noticeable in drafting rooms. Direct light will cause harsh shadows; indirect light is practically free from shadows; and intermediate equipment will vary in the degree of shadows produced. There are instances where shadows may aid in the inspection of details of manufactured parts.

The illumination should be uniform, and this uniformity is controlled by the spacing of lighting units. It is a good plan to place the lamps so that they will be about the same distance apart as the mounting height, and the spacing should never exceed one and one-half times the mounting height. It is desirable to reduce the number of units to a minimum, but this reduction should not be carried so far that the lighting will become "spotty." Table III–14 gives recommended spacing for rooms of different height and Table IV–14 gives the desirable mounting heights of equipment with various spacings.

The arrangement of the outlets is influenced by the arrangement of the equipment and the structural features of the room. It is well to locate the outlets so that they are placed at the corners of imaginary rectangles on the ceiling. In high-bay industrial lighting, the lighting units should be above the crane and, unless the bay is narrow, lights along the side of the bay will not be satisfactory. It is not advisable to place outlets on beams or roof girders unless the designer is positive that it will not be necessary at some future date to erect partitions. The arrangement of the outlets should be regular and should make a pleasing appearance, both when the units are idle and when they are lighted; therefore, peculiar and odd arrangements should be discouraged.

Both the color and the size of the room enter into the control of the illumination. The size of the room determines the absorption of the light, for the larger the room, with a given height, the less the absorption of light by the walls. Increasing the height without changing the other dimensions produces the same effect. Table V–14 gives the values of the room index, which is an arbitrary constant; these values are relative to a base and not absolute. In some published tables these values are represented by letters of the alphabet.

The coloring of the sidewalls and ceilings determines, in part, the efficiency of the installation. Colors containing blue and red absorb a high percentage of the light; those containing yellow are very good reflectors. White paints are better than those containing color, for light efficiency; that is, if a white appearance is not produced by the use of blue.

Frequently, it is necessary to control the color (Fig. 1–14) of the light source. The light from the incandescent lamp is high in the red portion of the spectrum and, therefore, does not show true colors. There are two methods used to obtain color correction when using artificial light

TABLE III–14

SPACING OF OUTLETS

Ceiling Height (or Height in the Clear)	Spacing between Outlets		Spacing between Outside Outlets and Wall		Approximate Area per Outlet (at Usual Spacings)
	Usual	Maximum (for units at ceiling)	Aisles or storage next to wall	Desks, work-benches, etc., against wall	
(Feet)	(Feet)	Not more than [1]		Not more than [1]	(Square Feet)
8	7	7½		3	50–60
9	8	8		3	60–70
10	9	9		3½	70–85
11	10	10½		3½	85–100
12	10–12	12	Usually one-half actual spacing between units	3½–4	100–150
13	10–12	13		3½–4½	100–150
14	10–13	15		4–5	100–170
15	10–13	17		4–5	100–170
16	10–13	19		4–6	100–170
18	10–20	21		4–6	100–400
20	18–24	24		5–7	300–500
22	20–25	27		5–7	400–600
24	20–30	30		6–8	400–900
26	25–30	33		8–9	600–900
30 and up	25–30	40		8–10	600–900

[1] Where it is definitely known that some form of indirect lighting will be used, the maximum spacing between outlets may be increased about 2 ft, and the distance from the outside outlets to the wall may be increased by 1 ft.

Alternate mercury and incandescent units should, as individual systems, provide uniform lighting and should overlap and blend when combined. The spacing of units should not exceed 80 per cent of recommended mounting height.

sources. The additive method uses a combination of light units, which correct each other so that the result produces white light effect, or fluorescent lamps of correct color temperature. A combination of mercury and incandescent light produces a white light almost like daylight. The second method consists in placing filters around the light and correcting it by subtraction. The daylight lamp is an example of partial correction. The complete correction, for color matching, requires filters which are expensive in first cost and also in operation because of the amount

TABLE IV–14

MOUNTING HEIGHT OF UNITS

Direct Lighting Units				Semi-Indirect and Indirect Lighting	
Actual spacing between units	Distance of units from floor not less than	Desirable mounting height in industrial interiors	Desirable mounting height in commercial interiors	Actual spacing between units	Recommended suspension length (top of bowl to ceiling)
(Feet)	(Feet)			(Feet)	(Feet)
7	8	12 ft above floor if possible—to avoid glare, and still be within reach from stepladder for cleaning.		7	1–3
8	8½			8	1–3
9	9			9	1–3
10	10		The actual hanging height should be governed largely by general appearance, but particularly in offices and drafting rooms the minimum values shown should not be violated.	10	1½–3
11	10½			11	2–3
12	11			12	2–3
14	12½	Where units are to be mounted much more than 12 ft it is usually desirable to mount the units at ceiling or on roof trusses.		14	2½–4
16	14			16	3–4
18	15			18	4–5
20	16			20	4–5
22	18			22	4–5
24	20			24	4–6
26	21			26	4–6
28	22			28	5–7
30	24			30	5–7

of light absorbed. These filters give results close to the natural white light, but are much more expensive than light correction by additive methods. The fluorescent lamp is at present without economic competition for control of the color temperature of light.

TABLE V–14

Room Index

ROOM INDEX FOR NARROW AND AVERAGE ROOMS

For Indirect and Semi-Indirect Lighting Use Ceiling Height		FEET						
		9 and 9½	10 to 11½	12 to 13½	14 to 16½	17 to 20	21 to 24	25 to 30
For Direct, Semi-Direct, and General Diffusing Lighting Use Mounting Height		FEET						
		7 and 7½	8 and 8½	9 and 9½	10 to 11½	12 to 13½	14 to 16½	17 to 20
Room width (feet)	**Room length (feet)**	ROOM INDEX						
9 (8½–9½)	8–10	1.0	0.8	0.6	0.6			
	10–14	1.0	0.8	0.8	0.6			
	14–20	1.2	1.0	0.8	0.6	0.6		
	20–30	1.2	1.2	1.0	0.8	0.6	0.6	
	30–42	1.5	1.2	1.0	0.8	0.6	0.6	0.6
	42–up	2.0	1.5	1.2	1.0	0.8	0.6	0.6
10 (9½–10½)	10–14	1.2	1.0	0.8	0.6	0.6		
	14–20	1.2	1.0	0.8	0.6	0.6	0.6	
	20–30	1.5	1.2	1.0	0.8	0.6	0.6	
	30–42	1.5	1.2	1.2	1.0	0.8	0.6	0.6
	42–60	2.0	1.5	1.2	1.0	0.8	0.6	0.6
	60–up	2.0	1.5	1.5	1.0	1.0	0.8	0.6
12 (11–12½)	10–14	1.2	1.0	0.8	0.8	0.6	0.6	
	14–20	1.5	1.2	1.0	0.8	0.6	0.6	
	20–30	1.5	1.2	1.2	1.0	0.8	0.6	0.6
	30–42	2.0	1.5	1.2	1.0	0.8	0.6	0.6
	42–60	2.0	1.5	1.5	1.2	1.0	0.8	0.6
	60–up	2.0	2.0	1.5	1.2	1.0	0.8	0.6
14 (13–15½)	14–20	1.5	1.2	1.0	1.0	0.8	0.6	0.6
	20–30	2.0	1.5	1.2	1.0	0.8	0.6	0.6
	30–42	2.0	1.5	1.5	1.2	1.0	0.8	0.6
	42–60	2.0	2.0	1.5	1.5	1.0	0.8	0.6
	60–90	2.5	2.0	2.0	1.5	1.2	1.0	0.6
	90–up	2.5	2.0	2.0	1.5	1.5	1.2	0.8
17 (16–18½)	14–20	2.0	1.5	1.2	1.0	0.8	0.6	0.6
	20–30	2.0	1.5	1.5	1.2	1.0	0.8	0.6
	30–42	2.5	2.0	1.5	1.2	1.0	1.0	0.6
	42–60	2.5	2.0	2.0	1.5	1.2	1.2	0.8
	60–110	2.5	2.0	2.0	1.5	1.2	1.2	0.8
	110–up	3.0	2.5	2.0	2.0	1.5	1.2	1.0
20 (19–21½)	20–30	2.5	2.0	1.5	1.2	1.0	0.8	0.6
	30–42	2.5	2.0	2.0	1.5	1.2	1.0	0.8
	42–60	2.5	2.5	2.0	2.0	1.5	1.2	0.8
	60–90	3.0	2.5	2.0	2.0	1.5	1.2	1.0
	90–140	3.0	2.5	2.5	2.0	1.5	1.5	1.0
	140–up	3.0	2.5	2.5	2.0	1.5	1.5	1.0
24 (22–26)	20–30	2.5	2.0	2.0	1.5	1.2	1.0	0.8
	30–42	3.0	2.5	2.0	1.5	1.2	1.2	0.8
	42–60	3.0	2.5	2.5	2.0	1.5	1.2	1.0
	60–90	3.0	2.5	2.5	2.0	1.5	1.5	1.0
	90–140	3.0	3.0	2.5	2.0	2.0	1.5	1.2
	140–up	3.0	3.0	2.5	2.0	2.0	1.5	1.2
30 (27–33)	30–42	3.0	2.5	2.5	2.0	1.5	1.2	1.0
	42–60	3.0	3.0	2.5	2.5	1.5	1.5	1.0
	60–90	4.0	3.0	3.0	2.5	2.0	1.5	1.2
	90–140	4.0	3.0	3.0	2.5	2.0	2.0	1.5
	140–180	4.0	3.0	3.0	2.5	2.0	2.0	1.5
	180–up	4.0	3.0	3.0	2.5	2.0	2.0	1.5
36 (34–39)	30–42	4.0	3.0	2.5	2.0	1.5	1.5	1.0
	42–60	4.0	3.0	3.0	2.5	2.0	1.5	1.2
	60–90	5.0	3.0	3.0	3.0	2.0	2.0	1.5
	90–140	5.0	4.0	3.0	3.0	2.5	2.0	1.5
	140–200	5.0	4.0	3.0	3.0	2.5	2.0	1.5
	200–up	5.0	4.0	3.0	3.0	2.5	2.0	1.5
40 or more	42–60	5.0	4.0	3.0				
	60–90	5.0	4.0	4.0				
	90–140	5.0	4.0	4.0				
	140–200	5.0	5.0	4.0				
	200–up	5.0	5.0	4.0				

TABLE V–14 (*Continued*)

ROOM INDEX FOR LARGE HIGH ROOMS

For Indirect and Semi-Indirect Lighting Use Ceiling Height (Feet)		14 to 16½	17 to 20	21 to 24	25 to 30	31 to 36	37 to 50		
For Direct, Semi-Direct, and General Diffusing Lighting Use Mounting Height (Feet)		**10 to 11½**	**12 to 13½**	**14 to 16½**	**17 to 20**	**21 to 24**	**25 to 30**	**31 to 36**	**37 to 50**
Room Width (Feet)	**Room Length (Feet)**	**ROOM INDEX**							
14 (13–15½)	14–20	1.0	0.8	0.6	0.6				
	20–30	1.0	0.8	0.6	0.6				
	30–42	1.2	1.0	0.8	0.6	0.6			
	42–60	1.5	1.0	0.8	0.6	0.6	0.6		
	60–90	1.5	1.2	1.0	0.6	0.6	0.6		
	90–up	1.5	1.5	1.2	0.8	0.6	0.6		
17 (16–18½)	14–20	1.0	0.8	0.6	0.6				
	20–30	1.2	1.0	0.8	0.6				
	30–42	1.2	1.0	1.0	0.6	0.6	0.6		
	42–60	1.5	1.2	1.2	0.8	0.6	0.6	0.6	
	60–110	1.5	1.2	1.2	0.8	0.6	0.6	0.6	
	110–up	2.0	1.5	1.2	1.0	0.8	0.6	0.6	
20 (19–21½)	20–30	1.2	1.0	0.8	0.6	0.6			
	30–42	1.5	1.2	1.0	0.8	0.6	0.6		
	42–60	2.0	1.5	1.2	0.8	0.6	0.6	0.6	
	60–90	2.0	1.5	1.2	1.0	0.6	0.6	0.6	
	90–140	2.0	1.5	1.5	1.0	0.8	0.8	0.6	0.6
	140–up	2.0	1.5	1.5	1.0	1.0	0.8	0.6	0.6
24 (22–26)	20–30	1.5	1.2	1.0	0.8	0.6	0.6		
	30–42	1.5	1.2	1.2	0.8	0.6	0.6		
	42–60	2.0	1.5	1.2	1.0	0.8	0.6	0.6	
	60–90	2.0	1.5	1.5	1.0	0.8	0.6	0.6	0.6
	90–140	2.0	2.0	1.5	1.2	1.0	0.8	0.6	0.6
	140–up	2.0	2.0	1.5	1.2	1.0	0.8	0.8	0.6
30 (27–33)	30–42	2.0	1.5	1.2	1.0	0.8	0.6	0.6	
	42–60	2.5	1.5	1.5	1.0	1.0	0.8	0.6	
	60–90	2.5	2.0	1.5	1.2	1.0	0.8	0.6	0.6
	90–140	2.5	2.0	2.0	1.5	1.2	1.0	0.8	0.6
	140–180	2.5	2.0	2.0	1.5	1.2	1.0	0.8	0.6
	180–up	2.5	2.0	2.0	1.5	1.2	1.0	0.8	0.6
36 (34–39)	30–42	2.0	1.5	1.5	1.0	0.8	0.8	0.6	
	42–60	2.5	2.0	1.5	1.2	1.0	0.8	0.6	0.6
	60–90	3.0	2.0	2.0	1.5	1.0	1.0	0.6	0.6
	90–140	3.0	2.5	2.0	1.5	1.2	1.0	0.8	0.6
	140–200	3.0	2.5	2.0	1.5	1.5	1.2	1.0	0.8
	200–up	3.0	2.5	2.0	1.5	1.5	1.2	1.0	0.8
42 (40–45)	42–60	3.0	2.0	1.5	1.2	1.0	0.8	0.8	0.6
	60–90	3.0	2.5	2.0	1.5	1.2	1.0	0.8	0.6
	90–140	3.0	2.5	2.5	2.0	1.5	1.2	1.0	0.6
	140–200	3.0	2.5	2.5	2.0	1.5	1.2	1.0	0.8
	200–up	3.0	2.5	2.5	2.0	1.5	1.5	1.2	0.8
50 (46–55)	42–60	3.0	2.5	2.0	1.5	1.2	1.0	0.8	0.6
	60–90	3.0	3.0	2.5	1.5	1.5	1.2	1.0	0.6
	90–140	3.0	3.0	2.5	2.0	1.5	1.5	1.2	0.8
	140–200	3.0	3.0	2.5	2.0	2.0	1.5	1.2	0.8
	200–up	3.0	3.0	2.5	2.0	2.0	1.5	1.2	1.0
60 (56–67)	60–90	4.0	3.0	2.5	2.0	1.5	1.2	1.0	0.8
	90–140	4.0	3.0	3.0	2.5	2.0	1.5	1.2	1.0
	140–200	4.0	3.0	3.0	2.5	2.0	1.5	1.5	1.0
	200–up	4.0	3.0	3.0	2.5	2.0	2.0	1.5	1.0
75 (68–90)	60–90	5.0	4.0	3.0	2.5	2.0	1.5	1.2	0.8
	90–140	5.0	4.0	3.0	2.5	2.0	1.5	1.5	1.0
	140–200	5.0	4.0	4.0	3.0	2.5	2.0	1.5	1.2
	200–up	5.0	4.0	4.0	3.0	2.5	2.0	1.5	1.2
90 or more	60–90	5.0	4.0	3.0	2.5	2.0	1.5	1.2	1.0
	90–140	5.0	5.0	4.0	3.0	2.5	2.0	1.5	1.2
	140–200	5.0	5.0	4.0	3.0	2.5	2.0	1.5	1.2
	200–up	5.0	5.0	4.0	3.0	3.0	2.5	2.0	1.5

An adequate and satisfactory lighting installation should meet the following requirements:

1. Quantity of light correct.
2. Quality of light.
   a. No glare.
      (1) No direct glare.
      (2) No reflected glare.
   b. No shadow.
   c. Uniform illumination.
   d. Surroundings illuminated.
3. Comfort.
   a. Previous experience.
   b. Time.

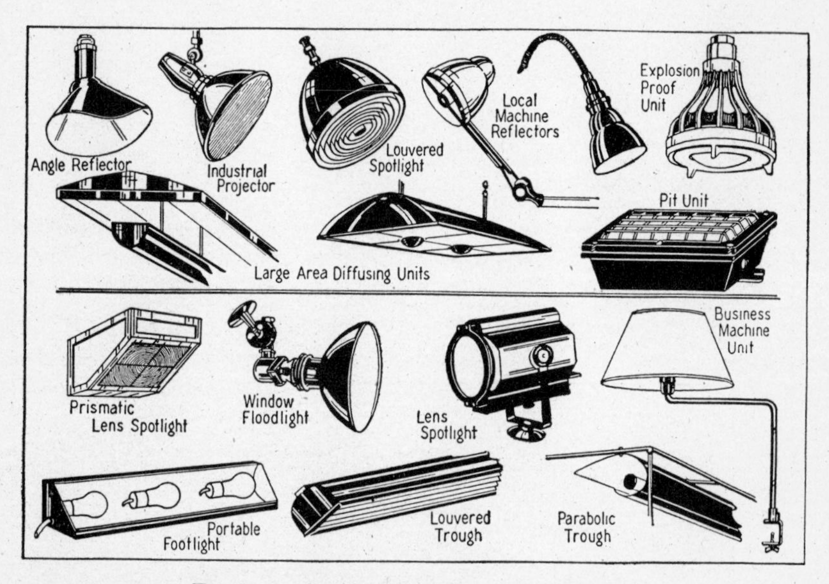

Fig. 2–14. Supplementary lighting equipment.

7. Selection of Lighting Equipment. Table VI–14 shows various types of lighting equipment. Regardless of the make or design of the equipment, it can usually be classified under one of the general classes listed (A to N). Figure 2–14 shows some types of units for local lighting which are outside the general design and are selected by judging the task requirements. It is seldom economical to have a general illumination above 20 foot-candles; therefore, the higher levels must be obtained by supplementary lighting units. Figures 3–14 and 4–14 show some typical manufactured units and give their efficiency.

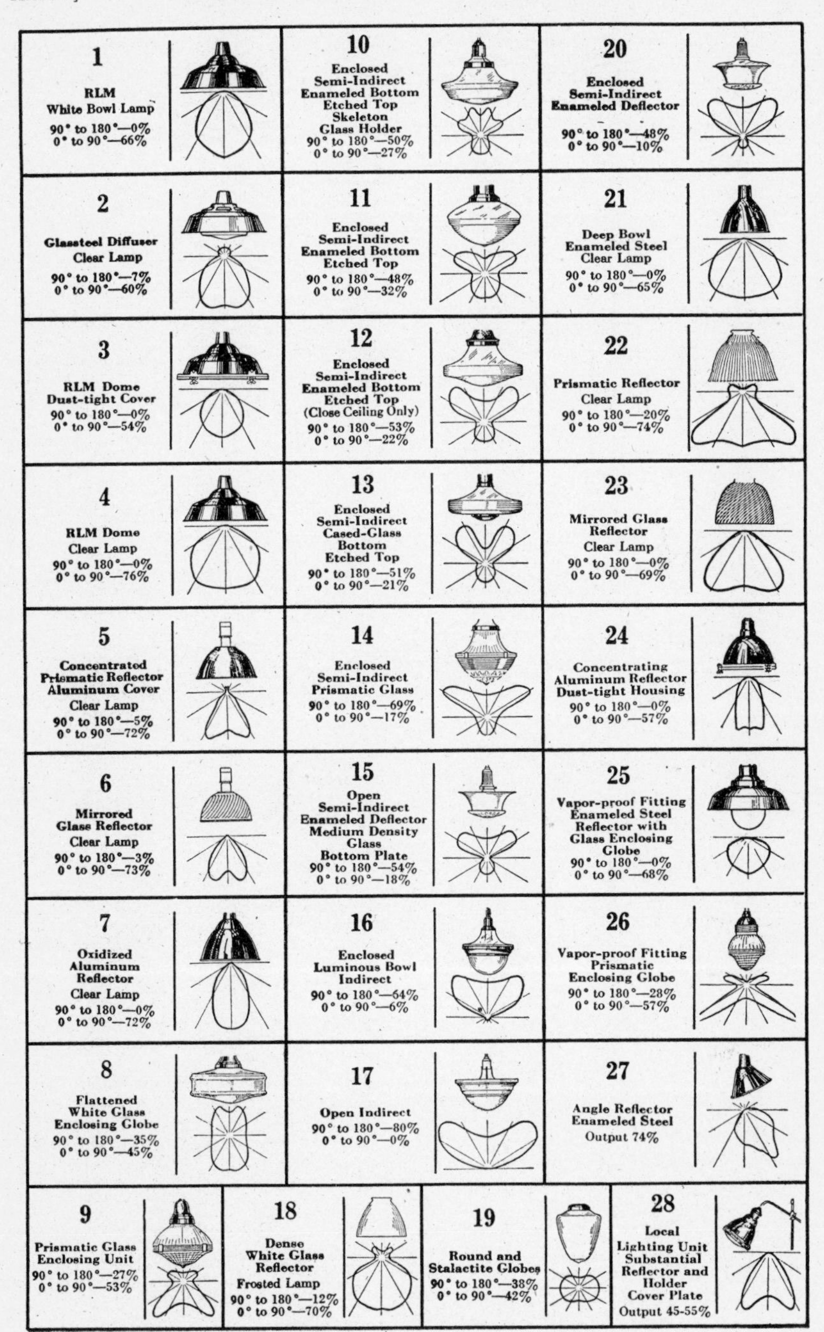

FIG. 3–14. Typical incandescent lighting equipment.

TABLE VI–14

Room Utilization Factors

Class	Type of Distribution	Ceiling	Very Light			Fairly Light			Fairly Dark	
		Walls	Fairly Light	Fairly Dark	Very Dark	Fairly Light	Fairly Dark	Very Dark	Fairly Dark	Very Dark
		Room Index	Room Utilization Factor							
DIRECT — CONCENTRATION	A 	0.6	57	54	51	56	54	51	56	51
		0.8	69	66	66	67	66	64	66	61
		1.0	73	73	71	71	71	70	71	69
		1.2	79	77	77	77	74	74	74	73
		1.5	83	80	79	79	79	77	79	76
		2.0	86	84	83	84	83	81	81	80
		2.5	91	87	86	89	86	86	86	84
		3.0	93	90	87	90	89	86	86	86
		4.0	93	91	90	91	89	89	89	87
		5.0	94	93	91	91	90	89	89	89
	B 	0.6	58	54	52	56	54	52	56	52
		0.8	68	66	64	68	64	64	64	62
		1.0	74	72	72	72	72	70	72	68
		1.2	78	78	76	76	76	74	76	72
		1.5	82	80	78	80	78	76	78	76
		2.0	86	84	84	84	84	80	82	80
		2.5	92	88	86	88	86	84	84	84
		3.0	92	90	88	90	88	86	86	84
		4.0	94	92	90	92	88	88	88	88
		5.0	94	92	92	92	90	88	88	88
	C 	0.6	57	53	53	57	53	53	57	50
		0.8	70	67	67	67	67	63	67	63
		1.0	73	73	70	73	70	70	70	70
		1.2	80	77	77	77	73	73	73	73
		1.5	83	80	80	80	77	77	77	77
		2.0	87	83	83	83	83	80	83	80
		2.5	90	87	87	87	87	87	87	83
		3.0	93	90	87	90	87	87	87	87
		4.0	93	90	90	90	90	87	87	87
		5.0	93	93	90	93	90	90	90	87
DIRECT — DISTRIBUTING	D 	0.6	45	39	32	45	39	32	37	32
		0.8	56	51	45	56	49	44	49	44
		1.0	61	57	52	60	56	52	56	52
		1.2	67	63	57	65	61	57	60	56
		1.5	71	67	61	69	65	61	64	60
		2.0	77	73	68	76	72	68	71	68
		2.5	83	79	75	81	77	75	77	75
		3.0	85	81	77	84	80	77	80	77
		4.0	89	87	84	88	85	83	84	81
		5.0	92	89	87	89	88	85	87	84
	E 	0.6	49	43	38	49	43	38	42	38
		0.8	61	55	52	60	54	51	54	51
		1.0	66	60	57	65	60	57	60	57
		1.2	71	66	63	69	66	63	66	63
		1.5	74	69	66	72	69	66	69	66
		2.0	80	77	74	78	75	72	75	72
		2.5	86	83	80	85	82	78	82	78
		3.0	88	85	82	86	83	80	83	80
		4.0	92	89	86	91	88	85	88	85
		5.0	94	91	88	92	89	88	89	86
	F 	0.6	48	40	35	47	40	35	38	35
		0.8	60	53	48	58	52	47	50	47
		1.0	65	60	55	63	58	55	57	53
		1.2	72	65	60	68	63	60	62	58
		1.5	75	70	65	72	67	63	65	63
		2.0	82	77	73	78	75	72	72	70
		2.5	88	83	78	85	80	77	78	77
		3.0	90	87	82	87	83	80	80	78
		4.0	95	92	88	92	87	85	85	83
		5.0	98	93	90	93	90	87	87	85
	G 	0.6	47	40	35	45	40	35	38	35
		0.8	58	53	47	56	51	47	51	47
		1.0	64	58	54	62	58	54	56	54
		1.2	69	64	60	67	64	58	62	58
		1.5	73	67	64	69	65	64	65	64
		2.0	78	75	71	76	73	69	73	69
		2.5	84	80	76	82	78	76	78	76
		3.0	87	84	78	84	82	78	80	78
		4.0	91	87	84	87	85	84	84	82
		5.0	93	89	87	91	87	85	85	84

TABLE VI-14 (*Continued*)

ROOM UTILIZATION FACTORS

	Type of Distribution	Ceiling	Very Light			Fairly Light			Fairly Dark	
		Walls	Fairly Light	Fairly Dark	Very Dark	Fairly Light	Fairly Dark	Very Dark	Fairly Dark	Very Dark
		Room Index	ROOM UTILIZATION FACTOR							
SEMI-DIRECT	H	0.6	36	30	27	34	29	26	27	25
		0.8	43	39	36	41	36	34	35	32
		1.0	49	44	41	45	41	39	39	36
		1.2	54	49	45	49	45	42	42	40
		1.5	57	52	47	52	49	45	46	42
		2.0	62	57	54	57	54	50	50	46
		2.5	67	61	57	61	57	54	54	51
		3.0	70	65	60	64	60	56	56	52
		4.0	75	70	65	68	62	60	59	56
		5.0	77	72	69	70	65	62	61	59
GENERAL DIFFUSING	I	0.6	30	25	21	27	22	20	20	17
		0.8	37	31	29	34	29	25	26	24
		1.0	42	36	32	37	32	30	30	27
		1.2	46	41	37	41	36	34	34	31
		1.5	51	45	40	45	40	36	36	34
		2.0	56	51	46	50	45	41	40	37
		2.5	61	55	50	54	49	45	44	41
		3.0	65	59	54	55	51	47	46	44
		4.0	69	64	59	60	55	52	50	47
		5.0	71	66	62	62	57	55	51	50
SEMI-INDIRECT	J	0.6	20	15	11	15	11	9	7	6
		0.8	25	20	16	20	15	12	11	9
		1.0	30	24	20	22	17	15	14	10
		1.2	34	29	24	26	21	17	15	12
		1.5	37	31	26	29	24	20	17	15
		2.0	44	37	32	34	27	25	21	17
		2.5	47	41	36	36	31	27	24	21
		3.0	51	45	40	39	34	30	26	24
		4.0	57	51	46	42	39	36	29	26
		5.0	60	55	50	46	41	39	31	29
	K	0.6	21	17	15	16	12	11	9	7
		0.8	27	22	20	20	16	15	11	10
		1.0	31	26	24	22	19	17	14	11
		1.2	36	31	26	26	22	20	15	14
		1.5	39	34	30	29	25	22	16	15
		2.0	44	39	35	32	27	25	19	17
		2.5	49	42	39	35	31	29	21	20
		3.0	51	46	42	37	34	31	22	21
		4.0	56	52	49	40	37	35	25	24
		5.0	59	55	51	42	40	37	27	25
INDIRECT	L	0.6	20	16	13	13	11	9	5	5
		0.8	25	20	19	17	13	12	8	7
		1.0	29	24	21	19	16	13	11	8
		1.2	33	28	24	23	19	17	11	11
		1.5	35	32	28	25	21	19	12	11
		2.0	41	36	33	28	24	21	13	13
		2.5	45	40	37	29	27	25	16	15
		3.0	48	44	40	32	29	27	17	16
		4.0	53	49	45	35	33	31	19	19
		5.0	56	52	49	37	35	33	21	19
	M	0.6	20	15	14	12	11	9	6	5
		0.8	25	20	18	17	14	12	8	8
		1.0	29	25	22	18	15	14	9	8
		1.2	34	29	25	23	18	17	11	9
		1.5	37	31	28	25	22	18	12	11
		2.0	42	37	31	28	25	22	14	12
		2.5	46	40	37	31	28	25	15	15
		3.0	49	45	40	32	29	28	17	15
		4.0	54	49	46	35	32	31	18	18
		5.0	55	52	49	38	35	32	22	18
	N	0.6	20	16	13	13	11	9	5	5
		0.8	25	20	18	16	15	13	7	7
		1.0	29	24	22	18	16	15	11	7
		1.2	33	29	24	24	18	16	11	11
		1.5	36	31	27	25	22	18	13	11
		2.0	42	36	33	27	24	22	15	13
		2.5	45	40	36	29	27	25	16	15
		3.0	49	44	40	33	29	27	16	16
		4.0	53	49	45	35	33	31	18	18
		5.0	57	53	49	38	35	33	22	18

Table VI–14 is useful in selecting the type of distribution desired. By comparing the distribution curves with the commercial products, units may be selected that will fit into the design.

TABLE VII–14

Maintenance Factors for the Equipment in Fig. 3–14

Equipment Number	Maintenance Factors (in Percentage)		
	Clean conditions	Average conditions	Dirty conditions
1	80	75	65
2	75	70	60
3	80	75	70
4	80	75	70
5	80	75	65
6	80	70	60
7	80	70	60
8	80	75	65
9	80	70	60
10	75	70	Not used
11	75	70	Not used
12	75	70	Not used
13	75	65	Not used
14	75	70	Not used
15	70	60	Not used
16	75	65	Not used
17	70	60	Not used

8. Design of Electrical Lighting Installations. The tables previously given contain all the constants necessary for use in the expression (*a*–14) to determine the size of lamp needed. Other tables give the limitations of the area per lighting unit, the spacing, and the mounting height. The design of lighting systems by the lumen method begins after the type of equipment has been selected and the height of the room determined. The equipment should be selected for the service, considering both the cost and the efficiency of the units. Manufacturers will furnish distribution curves obtained from tests performed by reliable testing laboratories, for it is seldom feasible for the purchaser to make these tests.

A systematic procedure gives the best results and the design should follow the suggested steps given below.

1. Determine the type of equipment that is to be used, its distribution characteristics, and its classification (Figs. 3–14 and 4–14 and Table VI–14).
2. From the last column of Table III–14 and the floor area, determine the limits of the economical number of units to use.
3. From Table III–14 determine the limits of spacing and arrange the outlets accordingly. It is best to locate the outlets as nearly on the corners of imaginary squares as possible.

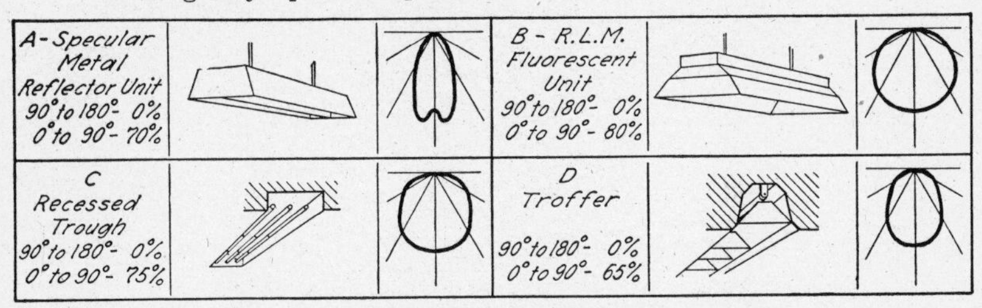

FIG. 4–14. Typical fluorescent lighting equipment.

4. From Table IV–14 select the mounting height for the equipment.
5. From Table I–14 select the desirable foot-candles for the task to be performed. This determines the required lumens per square foot.
6. From Table V–14 determine the "room index."
7. Having determined the *RI*, the class of equipment, the type and the constants for solving equation (*a*–14), constants must be obtained for

$$\text{Total lamp lumens per outlet} = \frac{E \times A}{MF \times UF \times \eta}$$

where E is the illumination as determined in item 5.
A is the floor area by measurement or from a drawing.
UF is the "utilization factor" from Table VI–14 for the class of equipment chosen and the room coloring, determined from the reflection factors of the walls and ceilings.
MF is the "maintenance factor" for the type of equipment chosen from Fig. 3–14 and listed in Table VII–14.
η is the "efficiency" of the type of equipment chosen; this is listed with the distribution curves in Figs. 3–14 and 4–14.

8. From Table II–14, select the lamp that comes closest to calculated lumens per outlet.
9. Calculate the average illumination which may be expected:

$$\text{Average foot-candles} = \frac{\text{lumens of lamp}}{\text{lumens required}} \times \text{selected foot-candles}$$

10. Determine the watts per square foot required to give the illumination for economic calculations and as a check on previous computations.

Example a. Determine the number, location, and size of lamps necessary for lighting the manufacturing plant shown in Fig. 5–14. The high bay is used for rough casting and core making; the low bay is used for rough machining and bench work. The ceiling is painted white and the side walls are of factory glass.

Refer to Fig. 5–14.

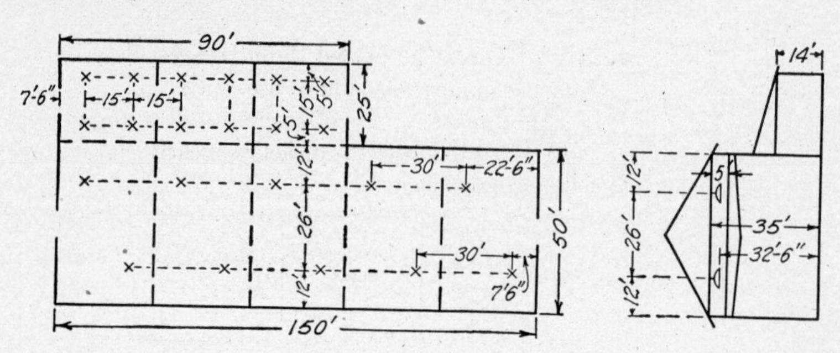

Fig. 5–14. Lighting a manufacturing plant.

High Bay:

1. Use equipment 5 — Fig. 3–14
   Class A — Table VI–14
2. With a 30-ft ceiling and up, adequacy and economy require 600 to 900 sq ft per outlet. The installation should use 8 to 12 units. Use two per bay. — Table III–14
3. A 35-ft ceiling permits a 25- to 30-ft spacing with a maximum of 40 ft allowing 8 to 10 ft to the side walls. Outlet location shown on Fig. 5–14. Stagger outlets so that the crane will not cover more than one outlet. — Table III–14
4. The equipment must be above the crane and should be serviced safely from the crane. Thirty inches above the crane is satisfactory. Mounting 32 ft 6 in. — Table IV–14
5. Desirable illumination, 10 ft-c — Table I–14
6. Room index (*RI*), 1.2 — Table V–14
7. $UF = 77$ per cent — Table VI–14
   $MF = 75$ per cent (average conditions) — Table VII–14
   $\eta = 77$ per cent — Fig. 3–14

$$\text{Total lamp lumens} = \frac{10 \times 50 \times 150}{0.75 \times 0.77 \times 0.77 \times 10} = 16{,}880 \text{ lumens}$$

8. Select 1000-watt lamp (21,000 lumens) — Table II–14
9. Average illumination $= \dfrac{21{,}000}{16{,}880} \times 10 = 12.5$ ft-c
10. Watts per square foot $\dfrac{10 \times 1000}{150 \times 50} = 1.33$ watts

Low Bay:

1. Use equipment 1 — Fig. 3–14
   Class E — Table VI–14
2. From 100 to 170 sq ft per outlet.
   Use 4 outlets per bay. — Table III–14

3. Spacing 10 to 13 ft, maximum 15 ft.
   Spacing to side wall 4 to 5 ft. Table III–14
4. Ceiling mounting (approximately 13 ft to bottom of equipment) Table IV–14
5. Desirable illumination, 12 ft-c (2 extra) Table I–14
6. Room index (RI), 1.5 or 2. Use 1.5 since this gives the lowest room efficiency. Table V–14
7. UF = 69 per cent Table VI–14
   MF = 75 per cent (average conditions) (Table VII–14
   η = 66 per cent Fig. 3–14

$$\text{Total lamp lumens} = \frac{12 \times 25 \times 90}{0.75 \times 0.69 \times 0.66 \times 12} = 6588 \text{ lumens}$$

8. Select 300-watt lamp (5650 lumens) Table II–14
9. Average illumination $= \frac{5650}{6588} \times 10 = 8.6$ ft-c
10. Watts per square foot $= \frac{300 \times 12}{25 \times 90} = 1.6$ watts

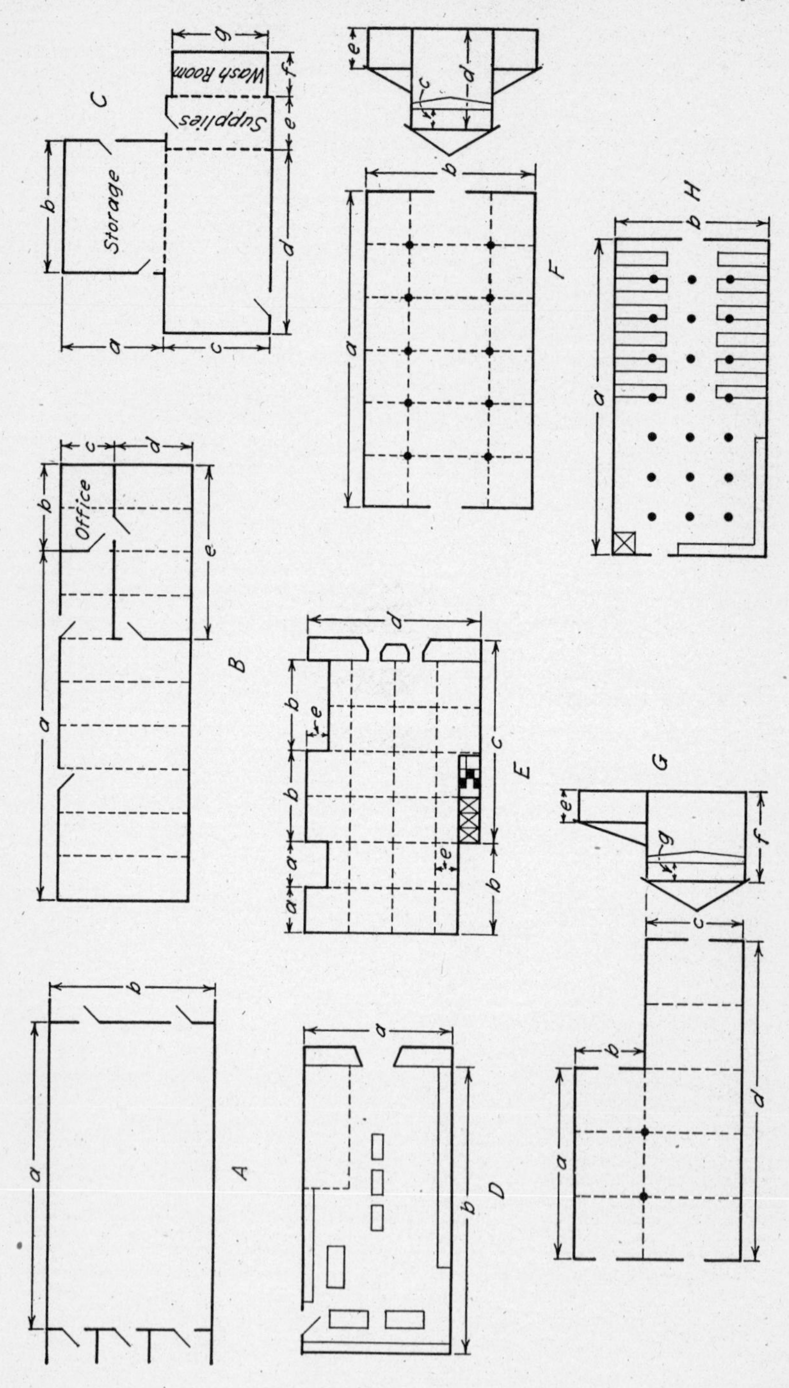
A
B
Office
C
Storage
Supplies
Wash Room
D
E
F
G
H

PROBLEMS IN ILLUMINATION DESIGN FOR INDUSTRIAL INTERIORS

The diagram gives the layout for the rooms and the buildings; the dimensions and other necessary information are listed in tabular form. Each area is planned for both incandescent and gaseous vapor discharge lamps. Tabulation for design data follow given form (p. 360).

Prob.[1] No.	Fig. No.	Kind of Work	Ceiling Height, Feet	Dimensions on Figure, Feet							Ceiling Color	Side Wall Color	Mounting Height, Feet	Luminaire Figs. 3–14, 4–14
				a	*b*	*c*	*d*	*e*	*f*	*g*				
1–14	*A*	Drafting	11	120	40						VL[2]	FL[3]	8	15
2–14	*A*													*D*
3–14	*B*	Medium Inspection	12	105	30	15	30	60			FL[3]	FL[3]	9	2
4–14	*B*													*C*
5–14	*C*	Candy Box Department	15	23	32	27	43	13	13	23	VL[2]	FL[3]	12	2
6–14	*C*													*B*
7–14	*D*	Bakery	13	24	46						VL[2]	FL[3]	12	1
8–14	*D*													*B*
9–14	*E*	Office	19.5	25	50	100	100	12.5			VL[2]	FL[3]	12	12
10–14	*E*													*D*
11–14	*F*	Medium—Shop and Assembly		140	76	9	34	14			FD[4]	FD[4]	28–12	5–2
12–14	*F*													*A, B*
13–14	*G*	Sheet Metal Work and Assembly		75	25	52	125				FL[3]	FD[4]	37–11	7–2
14–14	*G*													*A, B*
15–14	*H*	Forge and Welding	12	54	117.5						VD[5]	VD[5]	11	1
16–14	*H*													*B*

[1] Even numbers incandescent lighting. Odd numbers gaseous vapor discharge lighting. [2] VL—very light. [3] FL—fairly light. [4] FD—fairly dark. [5] VD—very dark.

PROBLEMS

Form for Tabulating Data for Lighting Designs

Layout

Use ____________________ Ceiling Color ____________________

Location ____________________ Side Wall Color ____________________

Kind of Work ____________________ Luminaire ____________________

Ceiling Height ____________________ Mounting ____________________

Outlet Spacing ____________________ Room Index ____________________

Side Wall Spacing ____________________ Class of Equipment ____________________

Number of Outlets ____________________ Luminaire Efficiency ____________________

Foot-Candles ____________________ Utilization Factor ____________________

Area per Outlet ____________________ Maintenance Factor ____________________

Lumens per Square Foot ____________________ Coefficient of Utilization ____________________

Lumens per Outlet ____________________ Average Illumination ____________________

Lamp Size ____________________ Initial Illumination ____________________

Watts per Square Foot ____________________

INDEX